The GI Cookbook

The GI Cookbook

delicious recipes for a healthier you

The GI Cookbook is published by
Reader's Digest (Australia) Pty Limited
80 Bay Street, Ultimo NSW 2007
www.readersdigest.com.au
www.readersdigest.co.nz
www.readersdigest.co.za

First published 2010. Reprinted 2010, 2012 (pbk. & hbk.).
Copyright © Reader's Digest (Australia) Pty Limited 2010
Copyright © Reader's Digest Association Far East Limited 2010
Philippines Copyright © Reader's Digest Association Far East
Limited 2010

GI Symbol on cover and page 244 ©, ® and ™ The University of
Sydney, used under licence

National Library of Australia Cataloguing-in-Publication entry

Title: The GI Cookbook.
ISBN: 978-1-921569-78-4 (hbk.)
ISBN: 978-1-921743-14-6 (pbk.)
Notes: Includes index.
Subjects: Glycemic index.
        Food–Carbohydrate content.
        Diet therapy.
Dewey Number: 613.283

Prepress by Sinnott Bros, Sydney
Printed and bound by Leo Paper Products, China

We are interested in receiving your comments on the
contents of this book. Write to: The Editor, General Books Editorial,
Reader's Digest (Australia) Pty Limited,
GPO Box 4353, Sydney, NSW 2001,
or email us at bookeditors.au@readersdigest.com

To order additional copies of *The GI Cookbook*,
please contact us as follows:
www.readersdigest.com.au, 1300 300 030 (Australia);
www.readersdigest.co.nz, 0800 400 060 (New Zealand);
www.readersdigest.co.za, 0800 980 572 (South Africa)
or email us at customerservice@readersdigest.com.au

The GI Cookbook

Consultants
Suzie Ferrie, Advanced Accredited Practising Dietitian
Dr Alan W Barclay, BSc; Grad Dip; PhD; APD; AN;
Glycemic Index Foundation

Project Editor Celia Coyne
Designer Clare Forte
Design Concept Donna Heldon
Nutritional Analysis Toni Gumley
Proofreader Susan McCreery
Indexer Diane Harriman
Senior Production Controller Monique Tesoriero
Editorial Project Manager General Books Deborah Nixon

READER'S DIGEST GENERAL BOOKS
Editorial Director Lynn Lewis
Managing Editor Rosemary McDonald
Art Director Carole Orbell

Note to readers The information in this book should not be
substituted for, or used to alter, medical therapy without your
doctor's advice. For a specific health problem, consult your
doctor for guidance. The mention of any products, businesses
or websites in this book does not imply or constitute an
endorsement by the authors, editors or Reader's Digest
(Australia) Pty Ltd.

Front cover (hbk): Spaghetti with a chickpea sauce, page 167
Back cover (hbk): *from left to right* Little custard pots, page 231;
Beef in red wine, page 77; Wholesome muffins, page 37; Simple
seafood broth, page 58
Front cover (pbk): Little custard pots, page 231
Back cover (pbk): *from left to right* Beef in red wine, page 77;
Wholesome muffins, page 37; Cannellini bean burgers, page 164;
Simple seafood broth, page 58
Page 2: Fruity Bircher muesli, page 18
Page 6: Fish en papillote, page 119

CONTENTS

GI eating explained ----------------- 8

Breakfasts ----------------- 18

Snacks and light bites -- 34

Soups ----------------- 52

Meat and poultry ----------- 74

Fish and seafood ----------- 114

Vegetarian dishes -------- 140

Salads ----------------- 186

Sweet treats ----------- 218

Putting it all into practice -------- 242
Meal plans ----------------- 246
Index ----------------- 250

HEALTHY EATING – THE GI WAY!

Ever since the positive effects of a low-GI eating plan were discovered in the 1980s, researchers have continued to gather evidence regarding the diet's far-reaching health benefits. Today most health professionals and nutritionists agree that a low-GI eating plan not only helps to keep you trim, but it can lower your chances of getting Type 2 diabetes, heart disease and possibly some forms of cancer. The diet has also been associated with improved memory, concentration and mood. Following the diet couldn't be simpler: there is no weighing of foods and obsessive counting of calories or kilojoules; no food is forbidden; and because of the way you are eating you are unlikely to feel hungry.

GI stands for Glycaemic Index, which is a measure of how quickly food is broken down into glucose. The key to the low-GI diet is its focus on slow-acting carbohydrate foods, which help to keep your blood glucose steady. How this happens is explained on pages 8–17, where you will also find lists of low-GI foods, smart substitutions and guidelines on choosing the right types of fat and the healthiest proteins. On pages 244–9 there are more hints and tips for putting the diet into practice, including two weeks of meal plans.

But the core of *The GI Cookbook* is the recipes, designed to ensure that your low-GI eating plan is never dull and always delicious. They range from soups, snacks and salads to satisfying main courses and dinner-party delights, as well as some healthy desserts. While most of the recipes are rated low GI, there are some dishes that are low–medium or medium GI. Opting for a medium-GI meal once in a while will do your diet no harm. This is not meant to be a gruelling dietary regime that is endured for a few weeks and dropped; this is a healthy eating plan for life, so feel free to choose the meals that entice you. But we appreciate that some of you may wish to stick to low-GI dishes, so on all medium-GI recipes we have added a 'For lower GI' option. The choice is yours.

After a few weeks of eating the GI way you'll wonder why you didn't start sooner. You may see that spare tyre melting away and feel more energetic. And if the nutritional experts are correct, adopting the low-GI eating plan may be the best thing you've ever done for your health.

GI EATING EXPLAINED

The low-GI eating plan, as described in this book, is more of a lifestyle change than a 'diet'. It will help you to lose weight – and keep it off – but there are other health benefits, including lowering your chances of getting Type 2 diabetes, protecting against heart disease and increasing your energy levels. Unlike fad diets that involve weird and unhealthy food restrictions and calorie counting, this eating plan couldn't be easier. By just incorporating a few simple principles you can enjoy all the benefits of healthy low-GI eating and have improved vitality for life.

What does GI mean?

GI stands for glycaemic index, which is a measure of how easily food is broken down by the body into glucose. Every carbohydrate food has a GI value and the higher the number, the more easily it is converted. Pure glucose, for example, has a GI value of 100 (the highest), while lentils have a GI value of just 31. When you eat a food with a high GI, the food is broken down quickly and causes a surge of glucose into the blood. Low-GI foods, on the other hand, release their sugars slowly, causing a steady release of glucose into the blood.

Why blood glucose matters

When you eat a meal that is full of high-GI foods, such as white bread, most types of potato, and processed foods such as cakes and biscuits, the glucose level in your blood may rise above the normal range. The body has a mechanism for coping with excess blood glucose – it releases insulin, a hormone produced by beta cells in the pancreas, which tells the body to use the glucose to fuel cells or to store it as fat. Although the body can deal with the excess glucose, continually loading your body with high-GI foods will keep your body in a state of 'red alert' as it tackles

Blood glucose ups and downs

The black dotted line shows the starting blood glucose level. Eating the high-GI rice raises blood glucose but even before 2 hours have passed the blood glucose has fallen lower than it was to begin with. The low-GI lentils produce a steady rise and slow fall of blood glucose, keeping hunger at bay for longer.

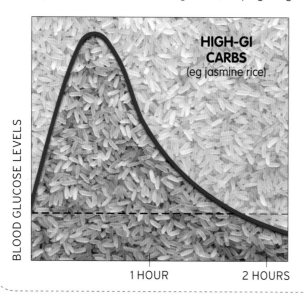

HIGH-GI CARBS (eg jasmine rice)

BLOOD GLUCOSE LEVELS

1 HOUR   2 HOURS

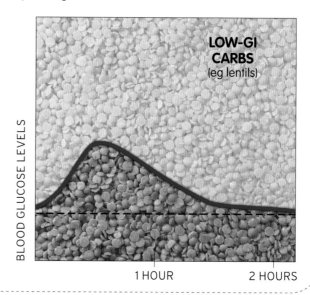

LOW-GI CARBS (eg lentils)

BLOOD GLUCOSE LEVELS

1 HOUR   2 HOURS

the blood glucose highs. Over time this can lead to health problems. Insulin in the blood has another effect: it prevents the body from releasing stored fat into the blood. This is certainly not what you need if you are trying to lose weight.

Another consequence of a high-GI diet is the rollercoaster effect. After you've eaten a meal that is heavy on high-GI foods, the body releases insulin, but it may release too much. This has the desired effect of bringing the blood glucose levels down, but it goes too far, making blood glucose levels dip. In fact, your blood glucose levels may be lower than before you ate anything. The result is that you feel sluggish and may even have a headache. Recognising the dip, the body signals that you are hungry. Even though you ate plenty of calories, the dip in your blood glucose makes your body think it needs more food. This is when you will be tempted to cram in a chocolate bar. Not only does this sabotage your diet, but it sets off the cycle again: a 'sugar high' followed by a 'sugar low' – and you feel hungry.

A high-GI diet affects more than your weight

Diets packed with high-GI foods not only promote weight gain, they have been shown to contribute to other serious health conditions. It's all to do with what happens when the body is continually being challenged to keep the blood glucose under control.

HEART HEALTH

Meals that cause blood glucose to spike tend to lower 'good' HDL cholesterol and raise triglycerides, the harmful fats that increase the risk of heart disease. High blood glucose also produces unstable forms of oxygen called free radicals that damage arteries and make cholesterol more likely to stick to artery walls. The raised levels of insulin produced to cope with surges of glucose in the blood set in motion changes that raise your blood pressure, make your blood more likely to form clots and increase inflammation, which doctors know is closely connected with heart attack risk.

CANCER CONNECTION

Recent research suggests that seesawing blood glucose levels may increase your chances of getting cancer. It seems that the high insulin levels promote an environment that makes it easier for certain tumours to grow. Research is ongoing, and it is too early to be absolutely certain about the connection between blood glucose and cancer, yet there is cause for concern in the following types of cancer: colon and rectal, breast, endometrial (womb lining), prostate and pancreatic.

MOOD AND MEMORY

The brain is very sensitive to the levels of glucose in the blood. Both high and low levels of blood glucose can cause problems with your mood and memory. Low levels may bring on symptoms of depression, poor memory and low concentration, while high levels of blood glucose also impair the brain, shrinking the part that stores memories and increasing the risk of dementia. The answer is to keep the levels steady by eating a diet rich in low-GI foods.

THE ROAD TO DIABETES

It has long been known that over time a diet packed with fast-acting, high-GI foods will greatly increase your risk of Type 2 diabetes. In Type 2 diabetes your body can't make enough insulin to keep your blood glucose levels under control. Before you reach that stage, your body may develop insulin resistance and/or metabolic syndrome (syndrome X) – pre-diabetic states where your body progressively struggles to control blood glucose. Many people are unaware that they have these conditions, yet studies show that they are increasingly common. In Australia, New Zealand, South Africa and the UK more than 10 per cent of adults have insulin resistance. Fortunately, you don't develop diabetes overnight and the journey towards diabetes can be redirected at any point. Eating more slow-acting foods is one of the most effective ways of preventing or reversing the condition. The earlier you start the better.

Step off the rollercoaster

As discussed on the previous page, the rollercoaster effect of high and low blood glucose levels can seriously damage your health. It can increase your risk of heart disease and it may even chip away at your memory and increase the risk of certain cancers. You may not even know you have a problem, but that doesn't mean it's not there. It's no longer just some people who need to worry about blood glucose. It's pretty much everyone.

Getting off the blood glucose rollercoaster means changing your diet so that you eat more of the low-GI foods that are gentle on your blood glucose and less of the high-GI foods. It means forgoing pies, cakes and sugary confectionery, but you will not feel hungry or deprived because the low-GI foods that you will be eating help to stave off hunger for longer. Because they release their sugars slowly, your blood glucose rises slowly and stays in the normal range for longer. The result is that you won't crave sugary snacks between meals, and sticking to a healthy diet becomes so much easier.

If you are overweight, the low-GI eating plan will help you to lose that spare tyre. In studies involving everyone from obese men to pregnant women and children, it has been found that a diet that stabilises blood glucose leads to

10 tips to lower the GI of your diet

The following are practical tips to help you make the switch to low-GI eating. There's no specific order. Essentially, you should attack the changes that you think you'll find easiest first. Make the changes gradually – it can take 6 weeks for a new behaviour to become a habit. Here's how you can get started:

1 Aim to eat 7 servings of vegetables every day, preferably of 3 or more colours. Make sure you fill half your dinner plate with vegetables.

2 Cut back on potatoes. Have one or two boiled new potatoes or make a cannellini bean and potato mash replacing half the potato with cannellini beans. Try other lower GI starchy vegetables for a change, such as a piece of orange sweet potato (kumara).

3 Choose a really grainy bread, such as stoneground wholemeal, real sourdough bread, or a soy and linseed bread. Look for the GI symbol on the breads you buy (see page 244).

4 Start the day with smart carbs like natural muesli or traditional (not instant) porridge oats or one of the lower GI processed breakfast cereals that will trickle fuel into your engine.

5 Look for the lower GI rices (basmati, Doongara Clever rice or Moolgiri), and choose low-GI whole grains such as pearl barley, buckwheat, burghul (bulgur) or quinoa.

6 Learn to love legumes and eat them often. Add red kidney beans to a chilli, chickpeas to a stir-fry, a 4-bean salad to a barbecue and beans or lentils to a casserole or soup.

7 Include at least one low-GI carb food at every meal and choose low-GI snacks. You'll find them in four of the food groups: fruit and vegetables, breads and cereals, legumes, and dairy foods.

8 Incorporate a lean protein source with every meal such as lean meat, skinless chicken, eggs, fish and seafood, or legumes and tofu if you are vegetarian.

9 Utilise the GI-lowering effect of acidic foods like vinegar, citrus fruit and sourdough: add vinaigrette dressing to salads and sprinkle lemon juice on vegetables like asparagus. Acids slow the digestion of carbs and lower the overall GI of the meal.

10 Limit (preferably avoid) high-GI refined flour products whether from the supermarket or home-baked, such as biscuits, cakes, pastries, crumpets, crackers and biscuits.

more body fat loss (or, in the case of pregnant women, less body fat gain during pregnancy). When the blood is flooded with insulin it makes the body want to hang on to fat, but with blood glucose levels kept steady, the body is always in the right 'mode' for fat burning. Another weight-loss barrier caused by rollercoaster blood glucose levels is that it may even slow your metabolism. This explains why people who follow a crash diet often end up piling back on the kilos – sometimes putting on more weight than they lost.

Get to know your GI-friendly foods

We have established that high-GI foods are bad for us and play havoc with our blood glucose and so we need to eat more of the low-GI foods – but how do we know which ones to choose? Foods don't come with labels explaining which is which, but read on and you will soon know how to tell the difference. The body obtains energy from all types of food – protein, fat and carbohydrate – but the main source of energy is carbohydrate, and this is what the low-GI eating plan focuses on. However, for overall health, you will also need to pay attention to the protein, fat and fibre in your diet, and we will discuss these later on (see pages 15–16).

The right carbohydrate

Carbohydrates include all kinds of sugar and starch (which is actually made up of sugar molecules linked together in long chains). Most types of food (apart from meats and oils) contain at least a little carbohydrate. But some contain more than others and some are made up of carbohydrates that are rapidly broken down by the body. Following a low-GI eating plan means incorporating more of the carbohydrates that are broken down slowly.

So why is it that one type of carbohydrate-rich food has a different GI from another? Why do potatoes, for example, have a higher GI than, say, lentils? It's all to do with the way Nature built them. Some starches, such as those found

As a general rule of thumb, the less processed a food is, the lower its GI value. The more work the body has to do in digesting it means the slower the sugar is released – and that's good news for keeping blood glucose steady.

in potatoes, are just very easy for the body to break down. Others such as those found in lentils are more difficult for the body to work on and so they break down more slowly. There are four main factors that determine how fast the body breaks down a carbohydrate-rich food: the type of starch it contains; the type of sugar it contains; how the food is cooked; and whether it is processed.

How do some popular foods rate?

Use the table as a rough guide to the GI of popular foods. To look up the GI of your favourite brands, check out the University of Sydney database at: **www.glycemicindex.com**

LOW-GI FOODS	MEDIUM-GI FOODS	HIGH-GI FOODS
All-Bran	Basmati rice	Cornflakes
Apples	Beetroot, canned	French fries
Baked beans	Couscous	Jasmine rice
Butternut pumpkin	Crumpets	Pikelets (flapjacks, drop scones)
Carrots	Good Start breakfast biscuits	Popcorn
Chickpeas	Honey, blended varieties	Potatoes
Corn (sweetcorn)	Muffins, fruit, commercially made	Pretzels, oven baked
Dried apricots	Pita bread	Puffed wheat
Fruit loaf	Potatoes, new	Rice cakes
Grainy breads	Shredded wheat biscuits	Scones
Honey, pure floral like yellow box	Sweet potatoes (kumara)	Water crackers
Hummus	Weet-Bix	White bread
Lentils		Wholemeal bread
Milk, lite or low-fat		
Muesli, natural		
Oranges		
Parsnips		
Pasta (made with durum wheat)		
Peaches and nectarines		
Pearl barley		
Pears		
Porridge made with traditional rolled oats		
Rice – Moolgiri or Doongara Clever rice		
Rye bread		
Soy milk, low-fat and calcium-enriched		
Stoneground wholemeal bread		
Sushi		
Tomato soup		
Yogurt, low-fat		

What is glycaemic load?

When reading about GI eating plans, you may come across the term 'glycaemic load' or GL. This is a measurement that takes into account both the quality of carbohydrate (its GI) in a food and the quantity. To get a bit technical, a food's GL is the GI multiplied by the amount of carbohydrate in one serving divided by 100. You can think of GL as the amount of carbohydrate in a food 'adjusted' for its glycaemic potency. Although the GL concept is useful in scientific research, it's the GI that's proven to be most helpful to people day to day. Emphasis on GL could lead to an unhealthy diet that is too high in saturated fat since the fattiest foods have the lowest GL values. If you choose low-GI foods – at least one at each meal – chances are you're eating a diet that not only keeps blood glucose within the healthy range, but contains balanced amounts of carbohydrates, fats and proteins.

Not all starches are equal

Starches are a type of carbohydrate, made of long chains of sugar molecules all joined together. Some of the long chains have straight edges, while others are branched. The straight-edged type, called amylose, is harder for the body's digestive enzymes to break down and turn into blood glucose. The branched type, called amylopectin, is much easier to break down because with its many branches, there are more places where the enzymes can get to work.

Most types of potato are high in amylopectin (the branched sugar chain), which is why they quickly raise your blood glucose, and have a high GI. Peas and beans, on the other hand, are high in amylose, the straight type of sugar chain, and so they are converted into blood glucose slowly. The more amylose a food contains, the more slowly it will be digested, so these are the types of food we should be looking for to tame our blood glucose levels.

Swapping to the right carbohydrate food is not as difficult as it at first sounds. You simply need to change a high-GI type for a low-GI type. Take rice, for example. Some contain less amylose (and so have a higher GI) than others. You can generally tell because low amylose types tend to be softer and stickier when cooked. Sticky rice is digested

Pasta is a GI favourite

Bread, even many wholemeal breads, can raise your blood glucose pretty quickly. Yet pasta, even if it's made from white flour, has a much lower GI. How can that be?

Imagine putting cooked pasta and a piece of bread in a bowl of water. The bread will fall apart, but the pasta won't. That's because in pasta dough, the starch granules get trapped in a network of protein molecules, so it takes more work – and more time – to get at them. That's why pasta releases its carbs much more slowly than potatoes or most breads do, especially if it's served al dente (slightly undercooked).

But watch your sauces. A huge bowl of overcooked pasta with a butter or cream sauce is not what the doctor ordered.

And remember, you can have too much of a good thing. Eating a huge amount of pasta will have a marked effect on your blood glucose. It's portion-caution time when it comes to serving up carb-rich foods.

quickly and so has a high GI, while a firmer type such as basmati, has more amylose and is therefore more slowly digested and has a lower GI. Make sure you don't overcook your basmati rice, though, as this will raise its GI.

Sweet enough?

You might assume that following a low-GI diet means avoiding sweet things at all costs, but this is not true. Different types of food contain different types of sugar and some are more quickly absorbed than others. Once again it is all about choosing the right type and eating more of that compared to the other types. There are three main types of sugar: sucrose (table sugar), fructose (found in fruit and non-starchy vegetables) and lactose (milk sugar). The sugars found in fruit and milk tend to be absorbed more slowly than table sugar. This is why low-fat milk and yogurt and all types of fruit are recommended on the low-GI eating plan.

Table sugar is not forbidden, but should be eaten in moderation and as part of a meal that has an overall low GI. For example, it is fine to add a little brown sugar to your porridge or a dollop of jam on a piece of grainy wholemeal toast. Or you could try some of the lower GI alternatives such as maple syrup, pure floral honey or agave syrup. A helpful side effect of following a low-GI diet is that your taste will change so that you need less of the 'pure' sugar – you'll be sweet enough without it!

Overcooking raises the GI

Another important factor in keeping GI levels in foods as low as possible is by not overcooking them. If we overcook rice or pasta, for instance, the GI increases, even in the better types. This is because the heat from cooking breaks down some of the chains of sugars so that when the food hits your stomach some of the work is done already and the body digests it more quickly.

Processed food: GI enemy number one

Although no food is prohibited on the GI eating plan, it has to be said that processed foods are best avoided as much as possible. Think of shop-bought pies, cakes and pastries. Not only are they laden

Top 10 GI Superfoods

The following GI 'Superfoods' are particularly nutritious as well as having a low GI. Feel free to incorporate as many of these foods into your diet as you can. You may be surprised to see vinegar on the list, yet it has been shown to lower the GI of any dish it is used in. Scientists think it may be to do with the way acid slows carbohydrate digestion. So make sure you have a vinaigrette dressing on your salad. The same is true for citrus fruit (and other acidic foods, see page 245).

- legumes
- rolled oats
- barley
- rye
- wholemeal pasta
- low-fat dairy foods
- citrus fruit
- apples and pears
- soy milk
- vinegar

with fats (including trans fats) and sugars, the commercial flour used has been milled and processed so much that it is extremely easy for the body to digest, making it high GI.

Up until the 19th century the main way of turning grain into flour was to grind it between stones. Today modern high-speed, high-heat rollers have replaced the millstones and the highly refined white flour produced is a blood glucose nightmare. White breads may be smooth and soft, but they are so quickly digested you might as well be eating a piece of cake. Even 'brown' bread may simply be made with white flour that has been artificially coloured. Do your blood sugar a favour and choose bread made with stoneground wholemeal flour that has been milled in an old-fashioned manner. When it comes to grains choose whole, intact grains such as pearl barley and buckwheat kernels. In fact, as a general rule of thumb, the less processed a food is,

the lower its GI value. The more work the body has to do in digesting it means the slower the sugar is released – and that's good news for keeping blood glucose steady.

The fibre factor

Dietary fibre is not a nutrient as such, since it is not actually absorbed into the body. Nevertheless it is an extremely important element in a healthy diet. It is no coincidence that many of the low-GI foods are high in fibre.

Dietary fibre is found only in plant foods. There are two types: soluble and insoluble. Soluble fibre dissolves in water and is found in oats, barley, beans and some fruit and vegetables and has been shown to reduce cholesterol in your blood, protecting your heart. It also helps to keep blood glucose levels steady. Insoluble fibre, or roughage, is found in wholegrains and most fruit and vegetables. It helps to keep the bowel working properly and provides bulk in your stomach, so that you feel full for longer.

Add some fibre

Eating more foods rich in soluble fibre is a good strategy for making your diet more GI friendly. It will also improve your health in other ways. Porridge is well known for lowering cholesterol, but scientists now think it may also lower levels of triglycerides and reduce blood pressure.

Lots of other foods are rich in soluble fibre, including barley, fruit and vegetables, beans, lentils, chickpeas, linseeds, psyllium, rice bran and soy products. Many health experts say that the average adult should aim to consume 20–30 g of dietary fibre a day. It's not difficult to achieve this; here are some ideas:

- Eat 2 servings of fruit and 5 servings of vegetables a day
- Eat porridge or muesli with fruit and nuts for breakfast
- Snack on fruit and nuts
- Choose low-GI grainy, stoneground wholemeal, or soy and linseed breads
- Pack in the pulses: try adding lentils to soups and sauces, add chickpeas to salads or serve as a side dish.

Protein

Protein is needed by the body to build tissues and muscles, among other things, so we need to include it in our diets. The plus point for anyone following a low-GI eating plan is

that most protein foods such as fish, meat, milk, eggs, cheese and soy have a low GI. The body also takes a long time to break down protein and this slows digestion of the whole meal, slowing the release of glucose into the blood – and making you feel fuller for longer. Protein also helps to keep your metabolism running at full speed, so you are more likely to burn fat rather than store it. It is a good idea to make sure you include some protein in every meal, even as part of a snack.

But you will need to be choosy about the type of protein you eat. Avoid fatty meat such as bacon, especially if you are trying to lose weight. Opt for lean meat, such as skinless chicken, fish and low-fat milk and yogurt. Pulses (beans and lentils) are a good source of protein as they are low in fat and high in fibre, making them a GI favourite. Nuts also provide protein, but eat them in moderation since they also have a high fat (and therefore calorie) content.

Good and bad fats

Like protein, fat doesn't affect your blood glucose levels and it takes a while to digest – both advantageous for a low-GI diet. In the past the perceived wisdom was that the less fat you ate, the better, but researchers are finding that this isn't true. Just as not all carbohydrates are equal, there are good

Drink in moderation is ok

According to research carried out at the University of Sydney, moderate drinking – up to one standard drink a day for women or two for men – is actually beneficial for your health. Researchers found that a drink before dinner (two 'standard' glasses of beer or wine) lowered blood glucose levels after the meal. But remember that the 'standard' amount is probably less than you think. It equates to just 285 ml of beer or half a glass (100 ml) of wine. Be careful not to overindulge: people who consume three or more drinks a day have a much higher risk of diabetes and heart disease.

fats and bad fats. Healthy eating means choosing the good fats in preference to the bad. Nevertheless, all fats are high in calories so you should still keep an eye on the amount you eat, especially if you wish to lose weight.

The good fats include:

● Monounsaturates: olive oil, canola (rapeseed) oil, avocados, nuts. These have a beneficial effect on cholesterol and help to reverse insulin resistance.

● Omega-3 fats: fatty fish such as salmon, sardines or mackerel; linseed and canola (rapeseed) oil. These help prevent heart disease and may improve insulin sensitivity.

● Polyunsaturated fats: corn, soy bean and safflower seeds.

The bad fats include:

● Saturated fats: red meat, butter, cheese, a few vegetable oils such as coconut or palm oil. These raise the levels of 'bad' LDL cholesterol, promote heart disease and reduce insulin sensitivity.

● Trans fats: found in solid margarine and hydrogenated vegetable oils as well as deep-fried snacks, commercial baked goods and fast foods. They raise 'bad' LDL cholesterol, lower 'good' HDL cholesterol, increase heart disease risk and may increase insulin resistance.

When and how much to eat

The amount of food you need to eat depends on your level of physical activity, but there are some GI principles you should follow. Aim to eat little and often, so that your calories are spread throughout the day. This will keep your blood sugar steady all day long. Always start the day with a healthy breakfast and follow this with a mid-morning snack, such as an apple and a few toasted almonds. After a healthy low-GI lunch, have a mid-afternoon snack of, say, a wholesome muffin. This should keep you going until the evening meal. With so many delicious recipes listed here for you to choose from, your food should never be dull.

Portion size is key

Although swapping low-GI foods for high-GI foods will go a long way to bringing your blood glucose under control and helping you to stay in the fat-burning zone, you will also need to look at your portion size. As mentioned, foods that have a low GI are not necessarily low in fat, and over-consumption will lead to weight gain. The recipes in this book specify the serving sizes, but if you begin to create your own meals, pay attention to the portion size and soon it will become second nature. Use the following guidelines:

● Pasta: $2/3$ cup (60 g) uncooked
● Rice: $1/3$ cup (65 g) uncooked
● Boiled new potatoes: 2 or 3 small
● Stoneground wholemeal, or any low-GI bread: 1 slice
● Meat or fish: 100 g, about the size of a deck of cards
● Non-starchy vegetables and fruit: unlimited.

Putting it all on your plate

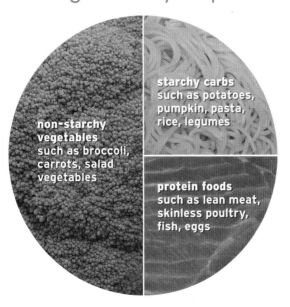

non-starchy vegetables such as broccoli, carrots, salad vegetables

starchy carbs such as potatoes, pumpkin, pasta, rice, legumes

protein foods such as lean meat, skinless poultry, fish, eggs

Here's an easy way to help you serve up balanced meals without having to fuss and weigh foods. After a few weeks it will become a habit.

● Fill $1/4$ of the plate with starchy carbs (preferably low GI) such as new potatoes, a small cob of corn (sweetcorn), pumpkin, pasta or legumes.

● Fill $1/4$ of the plate with protein foods such as lean meats, fish, skinless poultry, eggs or legumes.

● Fill $1/2$ the plate with non-starchy vegetables from green leafy vegetables, broccoli and carrots to salad vegetables.

● If you are trying to control your weight, it may be helpful to try using a smaller plate.

Smart substitutions

Following a low-GI eating plan is simple: just eat less of the high-GI foods, or replace them with lower-GI foods. Your main area to watch is processed foods as these contain large amounts of sugar as well as unhealthy fats. Making meals from scratch will do wonders for your diet and will save you money, too.

HIGH-GI FOOD	SUBSTITUTION
Mashed, baked, fried or instant potatoes	Sweet potato (kumara), pulses, boiled new potatoes (2 or 3 in a serving)
Processed breakfast cereals such as Cornflakes, shredded wheat and rice crispies	Homemade muesli, porridge (rolled oats), All-Bran
Shop-bought muffins	Homemade wholesome muffins
White and brown processed bread, bagels	Stoneground wholemeal bread, seedy mixed grain breads, sourdough, rye and pumpernickel breads, oatcakes
Jasmine rice, sticky rice, pudding rice	White and brown basmati rice, red and wild rice, brown rice
Wheat and rice noodles	Wholemeal or white pasta, cellophane and glass noodles (made from pea and bean flours)
Sweets and confectionery	Berries, cherries, grapes, toasted nuts, or dark chocolate made with 80% cocoa solids (in small amounts)
Cakes	Fruit, homemade sweet treats

A commonsense approach

The low-GI eating plan is not a rigid diet. Following the basic principles will make you healthier and full of energy. If you have weight to lose, you should see this starting to drop off – but don't expect to lose 3 kg in a week or anything as extreme. You should be aiming for $1/2$ kg a week. If, after a while, you notice that you have stopped losing weight and need to lose more, take a close look at what you are eating – and the amount. A calorie is a calorie and if you consume more than you expend – whether through low-GI foods or not – you will put on weight. Regular exercise can really boost your weight loss and make you feel good, too.

Seven steps to success

There are seven steps to staying on the GI wagon, and they couldn't be simpler:

1 Choose low-GI carbohydrates and keep an eye on the portion size
2 Eat regularly: three meals and two or three healthy snacks a day
3 Eat more whole grains, including pulses
4 Load your plate with fruit and vegetables
5 Eat healthy protein with every meal, even snacks
6 Favour the good fats and avoid the bad
7 Choose fresh produce over processed foods.

Fruity Bircher muesli **20**
Fruit and nut porridge **23**
Apricot pecan muffins **24**
Strawberry yogurt smoothie **25**
Blueberry and cranberry crunch **26**
Cottage cheese medley **28**
Mushroom and herb omelette **29**
Apple-berry soufflé omelette **31**
Orange and oat muesli squares **32**

Breakfasts

Fruity Bircher muesli

GI estimate LOW

Dr Bircher-Benner developed the original recipe for this nutritious breakfast cereal over a century ago. Soaking the cereal in milk makes it easier to digest, and also easier to eat. The combination of rolled oats, nuts and fruit makes a satisfying and low-GI meal.

PREPARATION: 10 minutes, plus overnight soaking   SERVES 4

1 cup (115 g) rolled oats
$3/4$ cup (115 g) sultanas
1 cup (250 ml) lite or low-fat milk
1 sweet red or green apple
2 teaspoons lemon juice
$1/4$ cup (30 g) roughly chopped
    hazelnuts
2 tablespoons pumpkin seeds
1 tablespoon sesame seeds
$2/3$ cup (100 g) strawberries,
    hulled and chopped
4 tablespoons low-fat natural yogurt
4 teaspoons pure floral honey

FOR EVEN LOWER GI
Replace the sultanas with peeled, pithed segments of orange, and add with the strawberries.

Each serving provides
1593 kJ, 380 kcal, 12 g protein, 12 g fat
(2 g saturated fat), 57 g carbohydrate
(38 g sugars), 7 g fibre

1   Place the oats and sultanas in a large bowl and add the milk. Stir to mix evenly, then cover and place in the refrigerator. Leave to soak overnight.

2   The next day, just before eating, grate the apple, discarding the core. Toss the apple with the lemon juice – this will prevent the flesh from browning.

3   Stir the hazelnuts, pumpkin seeds and sesame seeds into the oat mixture, then stir in the grated apple with the strawberries.

4   To serve, divide the muesli among 4 cereal bowls, and top each with a spoonful of yogurt and honey.

ANOTHER IDEA
● To make a mixed grain muesli, soak $1/4$ cup (25 g) rolled oats, $1/3$ cup (25 g) wheat bran flakes, 30 g flaked rice and $3/4$ cup (115 g) raisins in 1 cup (250 ml) buttermilk. Just before eating, stir in 1 tablespoon chopped almonds and 1 tablespoon sunflower seeds, then add the grated apple. Serve with natural yogurt.

HEALTHY EATING

● Oats have a low GI, and so produce a gentle, sustained rise in blood glucose levels. This breakfast should keep you going until lunchtime.

● The protein in the hazelnuts, pumpkin seeds and sesame seeds helps to keep hunger at bay and makes the meal more satisfying.

Fruit and nut porridge

There is nothing like a warm bowl of porridge on a winter's day, but you can eat this healthy breakfast all through the year. The nuts and almond meal boost the protein content, helping to make you feel full for longer. The grapes add natural sweetness.

GI estimate LOW

PREPARATION: 2 minutes COOKING: 4-8 minutes SERVES 1

1 Place the oats, milk and water in a small pan. Heat slowly and bring to a simmer. Cook for about 4-8 minutes (follow packet instructions), stirring, until the mixture thickens.

2 Stir in the almond meal and pour the porridge into a serving bowl. Sprinkle the wheat germ over the porridge, followed by the hazelnuts and grapes.

COOK'S TIP
● If you can't find toasted hazelnuts, buy whole nuts and chop and toast them in batches yourself. Just place them in a tray under a high grill for a few minutes, watching closely.

SOME MORE IDEAS
● Swap the grapes with berries, when in season, such as blackberries, raspberries or blueberries.

● If you don't have any fresh fruit, canned fruit (preferably canned in fruit juice or water with no added sugar) makes a handy year-round substitute.

● Add more crunch by finely chopping up a sweet red or green apple and adding it instead of the grapes.

● Try toasted almond flakes instead of hazelnuts.

● Add $1/2$ teaspoon cinnamon to the pan and then stir in some stewed apple to the cooked porridge.

$1/2$ cup (50 g) rolled oats
$1/2$ cup (125 ml) lite or low-fat milk
$1/2$ cup (125 ml) water
1 tablespoon almond meal (ground almonds)
2 teaspoons wheat germ
1 tablespoon hazelnuts, toasted and chopped
$1/2$ cup (90 g) black grapes, halved

Each serving provides
1734 kJ, 414 kcal, 16 g protein, 15 g fat (2 g saturated fat), 53 g carbohydrate (23 g sugars), 7 g fibre

HEALTHY EATING

● Oats not only have a low GI, they have other health benefits too, including lowering cholesterol.

● Hazelnuts contain 'good' fats, but you still need to limit your portions. If you're eating them as a snack, stick to a small handful (no more than 20) at a time.

● Wheat germ is a good source of B vitamins and vitamin E.

Apricot pecan muffins

GI estimate MEDIUM

PREPARATION: 25 minutes   COOKING: 20-25 minutes   MAKES 12 muffins

1 ³/₄ cups (220 g) plain flour
¹/₂ cup (75 g) strong bread flour
2 teaspoons baking powder
pinch of salt
¹/₂ cup (115 g) soft brown sugar
1 teaspoon ground cinnamon
3 tablespoons wheat bran
¹/₂ teaspoon grated lemon zest
240 ml lite or low-fat milk
2 eggs
4 tablespoons canola (rapeseed) oil
225 g ripe but firm apricots, stoned
    and diced
¹/₂ cup (60 g) chopped pecans

FOR LOWER GI
Replace the brown sugar with pure floral honey, reducing the amount of milk to 130 ml.

Each muffin provides
1012 kJ, 242 kcal, 6 g protein, 11 g fat
(1 g saturated fat), 31 g carbohydrate
(12 g sugars), 2 g fibre

1 Preheat the oven to 200°C (Gas 6). Lightly grease a deep 12-hole muffin tray.

2 Sift the flours, baking powder, salt, sugar and cinnamon into a bowl. Stir in the wheat bran and lemon zest. Combine the milk, eggs and oil in a jug, mixing well. Pour into the dry ingredients and add the diced apricots and pecans. Stir just until the dry ingredients are moistened. Do not overmix.

3 Spoon into the prepared muffin tray, filling the cups two-thirds full. Bake for 20-25 minutes or until risen and golden brown and a wooden cocktail stick inserted into the centre of a muffin comes out clean. Leave to cool in the tins for 2-3 minutes, then turn out onto a wire rack to finish cooling. The muffins are best served warm.

SOME MORE IDEAS

● For blueberry muffins, use 1¹/₂ cups (235 g) fresh blueberries instead of the apricots. Substitute 1 teaspoon grated orange zest for the lemon zest and omit the pecans.

● Chopped strawberries, peaches or nectarines can also be used, but the fruit must not be too ripe and mushy or it will make the muffin mixture too wet.

● Use ³/₄ cup (90 g) raisins or sultanas instead of apricots, with walnuts instead of pecans.

Strawberry yogurt smoothie

GI estimate LOW

PREPARATION: 5 minutes   SERVES 4

1   Tip the strawberries into a food processor or blender and
add the grated orange zest, orange juice and yogurt. Blend
to a smooth purée, scraping down the sides of the container
once or twice. Taste the mixture and sweeten with the sugar,
if necessary.

2   For a really smooth consistency, press through a nylon sieve
to remove the strawberry pips, although this is not essential.

3   Pour into glasses. If you like, decorate with small
strawberries and slices of orange, both split so they sit on
the rim of the glass.

3 cups (450 g) ripe strawberries, hulled
grated zest and juice of 1 large orange
$^2/_3$ cup (160 g) low-fat natural yogurt
1 tablespoon caster sugar, or to taste
   (optional)

TO DECORATE (OPTIONAL)
4 small strawberries
4 small slices of orange

Each serving provides
285 kJ, 68 kcal, 4 g protein, <1 g fat (0 g
saturated fat), 11 g carbohydrate (11 g sugars),
3 g fibre

HEALTHY EATING

● Strawberries, like most fresh
fruit, have a low GI. They are also
low in calories and are an excellent
source of vitamin C.

● By adding as little caster sugar as
possible you will keep the GI low.
After following the GI healthy eating
plan for a few weeks you will find
that your taste has changed and you
will naturally need less sugar to
sweeten your food.

Blueberry and cranberry crunch

GI estimate LOW

Stirring maple syrup and orange juice into the mix of grains, nuts and berries helps to keep this recipe lower in fat than most ready-made 'crunchy' cereals. This delicious toasted muesli is also low GI, so make up a big batch that will last you through the week.

PREPARATION: 40-50 minutes, plus cooling   MAKES 8 servings

2 ¼ cups (225 g) rolled oats
½ cup (45 g) wheat germ
⅔ cup (50 g) millet flakes
1 tablespoon sesame seeds
2 tablespoons sunflower seeds
2 tablespoons flaked almonds
½ cup (50 g) dried blueberries
½ cup (50 g) dried cranberries
1 tablespoon soft brown sugar
2 tablespoons pure maple syrup
2 tablespoons canola (rapeseed) oil
2 tablespoons orange juice

FOR EVEN LOWER GI
Use agave syrup instead of maple syrup as a sweetener.

Each serving provides
1101 kJ, 263 kcal, 6 g protein, 11 g fat
(2 g saturated fat), 35 g carbohydrate
(12 g sugars), 5 g fibre

1 Preheat the oven to 160°C (Gas 3). In a large bowl, combine the oats, wheat germ, millet flakes, sesame and sunflower seeds, almonds, dried berries and sugar. Stir until all the ingredients are thoroughly mixed.

2 Put the maple syrup, oil and orange juice in a small jug and whisk together. Pour this mixture slowly into the dry ingredients, stirring to ensure that the liquid is evenly distributed and coats everything lightly.

3 Spread the mixture out evenly in a non-stick baking tray. Bake for 30-40 minutes or until slightly crisp and lightly browned. Stir the mixture every 10 minutes to encourage even browning.

4 Remove from the oven and leave to cool. Store in an airtight container for up to two weeks. Serve with low-fat natural yogurt, low-fat milk or fruit juice.

COOK'S TIP
● Read the label to make sure you are using pure maple syrup and not a high-GI blend bulked out with corn syrup.

SOME MORE IDEAS
● For a chunkier muesli, replace the millet with barley flakes and the berries with a mixture of roughly chopped dried apples or apricots. A little shredded coconut can also be added, if liked.
● The maple syrup can be replaced with pure floral honey, and the flaked almonds with chopped hazelnuts.
● If you prefer, replace some of the berries with dried cherries.

HEALTHY EATING

● Maple syrup has a lower GI (54) than table sugar (68), although pure floral honey is even lower (44). The sweetener with the lowest GI of all is agave syrup (20).

● This breakfast supplies plenty of fibre, B vitamins and essential fatty acids. Wheat germ is especially rich in B vitamins and vitamin E.

Cottage cheese medley

PREPARATION: 5 minutes   SERVES 1

1 medium slice of wholemeal stoneground bread or rye bread, toasted

4 tablespoons (about 100 g) cottage cheese

1 tablespoon chopped walnuts

1 teaspoon ground linseeds (flax seeds)

handful sprouted alfalfa or mung beans

1 pear or apple, sliced

Each serving provides
1377 kJ, 329 kcal, 21 g protein, 15 g fat
(5 g saturated fat), 28 g carbohydrate
(20 g sugars), 8 g fibre

1 While the bread is toasting, mix the ground linseeds into the cottage cheese. Spread the mixture onto the toast. Sprinkle on the walnuts.

2 Wash and drain the alfalfa or mung bean sprouts and use enough to spread over the top of the cottage cheese mix.

3 Top with sliced pear or apple.

COOK'S TIP

● You can buy ground linseeds from health food shops, or buy them whole and grind them yourself in a coffee grinder or with a pestle and mortar. Store them in the refrigerator.

HEALTHY EATING

● Cottage cheese is low fat and has a low GI. It provides a healthy protein hit that will help to stop you feeling hungry right up to lunchtime.

● Linseeds contain omega-3 type fats, which keep your heart healthy and guard against insulin resistance and diabetes. They also contain useful amounts of magnesium, protein and fibre.

Mushroom and herb omelette

GI estimate LOW

PREPARATION: 5 minutes   COOKING: 10 minutes   SERVES 1

1   Crack the eggs into a bowl, then add the chervil, tarragon, chives, 1 tablespoon water and pepper to taste. Beat just enough to break up the eggs. Set on one side while preparing the mushrooms.

2   Heat an 18 cm omelette or non-stick frying pan. Add the sliced mushrooms and garlic, and cook gently for 3–4 minutes or until the mushrooms have softened and released their juices. Turn up the heat a little and continue cooking for a further minute or until the mushroom juices have evaporated. Tip the mushrooms into a small bowl and set aside. Wipe the pan clean with a paper towel.

3   Heat the pan over a high heat for a few seconds until hot. Add the oil, tilting the pan to coat the bottom. Pour in the egg and herb mixture. Cook for about 1 minute, stirring gently with a wooden spatula and letting the liquid egg spread out in the pan so that it cooks.

4   When the omelette holds together, stop stirring and cook for a further 30 seconds or until the underside is golden brown. The top surface should be just setting.

5   Scatter the mushrooms along the middle of the omelette. Using the spatula, fold an outside third of the omelette into the centre, over the mushrooms, then fold the opposite third over that. Quickly slide the folded omelette onto a warmed plate and serve immediately.

2 large eggs
1 tablespoon chopped fresh chervil
1 tablespoon chopped fresh tarragon
1 teaspoon snipped fresh chives
$^2/_3$ cup (60 g) sliced mushrooms
1 garlic clove, crushed
1 tablespoon canola (rapeseed) oil
freshly ground pepper

Each serving provides
1455 kJ, 348 kcal, 18 g protein, 30 g fat
(5 g saturated fat), 2 g carbohydrate
(1 g sugars), 2 g fibre

HEALTHY EATING

● The protein in eggs helps to make you feel full. They also contain useful amounts of vitamins A, D and K, as well as all the B vitamins, iron and zinc. White and brown eggs are nutritionally the same.

HEALTHY EATING

● Most types of fruit naturally have a low GI and poaching them in orange juice (which is acidic) lowers the GI even further.

● The use of eating apples instead of a cooking variety means that they need only light cooking and therefore not only retain their shape and texture but also much of their nutritive value too. They are naturally sweet, so require less added sugar, keeping the GI value low.

Apple-berry soufflé omelette

GI estimate LOW

This light, sweet omelette should be cooked just before serving. In late summer/early autumn it makes a special weekend breakfast, or can be served as a simple yet delectable dessert.

PREPARATION: 15 minutes   COOKING: 5-8 minutes   SERVES 2

1 Peel, core and thickly slice the apples. Put into a small saucepan and add the blackberries, ground allspice and orange juice. Cover and heat gently for 2-3 minutes, shaking the pan occasionally, until the fruit juices run. Remove the fruit from the heat and keep warm.

2 Put the egg yolks, caster sugar, orange zest and vanilla extract in a bowl, and whisk together until smooth and thick.

3 In a separate, clean bowl, whisk the eggwhites until they form soft peaks. Using a large spoon or spatula, fold the whites into the yolk mixture.

4 Preheat the grill to moderately hot. Heat the oil in a 20 cm non-stick frying pan with a heatproof handle. Tip in the egg mixture, spreading it evenly, and cook gently for 2-3 minutes or until set and golden on the base.

5 Place the pan under the grill and cook for 1-2 minutes or until the omelette is puffed up and just set on top. Remove from the heat and turn up the grill to high.

6 Spoon the fruit mixture on top of the omelette and fold it over in half. Sprinkle with raw sugar and grill for about 30 seconds or until the sugar caramelises. Cut the omelette in half and serve immediately, topped with the yogurt.

SOME MORE IDEAS

● For a cherry soufflé omelette, replace the apples and blackberries with 1 cup (150 g) pitted red cherries. Poach with 1 tablespoon caster sugar and a star anise until the juices run. Make the omelette as in the main recipe, but replace the vanilla extract with pure almond extract.

● Make a pear and ginger soufflé omelette. Peel, core and dice two pears and poach with orange juice plus $1/2$ teaspoon powdered ginger and $1/4$ teaspoon cinnamon. Use the fruit to fill the omelette made as in the main recipe.

2 crisp sweet apples
$1/2$ cup (65 g) blackberries
$1/2$ teaspoon ground allspice
finely grated zest and juice of $1/2$ orange
$1/2$ tablespoon caster sugar
2 eggs, separated
$1/2$ teaspoon pure vanilla extract
2 teaspoons canola (rapeseed) oil
1 teaspoon raw (demerara) sugar
2 tablespoons Greek-style yogurt

FOR EVEN LOWER GI

In step 6 do not grill the omelette or add sugar. Instead, drizzle some agave syrup or pure floral honey over the warm omelette.

Each serving provides
1363 kJ, 326 kcal, 9 g protein, 12 g fat (3 g saturated fat), 47 g carbohydrate (46 g sugars), 5 g fibre

Orange and oat muesli squares

GI estimate MEDIUM

These light and fruity muesli squares will appeal to the whole family. They are a little higher in their GI and calories than other breakfasts, so save them for special occasions or when you have a busy day ahead. Serve with fresh fruit for a 'get up and go' breakfast.

PREPARATION: 10 minutes   COOKING: 20-25 minutes   MAKES 9 squares

2 tablespoons sesame seeds
$^1/_4$ cup (60 g) non-hydrogenated soft
   margarine
4 tablespoons golden syrup
2 tablespoons soft brown sugar
grated zest of 1 orange
$^1/_2$ cup (125 ml) orange juice
$2^1/_2$ cups (250 g) rolled oats

FOR LOWER GI
Use agave syrup instead of golden syrup.

Each serving provides
881 kJ, 210 kcal, 4 g protein, 8 g fat
(2 g saturated fat), 29 g carbohydrate
(13 g sugars), 3 g fibre

1   Preheat the oven to 200°C (Gas 6). Toast the sesame seeds in a small dry frying pan for a few minutes or until golden, then tip out onto a plate and leave to cool.

2   Place the margarine, golden syrup, sugar, and orange zest and juice in a large saucepan and stir over a low heat for about 2 minutes or until the sugar has dissolved. Remove from the heat.

3   Add the sesame seeds and rolled oats to the melted mixture and stir until the oats are well moistened. Pour the mixture into a greased 19 cm square shallow cake tin and press down evenly with the back of a spoon. Bake for 20-25 minutes or until golden brown on top and firm to the touch.

4   Leave to cool in the tin for about 5 minutes, then cut the mixture into 9 squares. Leave in place in the tin for a further 10 minutes or until the muesli squares are quite firm. Remove from the tin with a palette knife and allow to cool further on a wire rack. They can be stored in an airtight container for up to 2 days.

SOME MORE IDEAS

● For honey and banana squares, use 3 tablespoons pure floral honey instead of the golden syrup, and the grated zest and juice of 1 large lemon instead of the orange. Add 1 diced banana to the mixture with the oats.

● For apricot and apple squares, add $^3/_4$ cup (100 g) chopped dried apricots and 2 peeled, cored and diced sweet apples with the oats. Omit the sesame seeds.

HEALTHY EATING

● Rolled oats are whole oat grains that have simply been husked and then rolled to flatten, and thus contain all of the nutrients of the whole grain. This is why they have a lower GI than the processed cereals on the market.

● Sesame seeds provide calcium, which is essential for healthy bones and teeth, as well as vitamin E, an antioxidant that helps to protect against cancer.

Wholesome muffins **37**

Garlicky fresh cheese **38**

Corn fritters **40**

Spiced couscous tomatoes **41**

Turkish eggplant and yogurt dip **42**

Spicy vegetable wedges **45**

High-vitality milk shake **46**

Spiced fruits, nuts and seeds **47**

Gravlax with ginger **48**

Sweet potato and celeriac purée **50**

Boston baked beans **51**

Snacks and light bites

HEALTHY EATING

● The stoneground flour and bran give these muffins a low GI. The apple and blueberries add natural sweetness and moisture.

● Apples and blueberries have a lower GI than the raisins and sultanas often used in shop-bought muffins.

● Wheat bran contains the indigestible fibrous part of the wheat grain. It helps to provide the bulk that keeps the digestive system healthy and it has a low GI.

Wholesome muffins

GI estimate LOW

Shop-bought muffins have earned themselves a bad reputation when it comes to healthy eating, but here is a recipe for a more virtuous kind using stoneground flour, nuts and fruit.

PREPARATION: 15 minutes   COOKING: 15–18 minutes   MAKES 12 muffins

1   Preheat the oven to 200°C (Gas 6). Lightly grease a deep 12-hole muffin tray.

2   Whisk the eggs and the sugar together in a large bowl until blended. In a small bowl, lightly mash the apple cubes so that about half are still in shape and stir into the egg-and-sugar mixture. Stir in the lemon juice. Measure out the milk and add the oil and vanilla extract to it. Now add the liquid to the bowl followed by the wheat bran. Mix well.

3   Measure out the flour and add the baking powder, bicarbonate of soda, spices and salt to it, giving it a stir to distribute the ingredients. Add this to the mixture in the large bowl, stirring lightly until all the dry ingredients are incorporated. Fold in the blueberries.

4   Spoon the mixture into the muffin tray and sprinkle with the chopped mixed nuts.

5   Bake near the top of the oven for 15–18 minutes. If the tops of the muffins spring back when lightly pressed, or a wooden cocktail stick inserted into the centre of a muffin comes out clean, the muffins are ready. If not give them another few minutes and check again. Don't let them overcook or they will be dry. Let the muffins cool in the tray for a few minutes, before easing them out and placing them on a cooling rack. Delicious served warm.

COOK'S TIP
● Make a batch of muffins for the week. They will keep for a couple of days, or you can wrap them individually in aluminium foil and freeze. Take out of the freezer and allow to thaw overnight, ready for a snack the next day.

2 medium eggs
1/2 cup (100 g) soft brown sugar
half a 400 g can of diced apple (unsweetened)
juice of half a lemon
200 ml lite or low-fat milk
3 tablespoons canola (rapeseed) oil
1 teaspoon vanilla extract
50 g wheat bran
1 cup (200 g) stoneground wholemeal flour
2 teaspoons baking powder
1 teaspoon bicarbonate of soda
2 teaspoons ground cinnamon
1/2 teaspoon ground nutmeg
pinch of salt
1/2 cup (85 g) blueberries, washed and dried
2 tablespoons chopped mixed nuts

Each muffin provides
740 kJ, 177 kcal, 5 g protein, 7 g fat
(1 g saturated fat), 23 g carbohydrate
(12 g sugars), 4 g fibre

Garlicky fresh cheese

This tangy, soft-textured yogurt cheese, flavoured with herbs and garlic, makes a healthy starter or snack, and is a great addition to a picnic basket, too. The garlic is blanched for a sweeter flavour. Serve with fresh vegetables for dipping and grainy low-GI bread.

PREPARATION and COOKING: 30–35 minutes, plus overnight draining   SERVES 4

^{2}/3 cup (160 g) low-fat natural yogurt

^{2}/3 cup (160 g) creamed cottage cheese
(or plain low-fat fromage frais)

2 large garlic cloves, unpeeled

1 tablespoon snipped fresh chives

1 tablespoon chopped parsley

2 teaspoons chopped fresh dill

1 teaspoon finely grated lemon zest

1 head witlof (Belgian endive/chicory),
leaves separated

4 carrots, peeled and cut into
5 cm sticks

1 bunch spring onions

4 celery sticks, cut into 5 cm sticks

4 slices stoneground wholemeal or
other grainy low-GI bread, cut into
large chunks

Each serving provides
744 kJ, 178 kcal, 15 g protein, 5 g fat
(2 g saturated fat), 17 g carbohydrate
(9 g sugars), 8 g fibre

1 Line a deep sieve with a double thickness of muslin and set over a bowl. Mix together the yogurt and cheese until smooth, then spoon into the muslin-lined sieve. Wrap the muslin over the top and put into the refrigerator. Leave to drain overnight.

2 The next day, drop the unpeeled garlic cloves into a small pan of boiling water and simmer for 3 minutes or until soft. Drain. Squeeze the garlic out of the skins and mash or chop.

3 Unwrap the drained yogurt mixture and put it into a clean bowl (discard the liquid that has drained from the mixture). Add the blanched garlic, herbs and lemon zest to the yogurt cheese, mix well and season to taste. (The yogurt cheese can be kept, covered, in the fridge for up to 4 days.)

4 Spoon the yogurt cheese into a small bowl and set on a platter. Arrange the witlof leaves, prepared vegetables and bread chunks around, and serve.

SOME MORE IDEAS

● Thoroughly chill the yogurt cheese, then form it into a small 'barrel' shape. Roll in ^{2}/3 cup (85 g) finely chopped walnuts or hazelnuts to coat on all sides.

● For an olive and caper cheese, mash ^{2}/3 cup (50 g) fetta and stir into the freshly drained yogurt cheese together with ^{1}/2 teaspoon crushed dried chillies, 1 crushed garlic clove, 1 tablespoon chopped capers, 1 tablespoon chopped black olives, 1 tablespoon chopped fresh oregano and seasoning to taste. Serve as a starter or snack for 6, with the crudités and pieces of toasted wholemeal pita bread.

HEALTHY EATING

● Look at the healthy balance of food groups in this dish: protein from the soft cheese, some low-GI carbohydrate from the bread and half of the plate covered in vegetables.

● This homemade soft cheese is much lower in fat than similar commercial cheeses, yet it is just as tasty. There is no need to add salt as the herbs, garlic and lemon provide lots of flavour.

Corn fritters

PREPARATION and COOKING: 30 minutes   SERVES 4 (makes 12 fritters)

1¼ cups (310 g) Greek-style yogurt

4 spring onions, finely chopped

2 tablespoons chopped fresh mint

grated zest and juice of 1 lime

pinch of salt

1 cup (150 g) plain flour

½ teaspoon baking powder

150 ml lite or low-fat milk

2 large eggs, lightly beaten

1⅔ cups (400 g) frozen corn
    (sweetcorn) kernels, thawed and
    drained

3 spring onions, finely chopped

1 red chilli, seeded and finely chopped

3 heaped tablespoons chopped fresh
    coriander

1 tablespoon canola (rapeseed) oil

3¾ cups (115 g) watercress

FOR LOWER GI

Make pea fritters by replacing the corn
with frozen peas. Use chopped fresh
basil in place of coriander.

Each serving provides
550 kJ, 131 kcal, 5 g protein, 5 g fat
(2 g saturated fat), 16 g carbohydrate
(4 g sugars), 2 g fibre

1   First make the yogurt sauce. Put the yogurt into a serving
    bowl and stir in the spring onions, mint, lime zest and a
    pinch of salt. Cover and chill while you make the fritters
    (keep the lime juice for use later).

2   Sift the flour and baking powder into a bowl. Make a well in
    the centre and add the milk and eggs. Using a wooden
    spoon, mix together the milk and eggs, then gradually draw
    in the flour from around the edges. Beat with the spoon to
    make a smooth, thick batter.

3   Add the corn kernels, spring onions, chilli and coriander to
    the batter, and season to taste. Mix together well.

4   Heat a griddle or large, heavy frying pan, then brush with
    a little of the oil. Drop large spoonfuls of the fritter batter
    onto the pan - make about 4 fritters at a time - and cook
    over a moderate heat for 2 minutes or until golden and firm
    on the underside. Turn the fritters over using a palette knife,
    and cook on the other side for about 2 minutes or until
    golden brown.

5   Remove the fritters from the pan and drain on a paper
    towel. Keep warm while cooking the rest of the fritters in the
    same way, adding more oil to the pan as necessary. Arrange
    the watercress on 4 plates and sprinkle with the lime juice.
    Arrange the corn fritters on top and serve hot, with the
    yogurt sauce to be drizzled over.

Spiced couscous tomatoes

PREPARATION and COOKING: 25 minutes   SERVES 4

1 Cut the tops off the tomatoes and scoop out the insides. Put the seeds and scooped-out flesh in a sieve set over a small jug or bowl and press with the back of a spoon to extract the juices; you will need about 4 tablespoons.

2 Sprinkle a little salt over the insides of the hollowed-out tomatoes. Place them upside down on a plate covered with a paper towel and leave to drain while making the filling.

3 Heat $^{1}/_{2}$ tablespoon of the olive oil in a non-stick saucepan. Add the flaked almonds and cook over a low heat for 2–3 minutes. Remove from the pan and set aside. Add the remaining oil to the pan. Stir in the eggplant and cook for 5 minutes until browned. Stir in the spices, and cook for a few more seconds, stirring constantly.

4 Pour in the stock and bring to a rapid boil, then add the couscous in a steady stream, stirring constantly. Remove from the heat, cover and leave to stand for 5 minutes.

5 Return pan to a low heat and cook for 2–3 minutes, stirring with a fork to fluff up the couscous grains. Stir in the toasted almonds, mint and dried apricots. Add the harissa sauce or chilli paste to the reserved tomato juices then pour over the couscous. Season to taste and mix well. Spoon into the tomatoes, replace the tops and serve.

8 large beefsteak tomatoes, about 170 g each

1$^{1}/_{2}$ tablespoons olive oil

$^{1}/_{2}$ cup (60 g) flaked almonds

1 small eggplant (aubergine), about 170 g, cut into 1 cm dice

1 teaspoon ground coriander

$^{1}/_{2}$ teaspoon ground cumin

pinch of ground cinnamon

1 cup (250 ml) boiling salt-reduced vegetable stock

$^{2}/_{3}$ cup (125 g) instant couscous

2 tablespoons chopped fresh mint

$^{1}/_{3}$ cup (60 g) dried apricots, chopped

1 teaspoon harissa sauce or chilli paste

FOR LOWER GI

Substitute burghul (bulgur) wheat for the couscous. You will need to simmer it for about 10 minutes to cook it in step 4.

Each serving provides
1183 kJ, 283 kcal, 9 g protein, 16 g fat (2 g saturated fat), 24 g carbohydrate (16 g sugars), 8 g fibre

HEALTHY EATING

● Couscous is low in fat and high in carbohydrates and fibre. The instant type has a moderate GI score, which is why this dish has a medium GI value overall.

● Vitamin C from the tomatoes improves the body's absorption of iron from the couscous.

SNACKS AND LIGHT BITES

41

Turkish eggplant and yogurt dip

Many versions of this dish can be found around the Mediterranean. This one is thickened with almond meal, which adds both texture and protein. Served with wholemeal pita bread and crunchy vegetable crudités, the dip makes a delicious snack or starter for 8.

PREPARATION and COOKING: about 1¹/₂ hours, plus 15 minutes draining SERVES 8

3 small eggplants (aubergines), about 675 g in total
2 large garlic cloves, unpeeled
¹/₃ cup (35 g) almond meal (ground almonds)
1 tablespoon lemon juice
1 teaspoon ground cumin
1 tablespoon extra virgin olive oil
²/₃ cup (160 g) Greek-style yogurt
¹/₃ cup (40 g) pitted black olives, roughly chopped
3 zucchini (courgettes)
3 celery sticks
¹/₂ cauliflower, broken into large florets
8 wholemeal pita breads

TO GARNISH
¹/₄ teaspoon paprika
4 pitted black olives, halved

Each serving provides
1376 kJ, 329 kcal, 11 g protein, 10 g fat
(2 g saturated fat), 48 g carbohydrate
(6 g sugars), 6 g fibre

1 Preheat the oven to 180°C (Gas 4). Prick the eggplants in several places with a fork and place in a lightly greased baking dish. Roast for 40 minutes, turning occasionally. Add the unpeeled garlic cloves to the baking dish and continue roasting for 20 minutes or until the eggplants feel very soft.

2 Remove from the oven and leave the eggplants until they are cool enough to handle, then cut them into quarters lengthwise. Strip off the skin and put the flesh into a colander. Leave to drain for about 15 minutes.

3 Squeeze out as much liquid from the eggplant flesh as possible. Squeeze the roasted garlic cloves from their skin. Purée the eggplant flesh, garlic, almond meal, lemon juice, cumin and olive oil in a food processor.

4 Stir in the yogurt and chopped olives. Season to taste. Cover and set aside.

5 Cut the zucchini and celery into finger-length sticks and arrange on a platter with the cauliflower florets. Toast the pita breads, cut each into 6 wedges and place on the platter.

6 Sprinkle paprika over the dip and garnish with the olives. Serve with the vegetable crudités and warm pita breads.

COOK'S TIP

● The dip can be made 1-2 hours in advance and kept in the refrigerator. Let it return to room temperature before serving.

ANOTHER IDEA

● For a white bean and yogurt dip, drain and rinse 2 cans of cannellini beans, about 410 g each. Put them in a food processor with 2 tablespoons tahini (sesame paste), 1 tablespoon lemon juice, ¹/₄ teaspoon ground cumin and ¹/₄ teaspoon ground coriander, and process until smooth. Stir in ²/₃ cup (160 g) Greek-style yogurt, 2 tablespoons chopped fresh coriander, 1 tablespoon chopped fresh mint, and seasoning to taste.

HEALTHY EATING

● In most recipes, eggplants are fried and they are notorious for soaking up the frying fat. For this dish they are dry-roasted, which keeps the overall fat content low.

● Garlic's medicinal properties have been recognised for centuries. Naturopaths and herbalists use it to treat dozens of ailments, from athlete's foot to colds.

● Olives contain healthy monounsaturated fat. They are also a source of vitamin E.

HEALTHY EATING

● Carrots, parsnips and sweet potatoes have much less of an effect on blood glucose levels compared to white potatoes, and make an interesting and tasty alternative.

● Sweet potatoes are an excellent source of beta-carotene, an antioxidant that helps to protect against free radical damage. They also provide vitamin C and potassium and contain more vitamin E than any other vegetable.

Spicy vegetable wedges

GI estimate MEDIUM

Here is a lower GI version of potato wedges, made with carrots, parsnips and sweet potatoes. Lightly crushed coriander seeds and a hint of cinnamon accentuate the flavours of the vegetables, which are served with a tangy mustard and yogurt dip.

PREPARATION: 35 minutes   COOKING: 40 minutes   SERVES 6

1 Preheat the oven to 220°C (Gas 7). Cut the carrots and parsnips into wedges. Place them in a saucepan and just cover with water. Bring to the boil; reduce the heat slightly and partially cover the pan. Cook for 2 minutes.

2 Meanwhile, mix together the lime juice, oil, coriander, cinnamon and pepper in a roasting pan. Cut the sweet potatoes across in half, then into thick wedges, about the same size as the carrots and parsnips. Add the sweet potatoes to the pan and coat in the spice mixture, then push them to one side of the pan.

3 Drain the carrots and parsnips and add them to the roasting pan. Use a spoon and fork to turn the hot vegetables and coat them with the spice mixture. Place the roasting pan in the oven and bake for 40 minutes, stirring and turning all the vegetables twice, until they are well browned in places and just tender.

4 Remove the vegetable wedges from the oven and leave them to cool slightly. Meanwhile make the dip, mixing together the mustard, sugar and lime zest, then stirring in the yogurt and dill. Transfer the dip to a serving bowl, garnish with a little extra chopped dill, and serve with the vegetables.

ANOTHER IDEA

● Make a spicy peanut dip to go with the vegetable wedges. Soften 1 finely chopped French shallot in 2 teaspoons canola (rapeseed) oil. Stir in $1/2$ teaspoon ground cumin and $1/4$ teaspoon ground coriander and cook for a few seconds then stir in $1/4$ cup (60 g) peanut butter and 1 tablespoon each of salt-reduced soy sauce and pure floral honey and 4 tablespoons of water. Stir over a gentle heat until ingredients are combined and smooth. Remove from the heat and stir in 1 tablespoon lemon juice.

2 large carrots
2 parsnips
juice of 1 lime
2 tablespoons canola (rapeseed) oil
2 tablespoons lightly crushed coriander seeds
$1/2$ teaspoon ground cinnamon
pepper to taste
600 g orange sweet potatoes (kumara), peeled

TANGY MUSTARD DIP
2 teaspoons wholegrain mustard
1 teaspoon caster sugar
grated zest of 1 lime
200 g low-fat natural yogurt
3 tablespoons chopped fresh dill, plus extra to garnish

FOR LOWER GI
Use beetroot instead of sweet potatoes.

Each serving provides
717 kJ, 171 kcal, 5 g protein, 7 g fat
(<1 g saturated fat), 24 g carbohydrate
(11 g sugars), 3 g fibre

SNACKS AND LIGHT BITES

45

High-vitality milk shake

PREPARATION: 5 minutes   SERVES 2

300 ml lite or low-fat milk, chilled
³/4 cup (185 g) Greek-style yogurt
juice of 1 large orange
1 large banana, sliced
1 teaspoon pure floral honey
1 tablespoon wheat germ

FOR LOWER GI

Use 1 cup (150 g) strawberries instead
of the banana (this is shown on the left
in the picture). Raspberries and
blueberries are good choices, too.

Each serving provides
1175 kJ, 281 kcal, 14 g protein, 10 g fat
(6 g saturated fat), 36 g carbohydrate
(33 g sugars), 2 g fibre

1   Place all the ingredients in a blender or food processor and
whizz for a couple of minutes until smooth and creamy.

2   Pour into 2 tall glasses and enjoy immediately, while the milk
shake is still frothy.

SOME MORE IDEAS

● Replace the wheat germ with 1 tablespoon ground sunflower
seeds (grind them in a coffee grinder or spice mill).

● Use vanilla frozen yogurt instead of Greek-style yogurt –
especially refreshing in the summer.

● Make a mixed fruit shake with frozen yogurt. Combine 300 ml
lite or low-fat milk, 1¹/3 cups (200 g) strawberry frozen yogurt,
1 large sliced banana, 1 skinned and chopped peach and
2 tablespoons rolled oats in a blender or food processor, and
whizz until creamy and frothy. Serve immediately.

HEALTHY EATING

● Milk is an important source of
riboflavin. It has a low GI and is a
good source of protein. Other
nutrients include calcium and
vitamin D.

● Greek-style yogurt may seem rich
and creamy in taste, but a level
tablespoon contains only 17 kcal. By
comparison, a level tablespoon of
whipping cream contains 67 kcal.

● The addition of wheat germ
boosts the content of vitamin E and
B vitamins in this recipe, and orange
juice provides vitamin C, so this is
truly a 'high vitality' drink.

Spiced fruits, nuts and seeds

PREPARATION and COOKING: about 1$^1/_4$ hours, plus cooling   MAKES 16 servings

1 teaspoon cardamom pods

2.5 cm (1 in) piece cinnamon stick

2 whole cloves

1 teaspoon black peppercorns

1 teaspoon cumin seeds

1 teaspoon coriander seeds

2 teaspoons finely chopped fresh
   root ginger

1 large eggwhite

$^1/_4$ cup (30 g) rolled oats

1 cup (155 g) blanched almonds

1 cup (100 g) pecan halves

1 cup (155 g) Brazil nuts

$^1/_2$ cup (75 g) pumpkin seeds

$^2/_3$ cup (85 g) sunflower seeds

$^3/_4$ cup (90 g) sultanas

1 cup (100 g) dried cranberries

FOR EVEN LOWER GI

Use $^3/_4$ cup (100 g) dried apricots, chopped, instead of the sultanas.

Each serving provides
1130 kJ, 270 kcal, 7 g protein, 22 g fat
(3 g saturated fat), 13 g carbohydrate
(9 g sugars), 4 g fibre

1   Preheat the oven to 130°C (Gas $^1/_2$). Lightly crush the cardamom pods using the side of a large knife, and discard the husks. Place the tiny seeds in a spice mill or coffee grinder, together with the piece of cinnamon stick, cloves, peppercorns, and cumin and coriander seeds, and grind to a fairly fine powder.

2   Mix the ground spices with the ginger, eggwhite and oats in a large bowl. Add the almonds, pecan halves, Brazil nuts, pumpkin seeds and sunflower seeds, and toss well to coat them all evenly with the spice mixture.

3   Tip the nuts and seeds into a large baking tray and spread out. Bake for 1 hour, stirring occasionally, until browned and crisp. Remove from the oven and cool in the baking tray.

4   Tip the nuts and seeds into a bowl. Add the sultanas and cranberries, mixing well. The mixture is ready to serve, but if not wanted immediately it can be stored in an airtight container for up to 2 weeks.

ANOTHER IDEA

● For hot-spiced nuts and seeds, add $^1/_2$ teaspoon crushed dried chillies and 1-2 cloves crushed garlic to the spice mixture. Use nuts and seeds only, omitting the dried fruit.

Gravlax with ginger

GI estimate LOW

The traditional Scandinavian recipe of marinated raw salmon served with a mustard and dill sauce is here given a modern twist, with fresh ginger and lemongrass added to the marinade. Be sure to use really fresh salmon as it needs to be marinated for 2 days.

PREPARATION: 20 minutes, plus 2 days marinating   SERVES 4

225 g piece of very fresh salmon fillet
(tail end)

MARINADE

1 tablespoon coarse sea salt

2 tablespoons caster sugar

1 teaspoon mixed black, green and red peppercorns, crushed

2 x 3 cm piece fresh root ginger, finely chopped

1 lemongrass stem, white part only, finely chopped

3 tablespoons chopped fresh dill

MUSTARD AND DILL SAUCE

3 tablespoons low-fat mayonnaise

3 tablespoons low-fat natural yogurt

2 tablespoons Dijon mustard

1 tablespoon chopped fresh dill

TO SERVE

1 small avocado

2 cups (50 g) mixed salad leaves

1 cucumber, halved and sliced

1/2 small red onion, thinly sliced

Each serving provides
762 kJ, 182 kcal, 13 g protein, 7 g fat
(1 g saturated fat), 17 g carbohydrate
(12 g sugars), <1 g fibre

1   Mix together all the marinade ingredients. Sprinkle half of the mixture over the bottom of a shallow, non-metallic dish. Lay the salmon on top, skin side down, and sprinkle over the remaining marinade, pressing the mixture well into the salmon flesh. Cover the salmon with cling film and place a board and a heavy weight on top. Leave to marinate in the refrigerator for 48 hours, turning the fish every 12 hours.

2   When the salmon is ready to serve, prepare the mustard and dill sauce. Combine all the ingredients, stirring well to mix smoothly, and spoon into a serving bowl.

3   Slice the salmon very thinly, cutting diagonally off the skin, so that each slice is edged with a little of the dill marinade. Arrange the salmon on serving plates.

4   Peel and stone the avocado and cut into chunky pieces. Arrange with the salad leaves and cucumber next to the salmon. Sprinkle over the sliced onion and serve with the mustard and dill sauce.

SOME MORE IDEAS

● For a quicker version of this dish, use 200 g sliced smoked salmon, spreading it out in a shallow dish. To make the marinade, roughly chop the ginger, put it in a garlic press and squeeze the ginger juice over the slices of salmon with the juice of 1/2 lemon. Scatter over the chopped lemongrass and dill, and leave in the fridge for several hours or overnight for the flavours to mingle.

● Make the sauce with crème fraîche (reduced-fat if you like) or light sour cream instead of the mayonnaise and yogurt combination.

HEALTHY EATING

● Fresh salmon is rich in heart-healthy omega-3 fats as well as being packed with protein. By marinating it, no fats are added through cooking and the fish remains as healthy for you as it possibly can be.

● Avocados contain mostly monounsaturated fats – the same heart-healthy kind found in olive oil. Use ripe avocados mashed with lemon juice as a spread for sandwiches instead of butter.

Sweet potato and celeriac purée

PREPARATION: 15 minutes   COOKING: 15-20 minutes   SERVES 4

500 g orange sweet potato (kumara)

400 g celeriac

juice of 1 lemon

2 tablespoons extra virgin olive oil

2 garlic cloves, finely chopped

1 tablespoon coarsely grated fresh
　　root ginger

$1/2$-1 teaspoon ground cumin

1 sweet red apple, peeled, cored and
　　finely chopped

1 tablespoon coriander seeds, roughly
　　crushed

Each serving provides
986 kJ, 235 kcal, 4 g protein, 10 g fat
(1 g saturated fat), 35 g carbohydrate
(13 g sugars), 5 g fibre

1　Peel then cut the sweet potato and celeriac into similar-sized chunks and place in a large saucepan. Add half the lemon juice, then pour in boiling water to cover the vegetables and bring back to the boil. Reduce the heat and simmer gently for 15-20 minutes or until the vegetables are tender.

2　Meanwhile, heat the oil in a small saucepan. Add the garlic, ginger and cumin, and cook for 30 seconds. Stir in the apple and remaining lemon juice and cook for 5 minutes.

3　Toast the crushed coriander seeds in a small dry pan, stirring occasionally, until they are fragrant.

4　Drain and mash the vegetables. Stir in the apple mixture and sprinkle with the toasted coriander seeds. Serve piping hot.

SOME MORE IDEAS

● For a creamy root vegetable purée, use 3 carrots, 3 parsnips and 1 turnip, 900 g in total, cooked and mashed with 5 tablespoons Greek-style yogurt. Stir in 4 finely chopped spring onions and sprinkle with toasted flaked almonds (*shown in picture on the left*).

● For a chilli spiced split pea purée, use 225 g yellow split peas, cooked and mashed with 5 tablespoons lite or low-fat milk. Stir in a finely chopped red chilli and 4 tablespoons chopped fresh coriander (*shown in picture on the right*).

Boston baked beans

GI estimate LOW

PREPARATION: 1-1^1/$_2$ hours, plus 8 hours soaking   COOKING: 3^1/$_2$ hours   SERVES 6

1   Drain the soaked beans and rinse under cold running water. Put them in a saucepan, cover with plenty of fresh cold water and bring to the boil. Boil rapidly for 10 minutes, then reduce the heat and simmer for 50-60 minutes or until tender. Drain well and place in a casserole dish.

2   Preheat the oven to 160°C (Gas 3). Heat the oil in a saucepan, add the shallots, garlic and celery, and sauté for about 5 minutes or until softened, stirring occasionally.

3   Stir in all the canned tomatoes with their juice, the dried herbs, cider and seasoning to taste. Cover and bring to the boil, then reduce the heat and simmer for 10 minutes, stirring occasionally.

4   Add the sugar, treacle and mustard to the tomato sauce and mix well. Pour the sauce over the beans and stir to mix. Cover the casserole and bake for 3^1/$_2$ hours, stirring occasionally. Serve the beans hot, garnished with sprigs of flat-leaf parsley.

1^1/$_4$ cups (250 g) dried haricot beans, soaked for at least 8 hours
1 tablespoon canola (rapeseed) oil
5 French shallots, finely chopped
2 garlic cloves, crushed
2 celery sticks, finely chopped
1 can chopped tomatoes, about 400 g
1 can chopped tomatoes, about 225 g
2 teaspoons mixed dried herbs
2 cups (500 ml) dry cider
1 tablespoon dark brown sugar
1 tablespoon treacle
1 teaspoon Dijon mustard
sprigs of fresh flat-leaf parsley to garnish

FOR EVEN LOWER GI
Replace the treacle with pure maple syrup.

Each serving provides
884 kJ, 211 kcal, 10 g protein, 4 g fat (<1 g saturated fat), 29 g carbohydrate (13 g sugars), 9 g fibre

HEALTHY EATING

● Haricot beans, like all pulses, are a GI 'superfood'. They provide hunger-satisfying fibre and protein and low-GI carbohydrate.

● Unrefined sugars such as dark brown or muscovado retain a proportion of molasses – the brown residue that contains the minerals and nutrients of the sugar cane.

Japanese miso soup **54**

Fresh fruit soup **57**

Simple seafood broth **58**

Golden lentil soup **59**

Lamb and barley soup **60**

Chilled leek and avocado soup **63**

Zesty turkey broth **64**

Turkey chilli soup with salsa **65**

Minestrone **66**

Chinese meatball broth **69**

Tuscan white bean soup **70**

Turkey, chestnut and barley broth **71**

Chickpea soup with asparagus **72**

Soups

Japanese miso soup

Shiitake mushrooms, ginger and a stock made with dried kombu seaweed bring rich savoury flavours to this quick and easy broth. With delicate tofu and slightly peppery watercress, the soup is ideal for a healthy first course before a mixed vegetable stir-fry.

GI estimate LOW

PREPARATION: 10 minutes, plus 5 minutes soaking   COOKING: about 20 minutes   SERVES 4

1 packet dried kombu seaweed (kelp), about 25 g

1 tablespoon sake, Chinese rice wine or dry sherry

2 teaspoons caster sugar

1/2 teaspoon finely grated fresh root ginger

2 tablespoons miso paste

4 spring onions, sliced at an angle

6 fresh shiitake mushrooms, thinly sliced

1/2 cup (95 g) diced tofu

3 cups (90 g) watercress leaves

Each serving provides
253 kJ, 60 kcal, 4 g protein, 2 g fat
(<1 g saturated fat), 8 g carbohydrate
(8 g sugars), 2 g fibre

1 Put the kombu seaweed in a saucepan and pour in 4 cups (1 litre) water. Bring slowly to the boil, then remove from the heat and cover the pan. Set aside for 5 minutes. Use a draining spoon to remove and discard the kombu seaweed.

2 Stir the sake, rice wine or sherry, sugar and ginger into the broth and bring back to the boil. Reduce the heat, and stir in the miso paste until it dissolves completely.

3 Add the spring onions, mushrooms, tofu and watercress. Cook very gently, stirring, for 2 minutes without allowing the soup to boil. Ladle the soup into small bowls and serve.

COOK'S TIP

● If you can't find fresh shiitake mushrooms, try your local health food shop for dried mushrooms and soak before use.

SOME MORE IDEAS

● The kombu seaweed can be finely shredded or snipped into fine strips with scissors and returned to the broth, if liked.

● For an intense herb flavour, add 2 tablespoons chopped fresh coriander with the watercress.

HEALTHY EATING

● Soybeans - and their products such as tofu and miso paste - are a lean and healthy form of protein. As well as having a low GI and being high in fibre, soybeans are rich in phytoestrogens. Including phytoestrogens in the diet may help to protect against heart disease, breast and prostate cancer, and osteoporosis (brittle bones).

● Kombu seaweed is rich in natural iodine and is an excellent source of minerals and vitamins.

HEALTHY EATING

● Nutritionists recommend a daily quota of 7 or more portions of fruit and vegetables for optimum health and wellbeing. This soup is a great way to help you meet the 7-a-day target.

● Studies into the incidence of bowel cancer within different population groups suggest that people who eat more fruit and vegetables are less likely to get this disease.

● Research at Harvard University found that drinking 1 glass of orange juice daily could reduce the risk of stroke by 25 per cent.

Fresh fruit soup

GI estimate LOW

Not only is this refreshing soup perfect on sweltering summer days, it could also give you a vitamin boost in winter. Stirred up from a variety of vitamin-packed raw fruit and vegetables, it is low GI and an easy way to top up on protective nutrients.

PREPARATION: 30 minutes, plus 1 hour chilling   SERVES 4

1   Mix together the pineapple and orange juices in a large bowl. Add the cucumber, onion, capsicum, chilli, lime juice and sugar, and stir well to mix. Cover and chill for 1 hour so that the flavours can mix and develop.

2   Peel, stone and dice the mango, and add to the soup. Halve the grapes, core and dice the pear, and add to the soup. Cut the passionfruit in half, scoop out the flesh with a teaspoon and stir into the soup with the chopped mint and coriander.

3   Ladle the soup into bowls and garnish with mint sprigs, if liked, then serve at once.

COOK'S TIP

● Whizz the soup in a blender or food processor to make a high-vitamin refreshing drink for any time of year.

SOME MORE IDEAS

● Make the soup as spicy as you like by adding more chopped fresh chilli - 1/2 chilli gives only the slightest of kicks.

● For a slightly thicker soup, purée the cucumber, onion, capsicum and chilli together in a blender or food processor until smooth, then add to the fruit juices in step 1.

● In place of the mango, cape gooseberries, pear and passion-fruit, use 1 peeled and diced kiwi fruit, 1 peeled and diced guava (or drained and diced canned guava) or 1 stoned and diced peach, 1/4 peeled and diced pineapple and 1 diced banana.

2 cups (500 ml) pineapple juice
2 cups (500 ml) orange juice
1/2 cucumber, diced
1/4 red onion, finely chopped
1 small red capsicum (pepper), seeded and chopped
1/2 red chilli, seeded and chopped
juice of 1 lime
1/2 teaspoon caster sugar
1 large mango
10 white grapes
1 firm pear
2 passionfruit
1 tablespoon chopped fresh mint
2 tablespoons chopped fresh coriander
sprigs of fresh mint to garnish (optional)

Each serving provides
560 kJ, 134 kcal, 2 g protein, <1 g fat (0 g saturated fat), 30 g carbohydrate (27 g sugars), 4 g fibre

Simple seafood broth

PREPARATION: 40 minutes   COOKING: 10 minutes   SERVES 4

1 small red capsicum (pepper), seeded
    and finely chopped
2/3 cup (160 g) ricotta cheese
pinch of cayenne pepper, or to taste
1 small celery stick, finely chopped
1 tablespoon snipped fresh chives
4 cups (1 litre) salt-reduced fish stock
1/4 teaspoon saffron threads
400 g mussels in shells, scrubbed
85 g raw king prawns, peeled and
    deveined
85 g scallops, shelled
85 g white fish fillet, such as ling or
    plaice, skinned
2 tomatoes, skinned and diced
1 zucchini (courgette), finely diced
freshly ground pepper
1 tablespoon snipped fresh chives
    to garnish

Each serving provides
965 kJ, 231 kcal, 30 g protein, 7 g fat
(4 g saturated fat), 9 g carbohydrate
(5 g sugars), 2 g fibre

1 The broth is served with a piquant spread, and this is
prepared first. Stir the red capsicum into the ricotta
together with the cayenne pepper, celery and chives. Cover
and chill until required.

2 Heat the fish stock in a large saucepan until boiling. Crumble
the saffron into the stock and stir well, then remove
from the heat and set aside. To prepare the mussels, discard
any broken shells or shells that do not close when tapped.
Put the wet mussels into a clean saucepan and cover tightly.
Cook over a moderate heat for 4 minutes, shaking the pan
occasionally. Check that the mussels have opened - if not,
cover and cook for a further 1-2 minutes.

3 Set a colander over the saucepan of stock and tip the
mussels into it so that the juices from the shells are added to
the stock. When cool enough to handle, remove the mussels
from their shells and set aside. Discard any unopened shells.

4 Cut each scallop into 2-3 thin slices, depending on size. Cut
the fish fillet into strips about 2 cm wide and 5 cm long.
Reheat the fish stock until simmering. Add the mussels,
prawns, scallops and fish. Stir then add the tomatoes and
zucchini with seasoning to taste. Simmer for 3 minutes.

5 Ladle the soup into warm bowls and scatter chives over to
garnish. Serve at once, with the piquant spread and warm
crusty bread (stoneground wholemeal is best).

Golden lentil soup

GI estimate LOW

PREPARATION: about 15 minutes   COOKING: about 1¼ hours   SERVES 6

1. Heat the oil in a large saucepan. Add the onion, stir well and cover the pan. Sweat the onion over a gentle heat for about 10 minutes or until softened. Stir in the parsnips, carrots and sherry. Bring to the boil, then cover the pan again and leave to simmer very gently for 40 minutes.

2. Add the lentils, stock and seasoning to taste. Bring to the boil, then reduce the heat and cover the pan. Simmer for a further 15-20 minutes or until the lentils are tender. Purée the soup in a blender until smooth or use a hand-held blender to purée the soup in the pan. Return the soup to the pan if necessary, and reheat it gently until boiling. If it seems a bit thick, add a little stock or water.

3. Stir the grated horseradish into the crème fraîche. Snip some of the chives for the garnish and leave a few whole. Ladle the soup into warm bowls and top each portion with a spoonful of the horseradish cream. Scatter snipped chives over the soup and add a few lengths of whole chive across the top of each bowl. Serve at once.

1 tablespoon canola (rapeseed) oil
1 large onion, finely chopped
450 g parsnips, cut into small cubes
340 g carrots, cut into small cubes
150 ml dry sherry
⅓ cup (90 g) red lentils
5 cups (1.25 litres) salt-reduced
    vegetable stock
2 teaspoons grated horseradish
6 tablespoons crème fraîche
fresh chives to garnish

Each serving provides
1076 kJ, 257 kcal, 7 g protein, 13 g fat
(7 g saturated fat), 23 g carbohydrate
(13 g sugars), 6 g fibre

HEALTHY EATING

● Lentils are a good source of protein and an excellent source of fibre. High-fibre foods are bulky and make you feel full for longer, so are very satisfying. They have a low GI too, making them a sensible choice for a low-GI diet.

● Root vegetables have long been enjoyed as a good source of vitamins and minerals during the winter months.

● Children who are reluctant to sample plain cooked vegetables will not even realise they are eating them in this tasty, colourful soup.

SOUPS

59

Lamb and barley soup

GI estimate LOW

Full of tender lamb, deliciously nutty pearl barley and chunky vegetables, this substantial soup is a hearty meal in a bowl. Savoury herb-scented scones are served alongside.

PREPARATION: 20 minutes   COOKING: about 1¹/₄ hours   SERVES 4

1 tablespoon olive oil

340 g lean boneless lamb, cut into
   2 cm cubes

1 onion, chopped

2 carrots, cut into 1 cm dice

250 g turnips, cut into 1 cm dice

250 g swede, cut into 1 cm dice

¹/₂ cup (110 g) pearl barley

5 cups (1.25 litres) lamb or chicken
   salt-reduced stock

2 teaspoons chopped fresh rosemary

1 teaspoon chopped fresh thyme

freshly ground pepper

²/₃ cup (100 g) frozen peas

HERB SCONES

1 ¹/₂ cups (225 g) plain flour

1 tablespoon baking powder

55 g non-hydrogenated soft margarine

3 tablespoons chopped parsley

3 tablespoons snipped fresh chives

1 tablespoon finely chopped fresh
   rosemary

150 ml lite or low-fat milk

FOR EVEN LOWER GI

Use barley groats instead of pearl barley. Barley groats are less processed and retain more fibre than pearl barley and so have a lower GI.

Each serving provides
2967 kJ, 709 kcal, 35 g protein, 30 g fat
(10 g saturated fat), 75 g carbohydrate
(14 g sugars), 11 g fibre

1 Heat the oil in a large saucepan and fry the lamb over a high heat for about 5 minutes or until browned, stirring frequently. Use a draining spoon to transfer the lamb to a plate. Add the onion, carrots, turnips and swede to the oil remaining in the pan. Stir well and cook for 2–3 minutes or until the vegetables are starting to soften.

2 Return the lamb to the saucepan and stir in the pearl barley, stock, rosemary and thyme with seasoning to taste. Heat until simmering, then reduce the heat and cover the pan. Simmer gently for 40 minutes.

3 Meanwhile, make the scones. Preheat the oven to 230°C (Gas 8) and grease a baking tray. Sift the flour and baking powder into a bowl. With your fingertips, rub in the fat until the mixture resembles fine breadcrumbs. Stir in the parsley, chives and rosemary, then make a well in the middle and pour in all but about 1 tablespoon of the milk. Gradually mix the dry ingredients into the milk to make a fairly soft dough.

4 Turn the scone dough out onto a well-floured surface. Dust your hands with a little flour, then lightly pat and knead the dough into a smooth ball. Flatten the dough and roll it out into a round about 2.5 cm thick and 13 cm across.

5 Place the dough round on the baking tray and use a large sharp knife to cut it into 8 wedges, leaving them in place. Wipe the knife with a damp cloth between cuts to prevent the dough from sticking to it. Brush with the reserved milk and bake immediately for 10–15 minutes or until well risen and deep golden brown on top. Slide the scone round onto a wire rack to cool.

6 Add the peas to the soup and simmer for 10 minutes. Taste for seasoning, then ladle the soup into large bowls and serve with the scones. If you like, wrap the scone round loosely in a folded napkin or clean tea towel and take it to the table on a large flat basket or board. Break it into wedges to serve.

HEALTHY EATING

● Barley is a GI 'superfood'. It is full of fibre and has a low GI – lower than brown rice. It contains traces of gluten and is therefore unsuitable for anyone following a gluten-free diet, but it is useful for those on wheat-free diets.

● Unlike the majority of vegetables, which are most nutritious when eaten raw, carrots are a better source of beta-carotene when they are cooked.

HEALTHY EATING

● Though avocados contain large amounts of fat, most of it is monounsaturated - the same heart-healthy kind found in olive oil. Half an avocado provides a quarter of the recommended daily intake of vitamin B6 and useful amounts of vitamin E and potassium. Other substances in avocados are good for the skin.

● Leeks provide useful amounts of folate, which is important for proper blood cell formation and development of the nervous system in an unborn baby.

Chilled leek and avocado soup

Coriander and lime juice accentuate the delicate avocado flavour in this refreshing soup. It is simple yet interesting, and ideal for a summer's dinner-party first course or a light lunch. Add the avocado at the last moment to avoid discoloration.

PREPARATION and COOKING: 30 minutes, plus cooling and chilling SERVES 4

1   Heat the oil in a saucepan, add the leeks and garlic, and cook for 10 minutes, stirring frequently, until the leeks are slightly softened but not coloured. Pour in the stock and bring to the boil. Cover the pan, reduce the heat and simmer for 10 minutes or until the leeks are cooked.

2   Remove the soup from the heat and let it cool slightly, then purée it in a blender or food processor. Alternatively the soup can be puréed in the saucepan with a hand-held blender. Pour the soup into a bowl and leave it to cool, then chill well.

3   Just before serving the soup, prepare the avocado. Halve the avocado and discard the stone. Scoop the flesh from the peel and press through a fine stainless steel or nylon sieve. The avocado can also be puréed in a blender or food processor until smooth, adding a little of the chilled soup to thin the purée if necessary.

4   Stir the avocado purée into the soup together with the yogurt, lime juice and coriander. Add seasoning to taste, then ladle the soup into 4 bowls. Float 2-3 ice cubes in each bowl, if you wish, then add slices of lime and sprigs of coriander. Serve at once.

SOME MORE IDEAS

● This soup is also good hot. Purée the hot soup with the avocado and stir in crème fraîche instead of yogurt.

● For a soup with Mexican flavours, cook 1-2 seeded and finely chopped green chillies with the leeks.

● For a simple no-cook avocado soup, blend 2 avocados with 2 cups (500 ml) vegetable stock, then add the yogurt and lime juice, and season to taste.

1 tablespoon olive oil

450 g leeks, halved lengthwise and thinly sliced

1 garlic clove, finely chopped

3 cups (750 ml) salt-reduced vegetable or chicken stock

1 large ripe avocado

$1/2$ cup (125 g) low-fat natural yogurt

1 tablespoon lime juice

2 tablespoons chopped fresh coriander

freshly ground pepper

TO GARNISH

8-12 ice cubes (optional)

slices of lime

sprigs of fresh coriander

Each serving provides
1006 kJ, 240 kcal, 6 g protein, 19 g fat (4 g saturated fat), 11 g carbohydrate (10 g sugars), 5 g fibre

Zesty turkey broth

GI estimate LOW

PREPARATION: 15 minutes   COOKING: about 20 minutes   SERVES 4

1 lemon

bunch parsley sprigs (about 15 g)

4 cups (1 litre) salt-reduced chicken
   stock

2 carrots, cut into 1 cm dice

2 celery sticks, cut into 1 cm dice

225 g skinless, boneless turkey breasts
   (fillets), cut into 1 x 4 cm strips

100 g small broccoli florets

Each serving provides
494 kJ, 118 kcal, 18 g protein, 3 g fat
(1 g saturated fat), 6 g carbohydrate
(5 g sugars), 3 g fibre

HEALTHY EATING

● Turkey is a lean and healthy form
of protein.

● As well as being extremely low in
fat, this soup is full of vitamins and
disease-fighting phytochemicals.

● Broccoli provides beta-carotene
along with vitamin C and several of
the B vitamins.

● Carrots are one of the richest
sources of beta-carotene.

1 Using a vegetable peeler, pare the zest off half the lemon in
one long strip and place it in a large saucepan. Cut the
thicker stalks off the parsley, tie them together in a neat
bunch with fine string and add to the pan. Set aside the rest
of the lemon and parsley. Pour the stock into the pan and
bring to the boil. Add the carrots and celery, reduce the
heat, cover and simmer for 5 minutes.

2 Add the turkey strips and reduce the heat so that the soup
barely simmers. Cover and cook very gently for 5 minutes.
Bring the soup back to the boil. Add the broccoli and cook,
uncovered, for 3 minutes or until the broccoli is just tender.

3 Meanwhile, use a citrus zester to remove the remaining zest
from the lemon in fine shreds. Halve the lemon and squeeze
its juice. Chop the reserved parsley. Remove the long strip of
lemon zest and the bunch of parsley stalks from the soup.
Stir in the lemon juice with most of the shreds of zest and
most of the chopped parsley. Season the soup to taste.

4 Ladle the soup into warm soup bowls. Garnish with the
remaining lemon zest and parsley and serve hot.

ANOTHER IDEA

● Use skinless, boneless chicken breasts (fillets), lean pork or
beef instead of the turkey and vary the vegetables.

Turkey chilli soup with salsa

GI estimate LOW

PREPARATION: 35 minutes   COOKING: 50 minutes   SERVES 6

1 Heat the oil in a large saucepan over a high heat. Add the turkey and cook for about 4 minutes, stirring occasionally, until lightly browned. Reduce the heat to moderate and add the onion, celery, capsicum and garlic. Continue cooking, stirring frequently, for about 2 minutes or until the onion begins to soften. Stir in the tomatoes with the juice from the can, the stock, coriander, cumin, oregano and chilli powder. Bring to the boil, then reduce the heat to low, cover the pan and simmer for 20 minutes.

2 Preheat the oven to 160°C (Gas 3). Add the zucchini, corn and borlotti or kidney beans to the soup. Bring back to the boil, then reduce the heat to low and cover the pan again. Simmer the soup for a further 10 minutes or until the zucchini are just tender.

3 Meanwhile, wrap the stack of tortillas tightly in foil and heat in the oven for about 10 minutes or until warmed through.

4 To make the salsa, place the lime juice in a bowl. Halve, stone, peel and dice the avocados, then add to the bowl and toss them in the lime juice. Gently mix in the tomatoes, spring onions and rocket, adding seasoning to taste. Take care not to break up the diced avocados.

5 Season the soup to taste. Ladle the soup into warm bowls and serve. The salsa can either be spooned on top of the soup or wrapped in the warm tortillas as a side dish.

2 tablespoons olive oil

450 g minced turkey

1 onion, finely chopped

2 celery sticks, finely chopped

1 red or yellow capsicum (pepper), seeded and finely chopped

3 garlic cloves, finely chopped

1 can chopped tomatoes, about 400 g

4 cups (1 litre) salt-reduced turkey or chicken stock

1/4 teaspoon ground coriander

1/4 teaspoon ground cumin

1/4 teaspoon dried oregano

1/2 teaspoon chilli powder, or to taste

3 zucchini (courgettes), diced

3/4 cup (150 g) fresh or frozen corn (sweetcorn), thawed if necessary

1 can borlotti or kidney beans, about 400 g, drained and rinsed

AVOCADO SALSA

2 tablespoons fresh lime juice

2 avocados

8 cherry tomatoes (about 100 g), quartered

6 spring onions, finely chopped

1 cup (45 g) chopped rocket

TO SERVE

12 wheat tortillas (1 packet, about 312 g)

Each serving provides
2150 kJ, 514 kcal, 38 g protein, 31 g fat
(7 g saturated fat), 21 g carbohydrate
(11 g sugars), 8 g fibre

Minestrone

GI estimate LOW

This soup makes the most of winter vegetables, and is full of vitamin goodness. Beans and pasta make it even more nourishing - and low GI. Serve with chunks of low-GI bread for a satisfying meal.

PREPARATION: 30 minutes, plus overnight soaking   COOKING: about 1$\frac{1}{2}$ hours   SERVES 6

1 tablespoon olive oil

1 large onion, finely chopped

3-4 garlic cloves, finely chopped

1 cup (200 g) dried cannellini or borlotti beans, soaked overnight, rinsed and drained

1 can roma (plum) tomatoes, about 400 g

2 tablespoons tomato purée

2 carrots, finely diced

150 g swede, finely diced

150 g celeriac, finely diced

250 g peeled pumpkin flesh, finely diced

1 teaspoon fresh thyme leaves

1 bay leaf

$\frac{1}{2}$ teaspoon ground allspice

1 potato (about 200 g), peeled and finely diced

150 g green beans, cut into short lengths

1$\frac{1}{4}$ cups (100 g) small pasta shapes, such as conchigliette (shells), or broken-up spaghetti

125 g spinach, chopped

4 tablespoons shredded fresh basil

freshly ground pepper

$\frac{1}{2}$ cup (50 g) freshly grated parmesan

Each serving provides
1230 kJ, 294 kcal, 17 g protein, 7 g fat
(2 g saturated fat), 42 g carbohydrate
(9 g sugars), 12 g fibre

1 Heat the oil in a large saucepan. Add the onion and garlic, and cook for 4-5 minutes, until the onion is translucent. Add the cannellini or borlotti beans and 8 cups (2 litres) water. Bring to the boil and boil for 10 minutes. Reduce the heat, cover and simmer for 30 minutes.

2 Add the tomatoes with their juice, breaking them up with a fork, then add the tomato purée, carrots, swede, celeriac and pumpkin. Stir in the thyme, bay leaf and ground allspice. Bring back to simmering point, then cover the pan again and simmer for 20 minutes.

3 Stir in the potato and green beans. Continue simmering, covered, for 15 minutes. Stir in the pasta and cook, still covered, for a further 10 minutes or until the cannellini or borlotti beans are tender and the pasta is cooked.

4 Add the spinach and basil, and season to taste. Simmer uncovered for 2-3 minutes until the spinach has wilted. Ladle the soup into warm bowls and serve at once, with the parmesan cheese to sprinkle on top.

COOK'S TIP

● Cheese is high in saturated fat, so you should limit your portions. Using a strong cheese such as parmesan means that you only need a little for plenty of flavour.

HEALTHY EATING

● Beans and pulses are a GI 'superfood': they provide hunger-satisfying protein, soluble fibre and low-GI carbohydrate.

● Pasta scores healthily low on the Glycaemic Index because it breaks down slowly into glucose in the body, providing long-lasting energy. For the lowest GI choose wholemeal pasta and be careful not to overcook it.

HEALTHY EATING

● Basmati rice has a lower GI than the jasmine rice that would traditionally be used in this recipe, yet it is just as delicious.

● Shiitake mushrooms contain lentinan, a special starch, which is believed to help strengthen the immune system and may even protect against cancer. If you can't find fresh mushrooms used dried ones and soak before using.

● As well as protein, pork is a good source of thiamin and several other B vitamins.

Chinese meatball broth

Rice-and-pork meatballs and lots of interesting vegetables bring savoury flavours to this satisfying main-meal soup. Serve it at the table in a warmed tureen or straight from the pan.

PREPARATION: 20 minutes   COOKING: about 40 minutes   SERVES 4

1 First prepare the meatballs. Rinse the rice with cold water then place in a saucepan with plenty of water to cover. Bring to the boil and boil for 5 minutes, then drain the rice in a sieve, rinse, and leave to cool.

2 Mix the pork with the ginger, spring onions, garlic, sesame oil, 2 tablespoons of soy sauce, Chinese five-spice and chilli powder. Strip the green leaves of the bok choy off the thick white stalks. Finely chop the leaves and add them to the pork. Reserve the stalks for the broth. Pound the mixture with a spoon until thoroughly combined.

3 Turn the drained rice into a large shallow bowl and separate the grains with a fork. Rinse your hands, then take a small lump of pork mixture, squeeze it together and roll it into a small ball about the size of a walnut. Roll the meatball in the rice, pressing it into the grains to coat it thickly. Press the rice firmly onto the meatball and set aside on a plate or dish. Shape the remaining pork mixture to make about 20 balls.

4 Cover the bottom of a steamer rack with a single layer of red chard, leaving gaps between the leaves. Add the meatballs in one layer, leaving space between them for the rice to swell. Bring the stock and ginger to the boil in the steamer base. Set the steamer on top and cover. Steam the meatballs for 35 minutes.

5 While the meatballs are cooking, cut the stalks of the bok choy across into 1 cm pieces. Remove the steamer from the pan and set it aside on a plate. Add the sherry, the rest of the soy sauce, baby corn, shiitake mushrooms, snow peas, remaining red chard leaves, bamboo shoots and spring onions to the stock. Bring back to the boil, then replace the steamer rack and steam for a further 5 minutes.

6 Transfer the meatballs to a warm serving bowl. Add the chard leaves from the steamer to the broth. Add more soy sauce, if liked. To serve, ladle some broth and vegetables into bowls and add a few meatballs to each.

3/4 cup (150 g) white basmati rice
340 g lean minced pork
2 x 3 cm piece fresh root ginger, peeled and grated
6 spring onions, chopped
1 garlic clove, finely chopped
1/2 teaspoon toasted sesame oil
4 tablespoons salt-reduced soy sauce
1/2 teaspoon Chinese five-spice
pinch of chilli powder
2 bok choy, about 225 g
2 stalks (about 250 g) red chard leaves
6 cups (1.5 litres) salt-reduced chicken stock
2 x 3 cm piece fresh root ginger, peeled and cut into thin strips
3 tablespoons dry sherry
200 g baby corn (sweetcorn), sliced diagonally into 2-3 pieces
115 g shiitake mushrooms, thinly sliced
200 g snow peas (mangetout), each cut diagonally into 2-3 pieces
1 can sliced bamboo shoots, about 220 g, drained
6 spring onions, thinly sliced diagonally

Each serving provides
1709 kJ, 408 kcal, 32 g protein, 8 g fat (3 g saturated fat), 47 g carbohydrate (11 g sugars), 6 g fibre

Tuscan white bean soup

PREPARATION: 10 minutes, plus 8 hours soaking   COOKING: 1¹/₂ hours   SERVES 4

GI estimate LOW

1 Heat the oil in a large saucepan, add the bacon and onion, and cook gently for 5 minutes or until the onion is softened. Add the garlic and red capsicum, and cook gently for a further 2 minutes.

2 Drain the soaked beans and rinse under cold running water. Add them to the pan together with the stock. Bring to the boil and boil rapidly for 10 minutes, then reduce the heat so the liquid is simmering. Skim off any froth.

3 Add the rosemary. Partly cover the pan and simmer for 45-60 minutes or until the beans are very tender.

4 Remove about 3 tablespoons of the beans with a draining spoon, place them in a basin and mash with a fork.

5 Add the cabbage to the soup and simmer for 5 minutes. Remove the rosemary twigs, if using fresh rosemary, then stir the mashed beans into the soup to thicken it slightly. Season to taste, and serve hot.

SOME MORE IDEAS

● For a very quick version of this soup, use 1 can cannellini beans, about 410 g, drained and rinsed, instead of dried beans. Cook the vegetables and bacon as in the main recipe, then add 5 cups (1.25 litres) stock and the rosemary, and bring to the boil. Add the beans and simmer gently for 5 minutes, to heat the beans through. Continue from step 4 as above.

● You can substitute dried haricot or flageolet beans for the cannellini beans.

1 tablespoon olive oil

2 slices lean smoked back bacon, rind removed and chopped

1 onion, chopped

2 garlic cloves, chopped

1 red capsicum (pepper), seeded and finely chopped

¹/₂ cup (100 g) dried cannellini beans, soaked for at least 8 hours

6 cups (1.5 litres) hot salt-reduced chicken or vegetable stock

2 sprigs fresh rosemary or 1 teaspoon dried rosemary

100 g Savoy cabbage, finely shredded

freshly ground pepper

Each serving provides
859 kJ, 205 kcal, 17 g protein, 8 g fat
(2 g saturated fat), 18 g carbohydrate
(8 g sugars), 6 g fibre

HEALTHY EATING

● Dried beans are an excellent source of low-GI carbohydrates and healthy protein. They contain soluble fibre, which can help to reduce high blood cholesterol levels.

● Savoy cabbage is easily recognised by its crinkly leaves. It contains a number of different phytochemicals that appear to help reduce the risk of various cancers.

Turkey, chestnut and barley broth

GI estimate LOW

PREPARATION: 15 minutes   COOKING: about 2^1/$_4$ hours   SERVES 6

1   First, make the stock. Break up the turkey carcass, discarding any skin, and place in a very large saucepan. Add the quartered onion, carrot and celery. Tie the herb sprigs and bay leaf into a bouquet garni and add to the pan. Cover generously with water and bring to the boil, skimming any scum from the surface with a draining spoon. Reduce the heat, cover the pan and simmer gently for 1^1/$_2$ hours. Strain the stock, and discard the bones and vegetables.

2   Measure the stock and, if necessary, make up to 7 cups (1.75 litres) with water. Skim off any fat and pour back into the cleaned saucepan.

3   Bring the stock back to the boil. Add the chopped vegetables, chestnuts and pearl barley and simmer for 35 minutes or until the pearl barley is tender.

4   Add the parsley and turkey and heat through thoroughly. Season to taste and serve.

ANOTHER IDEA

● For a turkey, lentil and sweet potato soup, add red lentils instead of pearl barley and use 1 large orange-fleshed sweet potato, 1 large parsnip and 225 g celeriac instead of the carrot, parsnip, celery, sprouts and leek. Stir in 1 tablespoon redcurrant jelly just before serving.

STOCK
1 roast turkey carcass
1 onion, cut into quarters
1 carrot, chopped
2 celery sticks, chopped
few sprigs of parsley
few sprigs of fresh thyme
1 bay leaf

SOUP
1 large carrot, chopped
1 large parsnip, chopped
3 celery sticks, chopped
4–6 Brussels sprouts, chopped
1 large leek, chopped
100 g freshly cooked or vacuum-packed chestnuts, roughly chopped
^{1}/$_3$ cup (75 g) pearl barley
3 tablespoons chopped parsley
100 g cooked turkey meat, without skin, chopped or shredded
freshly ground pepper

FOR EVEN LOWER GI

Use barley groats instead of pearl barley. Barley groats are less processed and retain more fibre than pearl barley and so have a lower GI.

Each serving provides
542 kJ, 129 kcal, 8 g protein, 2 g fat (<1 g saturated fat), 20 g carbohydrate (6 g sugars), 7 g fibre

Chickpea soup with asparagus

This filling soup is easy to make, low GI and virtually fat-free. Offer grainy wholemeal or other low-GI bread as an accompaniment. For a main meal, serve with a little strong-flavoured cheese, which tastes very good with the soup.

PREPARATION: 15 minutes   COOKING: about 40 minutes   SERVES 4

1 can chickpeas, about 400 g, drained

1 onion, coarsely chopped

2 garlic cloves, chopped

4 cups (1 litre) salt-reduced vegetable or chicken stock

8 asparagus spears (about 150 g), trimmed and cut into bite-sized pieces

1¼ cups (180 g) orzo (rice-shaped pasta) or other type of soup pasta

freshly ground pepper

TO SERVE

fine strips of zest from 1 lemon

2 tablespoons chopped fresh parsley, preferably flat-leaf

1 lemon, cut into wedges

FOR EVEN LOWER GI

Keep a look-out in health food shops for pasta shapes made from lentil flour – delicious in this soup and very low GI.

Each serving provides
1057 kJ, 253 kcal, 14 g protein, 2 g fat
(1 g saturated fat), 44 g carbohydrate
(5 g sugars), 5 g fibre

1 Put the chickpeas, onion, garlic and stock in a saucepan and bring to the boil. Reduce the heat and simmer for about 20 minutes or until the onion is very tender and the chickpeas are falling apart. If the mixture is becoming too thick, add a little more stock or water.

2 Ladle about one-third of the soup into a blender or food processor and purée until it is smooth. Return the puréed soup to the pan and bring back to simmering point. Add the asparagus, cover the pan and cook gently for 5-6 minutes or until the asparagus is just tender.

3 Meanwhile, cook the orzo or other pasta shapes in boiling water for 10-12 minutes, or according to the packet instructions, until al dente. Drain the pasta and add it to the soup with seasoning to taste.

4 Mix together the lemon zest and parsley for the garnish. Top each bowl of soup with a small spoonful of the lemon and parsley garnish, and serve immediately, offering lemon wedges so that the juice can be added to the soup to taste.

COOK'S TIP

● Orzo is a type of rice-shaped pasta. If you can't find it, any type of small pasta shape will do, such as stelline (stars), ditalini (tubes), conchigliette (shells) and farfallini (bow ties). You can also use regular-sized pasta shapes such as penne, for example.

SOME MORE IDEAS

● Use small broccoli florets instead of asparagus. Broccoli is an excellent source of vitamin C and the quantity in this soup will provide about a quarter of the recommended daily intake of that vital vitamin.

● For a spicier soup, season with cayenne instead of ground pepper, or add a few drops of hot chilli sauce.

HEALTHY EATING

● Chickpeas, along with other pulses, are a GI superfood, providing healthy protein, fibre and low-GI carbohydrate.

● Asparagus is a rich source of many of the B vitamins, especially folate, which is thought to help protect against developing Alzheimer's disease.

Beef in red wine **77**

Lamb, butternut and barley stew **79**

Fragrant lamb with spinach **80**

Rich lamb and apricot couscous **81**

Beef and mushroom pie **82**

Beef and cranberry rolls **84**

Spiced pork with sweet potatoes **85**

Cidered pork with herb dumplings **87**

Pork, prune and orange pie **88**

Ham with pears **90**

Ham and baby corn polenta tart **91**

Hungarian-style meatballs **92**

Goulash in a hurry **95**

Mexican pork **96**

Chinese-style lemon chicken **97**

One-pot Japanese chicken **98**

Aztec chicken pie **101**

Stuffed turkey rolls with lentils **102**

Chicken liver mousse **103**

Chicken satay **104**

Chicken and cashew pancakes **107**

Indian-style grilled chicken breasts **108**

Turkey and lentil pâté **109**

Spicy turkey chilli with spaghetti **110**

Turkey and celery casserole **112**

Turkey kebabs with relish **113**

Meat and poultry

HEALTHY EATING

● As well as providing protein, beef is a good source of iron, zinc and vitamins B6 and B12.

● Boiled new potatoes are acceptable on a low-GI eating plan – they have a moderate GI score (unlike mashed or baked potatoes, which have high GI scores). Make sure you don't overcook them, though, as this will raise the GI.

● Broad beans go well with beef and they bring valuable dietary fibre to the dish.

Beef in red wine

Long, slow cooking gives this casserole its inimitable flavour. The cooking liquid is reduced by removing the casserole lid to produce a deliciously aromatic sauce. Flambéing with brandy brings the cooking to a spectacular finale. Serve with boiled new potatoes.

GI estimate LOW

PREPARATION: 20 minutes   COOKING: about 2^1/$_2$ hours   SERVES 4

1   Preheat the oven to 150°C (Gas 2). Heat the oil in a large flameproof casserole dish. Add the onion and cook over a moderately high heat for 5 minutes or until softened and beginning to brown. Add the beef and fry for about 5 minutes, stirring frequently, until the pieces of meat are browned on all sides. Stir in the carrots, parsnips, mushrooms and garlic.

2   Pour in the wine, then stir in the orange zest and juice, thyme, rosemary, bay leaf and seasoning to taste. Bring to the boil, then cover the casserole and transfer it to the oven. Cook for 1^1/$_4$ hours.

3   Remove the lid from the casserole and cook for 30 minutes, stirring once or twice. Stir in the broad beans and continue to cook, uncovered, for another 30 minutes, again stirring once or twice.

4   Just before serving, adjust the seasoning and stir in the parsley. Warm the brandy in a small saucepan and pour it over the casserole. Immediately set the brandy alight and carry the casserole to the table while still flaming.

COOK'S TIP
● If you can't find baby carrots or parsnips, use large vegetables, cut into equal-sized chunks.

SOME MORE IDEAS
● Small broccoli florets or shelled peas can be added instead of the broad beans.
● For an everyday version, use 3 cups (750 ml) salt-reduced beef stock instead of wine. Omit the final stage of flambéing the casserole - it will still taste delicious.

2 tablespoons canola (rapeseed) oil

1 large onion, sliced

450 g lean stewing beef, cubed

250 g baby carrots

250 g baby parsnips

250 g button mushrooms

1 garlic clove, finely chopped

1 bottle full-bodied red wine

grated zest and juice of 1 orange

1 sprig thyme

1 sprig rosemary

1 bay leaf

freshly ground pepper

1 cup (185 g) shelled fresh broad beans, or frozen broad beans, thawed

TO SERVE

2 tablespoons chopped parsley

3 tablespoons brandy

Each serving provides
1961 kJ, 469 kcal, 31 g protein, 15 g fat
(3 g saturated fat), 21 g carbohydrate
(10 g sugars), 8 g fibre

Lamb, butternut and barley stew

GI estimate LOW

Like Irish stew and Lancashire hotpot, this hearty dish is made with good-quality lamb, plus lots of vegetables, pearl barley, and bay leaves and thyme for flavouring. Serve with steamed broccoli.

PREPARATION: 20 minutes, plus 10 minutes standing   COOKING: about 1¹/₂ hours   SERVES 4

1 Preheat the oven to 160ºC (Gas 3). Heat the oil in a large flameproof casserole dish, add the chops and brown them on both sides. Remove and set aside.

2 Add the onion wedges and fry for about 5 minutes or until browned on all sides. Stir in the leeks, butternut pumpkin and turnips. Cover and sweat gently for 5 minutes.

3 Sprinkle in the pearl barley and cook, stirring, for 1 minute, then pour in the hot stock. Tuck the chops in with the vegetables, and add the bay leaves, thyme and seasoning to taste. Bring to the boil, then cover the casserole. Transfer to the oven and cook for 1¹/₄ hours or until the meat and vegetables are very tender.

4 Remove the casserole from the oven and let stand for 10 minutes, to allow the barley to soak up more of the stock. Season to taste and serve hot, sprinkled with parsley.

SOME MORE IDEAS

● For extra piquancy, add a few dashes of Worcestershire sauce or a couple of crushed garlic cloves with the herbs in step 3.

● Try diced carrots and swede instead of the butternut pumpkin and turnips.

HEALTHY EATING

● Pearl barley is a GI 'superfood'. It is low in fat and rich in low-GI carbohydrate.

● Butternut pumpkin is an excellent source of beta-carotene (producing its orange colour). It is also a good source of vitamin C and a useful source of vitamin E. All of these vitamins act as antioxidants, fighting against some cancers and preventing heart disease.

1 tablespoon olive oil

4 lamb chops, about 450 g in total, trimmed of fat

2 onions, quartered lengthwise

2 large leeks, about 400 g in total, cut into 2.5 cm pieces

1 butternut pumpkin, about 600 g, peeled, seeded and cut into 2.5 cm chunks

2 turnips, about 200 g in total, quartered lengthwise

¹/₂ cup (110 g) pearl barley

900 ml hot salt-reduced lamb stock

2 bay leaves

2 large sprigs thyme

freshly ground pepper

2 tablespoons chopped parsley to garnish

FOR EVEN LOWER GI

Use barley groats instead of pearl barley. Barley groats are less processed and retain more fibre than pearl barley and so have a lower GI.

Each serving provides
1795 kJ, 429 kcal, 35 g protein, 14 g fat (5 g saturated fat), 44 g carbohydrate (10 g sugars), 10 g fibre

MEAT AND POULTRY

79

Fragrant lamb with spinach

GI estimate LOW

PREPARATION: 20-25 minutes   COOKING: 1 hour 20 minutes   SERVES 4

2 tablespoons canola (rapeseed) oil

2 onions, finely chopped

4 garlic cloves, crushed

2 x 3 cm piece fresh root ginger, peeled and chopped

1 red chilli, seeded and sliced

2 teaspoons paprika

2 teaspoons ground cumin

2 teaspoons ground coriander

1 teaspoon ground white pepper

$\frac{1}{2}$ teaspoon ground cinnamon

seeds from 8 green cardamom pods, crushed

2 bay leaves

200 g Greek-style yogurt

500 g lean boneless lamb, cubed

2 large tomatoes, chopped

$2\frac{1}{2}$ cups (225 g) fresh baby spinach

4 tablespoons chopped fresh coriander

sprigs of fresh coriander to garnish

Each serving provides
1612 kJ, 385 kcal, 34 g protein, 23 g fat
(7 g saturated fat), 15 g carbohydrate
(8 g sugars), 5 g fibre

1 Heat the oil in a large saucepan or flameproof casserole dish. Add the onions, garlic and ginger, and fry for about 15 minutes, stirring frequently, until the onions are golden.

2 Stir in the chilli, paprika, cumin, coriander, white pepper, cinnamon, crushed cardamom seeds and bay leaves. Stir briefly over a moderate heat, then stir in the yogurt and 150 ml water. Add the lamb, mix well and cover the pan. Simmer gently for $1\frac{1}{4}$ hours or until the lamb is tender.

3 Add the tomatoes, spinach and chopped coriander. Cook for 2-3 minutes, stirring, until the tomatoes have softened slightly and the spinach has wilted. Taste for seasoning and remove the bay leaf. Serve garnished with fresh coriander.

HEALTHY EATING

● As well as providing protein, lamb is a good source of vitamin B12, thiamin and iron. It contains saturated fat, so trim off as much as you can before cooking.

● Cardamom is believed to help relieve problems such as indigestion, flatulence and stomach cramps.

● Spinach is packed with nutrients, including vitamins C, E and K, the B vitamins, beta-carotene and iron.

Rich lamb and apricot couscous

GI estimate LOW

PREPARATION: 15 minutes, plus 12 hours marinating   COOKING: 2¹/₂ hours   SERVES 4

1   Place the lamb in a bowl with the mushrooms and onion. Tie the bay leaves and thyme together into a bouquet garni and add to the bowl with the garlic, carrots, celery and nutmeg. Pour on the ale and stir to mix, then cover and leave to marinate in the refrigerator for 12 hours.

2   Preheat the oven to 160°C (Gas 3). Transfer the lamb, mushrooms and flavouring to a large casserole dish and pour the marinade over. Add the tomatoes with their juice and the stock. Cover and cook in the oven for 2 hours.

3   Discard the bouquet garni from the casserole. Stir in the apricots and return the casserole to the oven to cook for a further 30 minutes.

4   Just before the casserole is ready, prepare the couscous. Bring the stock to the boil in a large saucepan. Add the cabbage and bring back to the boil, then remove from the heat and immediately add the couscous and mint. Stir once, then cover the pan and leave, off the heat, for about 5 minutes or until the couscous has absorbed all the stock. Use a fork to fluff up the couscous.

5   Divide the couscous among 4 bowls and ladle the lamb casserole over the top. Scatter on the chopped parsley and serve at once.

450 g lean boneless lamb, cut into chunks
340 g mushrooms, sliced
1 onion, thinly sliced
2 bay leaves
2 sprigs thyme
2 garlic cloves, crushed
2 carrots, sliced
2 celery sticks, sliced
¹/₄ teaspoon freshly grated nutmeg
2 cups (500 ml) strong brown ale (beer)
1 can chopped tomatoes, about 400 g
150 ml salt-reduced lamb or chicken stock
150 g dried apricots, halved
2 tablespoons chopped parsley to garnish

MINTED COUSCOUS WITH CABBAGE

3 cups (750 ml) salt-reduced vegetable stock
450 g green cabbage, such as Savoy, finely shredded
340 g instant couscous
4 tablespoons chopped fresh mint

FOR EVEN LOWER GI

Replace the couscous with burghul (bulgur) wheat. You will need to cook the burghul wheat separately, simmering in plenty of water for 10 minutes, and then drain before adding with the mint.

Each serving provides
2493 kJ, 596 kcal, 35 g protein, 21 g fat (9 g saturated fat), 59 g carbohydrate (28 g sugars), 13 g fibre

Beef and mushroom pie

A sweet potato mash flavoured with mustard and orange is the colourful top for this winter pie. Underneath is a hearty filling of lean beef simmered in red wine with baby onions and button mushrooms. Serve with steamed green vegetables.

GI estimate LOW

PREPARATION: 1¼ hours   COOKING: 20 minutes   SERVES 4

2 tablespoons olive oil
200 g baby onions, peeled and left whole
500 g lean stewing beef, cubed
150 g baby button mushrooms
3 celery sticks, thickly sliced
1 tablespoon fresh thyme leaves
300 ml full-bodied red wine
150 ml salt-reduced beef stock
1½ tablespoons cornflour
freshly ground pepper

SWEET POTATO MASH
2 large orange sweet potatoes (kumara), about 1 kg, peeled and cubed
1 tablespoon wholegrain mustard
grated zest and juice of 1 orange

Each serving provides
2201 kJ, 526 kcal, 34 g protein, 18 g fat (5 g saturated fat), 44 g carbohydrate (18 g sugars), 7 g fibre

1 Heat the oil in a large saucepan and add the onions. Cover and cook over a low heat for 8-10 minutes, shaking the pan occasionally, until the onions are lightly browned all over.

2 Remove the onions to a plate using a draining spoon. Add the beef to the pan and cook, uncovered, over a moderately high heat for 2-3 minutes or until the cubes are well browned.

3 Add the onions, mushrooms, celery and thyme. Pour in the wine and stock. Bring to the boil, then reduce the heat. Cover and simmer for 45 minutes or until the beef is tender.

4 Meanwhile, steam the sweet potatoes for 25 minutes or until tender. Alternatively, cook them in boiling water for about 15 minutes, then drain.

5 Preheat the oven to 190°C (Gas 5). Tip the sweet potatoes into a bowl and mash with the mustard, orange zest and juice, and seasoning to taste. Set aside.

6 Blend the cornflour with 2 tablespoons cold water. Stir into the beef mixture and cook, stirring, until lightly thickened. Season to taste. Spoon the filling into a 1.2 litre pie dish.

7 Spread the sweet potato mash over the beef filling to cover it completely. Bake for 20 minutes. Serve the pie hot.

COOK'S TIP
● The pie can be made ahead and chilled, then reheated in a preheated 190°C (Gas 5) oven for 45 minutes or until piping hot.

ANOTHER IDEA
● Cover the beef filling with a sweet potato and butternut mash. Steam 500 g each peeled sweet potato and butternut pumpkin for 25 minutes, or cook in boiling water for 15 minutes, until tender. Mash with a knob of non-hydrogenated soft margarine and 2 tablespoons snipped fresh chives.

HEALTHY EATING

● Although sweet potatoes have a moderate GI, it is much lower than that of white potatoes. Sweet potatoes contain beta-carotene (giving them their orange colour), an antioxidant that helps to protect against free radical damage, and they provide good amounts of vitamin C and potassium. Sweet potatoes contain more vitamin E than any other vegetable.

Beef and cranberry rolls

PREPARATION: 20 minutes   COOKING: about 1 hour   SERVES 4

550 g rump steak, cut into 4 thin slices

2 tablespoons canola (rapeseed) oil

2 sprigs thyme

1 bay leaf

10 black peppercorns, lightly crushed

8 juniper berries, lightly crushed

4 cloves

1/2 cup (125 ml) salt-reduced beef stock

1 1/2 cups (375 ml) red wine

1/2 cup (50 g) fresh cranberries (or frozen cranberries, thawed), finely chopped

1 carrot, thinly sliced

1 onion, sliced

1 garlic clove, sliced

leaves of fresh thyme to garnish

CRANBERRY STUFFING

1/3 cup (30 g) cranberries

1/2 cup (50 g) fresh wholemeal breadcrumbs

finely grated zest of 1 orange

1/4 cup (30 g) finely grated carrot

2 teaspoons fresh thyme leaves

2 tablespoons orange juice

Each serving provides
1696 kJ, 405 kcal, 34 g protein, 17 g fat
(4 g saturated fat), 15 g carbohydrate
(5 g sugars), 3 g fibre

1 First make the stuffing. Mix the cranberries with the breadcrumbs, orange zest, carrot, thyme and orange juice until thoroughly combined.

2 Place each slice of rump steak in turn between 2 sheets of cling film and use a rolling pin to bat them out until they are thin. Lay a slice of rump steak on a board and place a quarter of the stuffing in the centre. Flatten the stuffing slightly, leaving a border all around it, then fold the sides of the meat over it. Roll up the meat to enclose the stuffing in a neat package. Secure with a wooden cocktail stick. Repeat with the remaining beef slices and stuffing.

3 Heat the oil in a flameproof casserole dish. Add the beef rolls and cook for about 6 minutes, rolling them occasionally so that they brown evenly. Meanwhile, place the thyme, bay leaf, peppercorns, juniper berries and cloves in a small square of muslin and tie up into a bouquet garni. Add to the casserole with the stock, wine, cranberries, carrot, onion and garlic. Bring slowly to the boil, then reduce the heat, cover and simmer for 40 minutes until the beef is tender.

4 Discard the bouquet garni. Place the beef rolls in a warm serving dish. Transfer the cooked vegetables to a blender with a ladleful of the cooking liquid, then purée until smooth. Boil the remaining cooking liquid for 2–3 minutes. Return the puréed vegetables to the pan, stir and reheat.

5 Remove the cocktail sticks from the beef rolls, slice them and arrange on warmed plates with some of the sauce. Garnish with fresh thyme sprigs and serve.

Spiced pork with sweet potatoes

PREPARATION: 30 minutes   COOKING: about 30 minutes   SERVES 4

1 tablespoon canola (rapeseed) oil

4 pork loin steaks or boneless pork chops, about 140 g each, trimmed of fat

1 red onion, coarsely chopped

2 celery sticks, chopped

1 large orange sweet potato (kumara), about 400 g, peeled and cut into sticks

150 ml sweetened cranberry juice

150 ml salt-reduced chicken stock

1 piece of stem ginger, drained of syrup and cut into fine sticks

1 tablespoon thick-cut orange marmalade

1 tablespoon dry sherry

1 teaspoon Chinese five-spice

2 star anise

4 roma (plum) tomatoes, quartered

freshly ground pepper

3 spring onions, shredded, to garnish

Each serving provides
1756 kJ, 420 kcal, 35 g protein, 16 g fat (5 g saturated fat), 32 g carbohydrate (19 g sugars), 5 g fibre

1 Heat the oil in a large flameproof casserole dish or deep sauté pan. Add the pork steaks and brown for 3–4 minutes on each side. Transfer to a plate and set aside.

2 Add the onion and celery to the oil remaining in the casserole dish and cook, stirring, over a moderate heat for 2–3 minutes. Add the sweet potato, cover the pan and sweat the vegetables for 3–4 minutes or until softened.

3 Stir in the cranberry juice, stock, ginger, marmalade, sherry, five-spice, star anise and a little pepper to taste. Bring to the boil, then reduce the heat and return the pork to the casserole. Cover and cook gently for 15 minutes.

4 Add the tomatoes to the casserole, cover and cook gently for a further 5 minutes or until the tomatoes are lightly cooked, but still hold their shape. Season to taste and serve, garnished with spring onions.

SOME MORE IDEAS

● Add 400 g cubed pumpkin instead of the sweet potato, and 1 small bulb of fennel, chopped, instead of the celery sticks.

● Add 1¼ cups (200 g) pitted prunes and 2 cored and thickly sliced sweet red apples instead of the tomatoes. Omit the sherry.

HEALTHY EATING

● Sweet potatoes have a natural sweetness that intensifies during cooking. They have a moderate GI score and are an excellent source of beta-carotene and vitamin E.

● Lean pork has a lower fat content than beef or lamb. It is a good source of zinc and iron.

HEALTHY EATING

● The potatoes and dumplings conspire to raise the GI of this dish to medium, but if eaten only occasionally it will do your low-GI diet no harm.

● Swede is a member of the cruciferous family of vegetables. It is rich in cancer-fighting phytochemicals and a useful source of vitamin C and beta-carotene.

● Leeks are thought to assist in preventing heart disease and stroke. They are also a source of folate and beta-carotene.

Cidered pork with herb dumplings

GI estimate MEDIUM

Mustard peps up this simple, vegetable-rich pork stew. Fluffy dumplings help to mop up the full-flavoured sauce, and turn the stew into a well-balanced meal in a bowl.

PREPARATION: 30 minutes   COOKING: about 1³/4 hours   SERVES 4

1 Heat the olive oil in a large flameproof casserole dish and add the chunks of pork. Cook over a high heat for 10 minutes or until well browned, stirring frequently. Use a draining spoon to transfer the meat to a plate.

2 Reduce the heat to moderate and add the carrots, celery, leeks, bay leaves and sage to the casserole dish. Cook for 5 minutes, stirring frequently, until the leeks are softened. Pour in the cider and stock. Return the pork to the casserole dish with any juices. Add the mustard and mix well.

3 Bring to the boil, then reduce the heat to low and cover. Simmer gently for 45 minutes, stirring occasionally. Stir in the potatoes and swede. Bring back to simmering point, cover again and cook over a low heat for a further 30 minutes or until the pork and vegetables are cooked.

4 Meanwhile, prepare the dumplings. Mix together the breadcrumbs, flour, baking powder, chives, parsley and a generous pinch of salt in a bowl. Make a well in the centre and add the egg, milk and oil. Mix the liquids together, then gradually stir in the dry ingredients to make a dough.

5 Bring a saucepan of water to a steady boil. Dust your hands with flour, then divide the dumpling mixture into 12 portions and roll each one into a round dumpling. Keep dusting your hands with flour to prevent the mixture from sticking. Add the dumplings to the water, adjust the heat so that they simmer gently for about 10 minutes or until risen and firm.

6 Taste the casserole and season, if necessary. Use a draining spoon to lift the dumplings out of the water, shaking gently to drain them well. Arrange them on top of the casserole and serve at once.

COOK'S TIP

● For high-fibre dumplings, use wholemeal breadcrumbs and stoneground wholemeal self-raising flour (which you should be able to buy in a health food shop).

1 tablespoon olive oil

450 g lean boneless pork, cut into 2.5 cm chunks

2 carrots, cut into 1 cm dice

2 celery sticks, sliced

2 leeks, sliced

2 bay leaves

2 tablespoons finely shredded fresh sage or 1 teaspoon dried sage

300 ml dry cider

300 ml salt-reduced pork or chicken stock

1 tablespoon Dijon mustard

675 g new potatoes, peeled and cut into 1 cm dice

225 g swede, cut into 1 cm dice

HERB DUMPLINGS

1¹/4 cup (100 g) fresh breadcrumbs

¹/2 cup (50 g) self-raising flour

¹/2 teaspoon baking powder

3 tablespoons snipped fresh chives

3 tablespoons chopped parsley

1 egg, lightly beaten

3 tablespoons lite or low-fat milk

1 tablespoon canola (rapeseed) oil

FOR LOWER GI

Use orange sweet potatoes (kumara) instead of new potatoes. Serve the stew with pasta instead of dumplings.

Each serving provides
2427 kJ, 580 kcal, 37 g protein, 19 g fat (4 g saturated fat), 61 g carbohydrate (12 g sugars), 7 g fibre

Pork, prune and orange pie

GI estimate LOW–MED

Pastry raises the GI of a dish, so is best eaten only occasionally. When a recipe requires it, roll it thinly and use it sparingly for the minimum impact on the overall GI of the meal. Here a layer of shortcrust pastry covers a delicious filling of pork and prunes.

PREPARATION: 50 minutes (including making the pastry) COOKING: 35 minutes SERVES 4

SHORTCRUST PASTRY

3/4 cup (110 g) plain flour

pinch of salt

60 g non-hydrogenated soft margarine

PORK AND PRUNE FILLING

1 tablespoon canola (rapeseed) oil

400 g pork fillet (tenderloin), trimmed of all fat and cut into bite-sized pieces

2 leeks, sliced

150 ml apple juice

200 ml salt-reduced chicken or vegetable stock

1 tablespoon dry sherry

grated zest of 1 orange

1 tablespoon chopped fresh sage or 1 teaspoon dried sage

3/4 cup (165 g) pitted prunes

2 teaspoons cornflour

FOR LOWER GI
Replace half the flour with stoneground wholemeal flour to make the pastry.

Each serving provides
2081 kJ, 497 kcal, 27 g protein, 23 g fat (4 g saturated fat), 46 g carbohydrate (19 g sugars), 6 g fibre

1 Sift the flour and salt into a large mixing bowl. Rub in the margarine until the mixture resembles fine breadcrumbs. Sprinkle on 2 tablespoons cold water and mix using a round-bladed knife. Add a drop more water only if the dough will not clump together. Gather into a firm dough, wrap in cling film and leave in the refrigerator to chill while making the filling.

2 To make the filling, heat the oil in a large non-stick frying pan over a moderately high heat. Add the pieces of pork and cook for 3–4 minutes or until lightly browned on all sides. Remove to a plate using a draining spoon. Add the leeks to the frying pan and cook for 2–3 minutes or until softened.

3 Add the apple juice, stock, sherry, orange zest and sage. Bring to the boil, then reduce the heat. Return the pork to the pan and add the prunes. Cover and cook gently for 20 minutes or until the pork is tender. Preheat the oven to 220°C (Gas 7).

4 Using a draining spoon, transfer the pork, prunes and vegetables to a 1.2 litre pie dish. Blend the cornflour with 2 teaspoons cold water, then stir into the cooking liquid left in the pan. Bring to the boil, stirring, and cook until the sauce has thickened slightly. Season to taste, then pour into the pie dish.

5 Roll out the pastry dough thinly to a round to cover the pie dish. Lay the dough over the filling, crimp the edges and make a small hole in the centre so the steam can escape. Bake for 15 minutes, then reduce the oven temperature to 180°C (Gas 4). Bake for a further 20 minutes or until golden. Serve hot.

ANOTHER IDEA
● Use skinless, boneless chicken breasts (fillets) instead of pork, and dried apricots rather than prunes.

HEALTHY EATING

● Pork is a first-class source of protein, B vitamins (especially B12), iron and zinc.

● Prunes are a good source of dietary fibre and contain a natural laxative.

Ham with pears

GI estimate LOW

PREPARATION: 20 minutes   COOKING: about 1 hour   SERVES 4

2 tablespoons olive oil

340 g lean cooked ham, cut into
2 cm cubes

2 onions, chopped

2 red capsicums (peppers), seeded and
diced

3 hard cooking pears

juice of 1 lemon

2 teaspoons soft light brown sugar

3 large sprigs thyme

600 ml salt-reduced vegetable stock

675 g orange sweet potatoes (kumara),
peeled and cut into 2 cm chunks

2 tablespoons cornflour

a good pinch of freshly grated nutmeg

freshly ground pepper

sprigs of fresh thyme to garnish

FOR EVEN LOWER GI

Cook without the sweet potatoes and
serve with a low-GI grain such as
burghul (bulgur) wheat.

Each serving provides
1789 kJ, 427 kcal, 20 g protein, 12 g fat
(2 g saturated fat), 58 g carbohydrate
(31 g sugars), 7 g fibre

1 Heat the oil in a large saucepan. Add the ham and cook over
a fairly high heat for about 5 minutes, turning the pieces
frequently until they are browned all over. Use a draining
spoon to remove the ham from the pan and set aside.

2 Add the onions and capsicums to the oil remaining in the
pan. Stir well, then cover and cook for 10 minutes or until the
vegetables are softened. While the vegetables are cooking,
peel the pears, quarter them lengthwise and remove the
cores. Toss the pears with the lemon juice to prevent them
from turning brown.

3 Return the ham cubes to the saucepan. Add the pears with
the lemon juice, the sugar and thyme, and pour in the stock.
Bring to the boil, then reduce the heat to low and cover the
pan. Simmer gently for about 20 minutes or until the pears
are tender.

4 Use a draining spoon to transfer the pears to a bowl; cover
and set aside. Stir the sweet potatoes into the stew and
bring back to simmering point, then cover and cook for a
further 10 minutes. Mix the cornflour to a smooth paste with
2 tablespoons cold water and stir into the stew. Bring to the
boil, stirring. Reduce the heat, cover and cook for 5 more
minutes until the ham and sweet potatoes are tender.

5 Discard the thyme sprigs. Add the nutmeg and pepper to
taste. Ladle the stew into bowls and add the pears. Garnish
with thyme sprigs and serve.

Ham and baby corn polenta tart

GI estimate LOW

PREPARATION: 25 minutes, plus 10 minutes cooling   COOKING: 35-40 minutes   SERVES 4

1. Preheat the oven to 190°C (Gas 5). Heat the stock in a large saucepan until boiling, then pour in the polenta in a steady stream, stirring constantly with a wooden spoon to prevent lumps from forming. Cook over a moderate heat, stirring, for about 5 minutes or until thick and smooth, and pulling away from the sides of the pan. Remove from the heat and beat in the margarine, chives, parsley, and seasoning to taste. Set aside to cool for about 10 minutes.

2. Spoon the polenta into a lightly oiled, 25 cm loose-bottomed flan tin that is about 4 cm deep. Spread out the polenta with the back of a metal spoon. Set the tin on a baking tray.

3. To make the filling, cook the broccoli and corn in a saucepan of boiling water for 3 minutes. Drain well and spoon into the polenta case. Scatter over the diced ham and spring onions.

4. Whisk together the eggs, milk, mustard and seasoning to taste. Pour over the ham and vegetables. Bake for about 35-40 minutes or until golden brown and just set.

5. To serve, carefully remove the tart from the tin and sprinkle the top with the chives. Serve warm.

COOK'S TIP

● If you can't find fresh baby corn, use canned. Alternatively, try canned corn kernels.

HERBED POLENTA

600 ml salt-reduced chicken stock

1 cup (150 g) polenta

1 tablespoon non-hydrogenated soft margarine

2 tablespoons chopped fresh chives

2 tablespoons chopped parsley

freshly ground pepper

HAM AND CORN FILLING

250 g broccoli, cut into small florets

85 g baby corn (sweetcorn), halved lengthwise

200 g lean cooked ham, diced

3 spring onions, thinly sliced

3 eggs, beaten

1 cup (250 ml) lite or low-fat milk

1 teaspoon Dijon mustard

2 tablespoons snipped fresh chives to garnish

Each serving provides
1395 kJ, 333 kcal, 25 g protein, 10 g fat
(2 g saturated fat), 36 g carbohydrate
(7 g sugars), 5 g fibre

HEALTHY EATING

● Polenta is low in fat with a moderate GI score, so it makes a healthy alternative to pastry.

● Ham is a good source of iron and zinc but is high in sodium so is best used in small amounts to add flavour, as in this recipe.

● Broccoli is packed with vitamins, including B6, folate and niacin.

Hungarian-style meatballs

Minced turkey and mushrooms make succulent, low-fat meatballs – delicious simmered in a sauce of smooth passata with red and green capsicums. Paprika warms the dish and new potatoes turn it into a complete one-pot meal.

GI estimate LOW–MED

PREPARATION: 35 minutes   COOKING: about 45 minutes   SERVES 4

1 tablespoon canola (rapeseed) oil

1 small onion, finely chopped

340 g mushrooms, finely chopped

340 g minced turkey

$^2/_3$ cup (55 g) fresh wholemeal breadcrumbs

1 egg, beaten

2 tablespoons chopped parsley

550 g small new potatoes

freshly ground pepper

4 tablespoons low-fat natural yogurt to serve

fresh flat-leaf parsley to garnish

PAPRIKA SAUCE

2 tablespoons olive oil

1 onion, finely chopped

2 garlic cloves, crushed

1 red capsicum (pepper), seeded and thinly sliced

1 green capsicum (pepper), seeded and thinly sliced

1 tablespoon paprika

4 cups (1 litre) passata

pinch of caraway seeds

FOR LOWER GI

Omit the potatoes and serve the meatballs with wholemeal spaghetti.

Each serving provides
2150 kJ, 514 kcal, 43 g protein, 22 g fat
(4 g saturated fat), 35 g carbohydrate
(6 g sugars), 8 g fibre

1   Heat the oil in a heavy-based frying pan. Add the onion and mushrooms, and cook over a moderate heat, stirring frequently, for about 10 minutes. The mushrooms give up their liquid initially, but this evaporates to leave the mixture greatly reduced, dark in colour and very thick. Transfer the mixture to a bowl and allow it to cool slightly.

2   Add the minced turkey to the mushroom mixture and use a fork to break up the mince. Add the breadcrumbs, egg, parsley and a little pepper. Mix the ingredients until thoroughly combined. Wet your hands to prevent the mixture from sticking to them, then shape it into 20 walnut-sized balls. Set aside.

3   To prepare the sauce, heat the oil in a large flameproof casserole dish. Add the onion and cook for 4–5 minutes, stirring frequently, until softened. Add the garlic and red and green capsicums and cook, stirring constantly, for 2–3 minutes. Stir in the paprika and cook for 1 minute, then pour in the passata and bring to the boil over a high heat.

4   Stir in the caraway seeds and season to taste. Add the meatballs and potatoes to the simmering sauce. Cover and simmer gently for 35 minutes until the potatoes are tender. Taste and adjust the seasoning, if necessary.

5   Ladle the meatballs, potatoes and sauce into bowls. Serve with a swirl of yogurt and a sprig of parsley.

HEALTHY EATING

● Boiled new potatoes are acceptable on a low-GI eating plan – they have a moderate GI score (unlike mashed or baked potatoes, which have high GI scores). Watch your portion size, though. One serving is 2 or 3 new potatoes.

Goulash in a hurry

GI estimate LOW

This short-cut version of classic Hungarian goulash is rich and delicious. Strips of lean pork, shredded red cabbage and green capsicum taste excellent with the traditional flavourings of paprika and caraway seeds. Serve with noodles and a green salad.

PREPARATION: 10 minutes   COOKING: about 20 minutes   SERVES 4

1 Heat the oil in a large frying pan or saucepan. Add the onion, garlic and pork, and cook over a high heat for about 3 minutes or until the meat has changed colour and become firm and the onion is slightly softened. Meanwhile, blend the flour with 4 tablespoons juice from the canned tomatoes to make a smooth paste; set aside.

2 Add the vermouth, paprika, caraway seeds and sugar to the pan and stir, then add the tomatoes with the rest of their juice, breaking them up as you mix them in. Stir in the flour and tomato juice mixture. Bring to the boil, stirring, and cook until the juices thicken.

3 Stir in the green capsicum and red cabbage. Reduce the heat, cover and simmer for 15 minutes or until the meat is cooked and the vegetables are just tender.

4 Season to taste. Ladle the goulash into bowls and top each portion with a spoonful of Greek-style yogurt and a sprinkle of paprika. Garnish with chives.

ANOTHER IDEA

● To make a vegetarian goulash, omit the pork and red cabbage. Cut 1 eggplant (aubergine) into chunks and add to the onion and garlic in step 1 with 2 sliced celery sticks and 2 sliced zucchini (courgettes). Follow the main recipe, using salt-reduced vegetable stock. Simmer until the vegetables are tender, then stir in 1 can chickpeas, about 400 g, and 1 can red kidney beans, about 200 g, well drained. Cook for 5 minutes.

2 tablespoons olive oil

1 large onion, finely chopped

2 garlic cloves, crushed

3 thick lean pork loin steaks, about 300 g total, cut into thin strips

1 tablespoon plain flour

1 large can tomatoes, about 800 g

1/2 cup (125 ml) extra dry white vermouth

2 tablespoons paprika

1 teaspoon caraway seeds

1 teaspoon caster sugar

1 large green capsicum (pepper), seeded and chopped

200 g red cabbage, finely shredded

freshly ground pepper

TO SERVE

4 tablespoons Greek-style yogurt

extra paprika

fresh chives

Each serving provides
1335 kJ, 319 kcal, 21 g protein, 16 g fat
(4 g saturated fat), 17 g carbohydrate
(11 g sugars), 7 g fibre

HEALTHY EATING

● Several studies have shown that eating garlic can reduce the risk of heart attack and stroke by making the blood less sticky and less likely to clot.

Mexican pork

PREPARATION and COOKING: about 50 minutes, plus at least 30 minutes marinating   SERVES 4

400 g pork fillet (tenderloin), trimmed
of fat

2 teaspoons olive oil

2 onions, thickly sliced

1 red and 1 yellow capsicum (pepper),
seeded and cut into chunks

4 large wheat tortillas

CITRUS MARINADE

3 garlic cloves, chopped

juice of 1 lime

juice of $1/2$ grapefruit or 1 small blood
orange

2 teaspoons mild chilli powder

1 teaspoon paprika

$1/2$ teaspoon ground cumin

$1/4$ teaspoon dried oregano or mixed
herbs

pinch of ground cinnamon

3 spring onions, chopped

1 tablespoon olive oil

AVOCADO AND RADISH SALSA

1 avocado

3 radishes, diced

1 garlic clove, chopped

1 ripe tomato, diced

juice of $1/2$ lime, or to taste

1 spring onion, chopped

1 tablespoon chopped fresh coriander

freshly ground pepper

Each serving provides
1757 kJ, 420 kcal, 27 g protein, 24 g fat
(5 g saturated fat), 23 g carbohydrate
(8 g sugars), 6 g fibre

1   Mix together all the ingredients for the marinade in a
shallow dish. Add the pork fillet and turn to coat. Cover and
marinate for at least 30 minutes, or overnight.

2   To prepare the salsa, halve, stone and peel the avocado,
then mash the flesh in a bowl. Add the remaining salsa
ingredients and mix well, then season to taste. Cover and
chill until serving time.

3   Preheat the oven to 180°C (Gas 4). Heat a ridged cast-iron
grill pan or non-stick frying pan over a moderate heat until
hot. Remove the meat from its marinade and pat it dry with
a paper towel. Brush the pan with the olive oil, then add the
pork and sear on all sides. Push the pork to one side and add
the onions and capsicums to the pan. Cook for 12-15 minutes
or until the vegetables are tender and lightly charred and
the pork is cooked through.

4   Meanwhile, wrap the tortillas, stacked up, in foil and put into
the oven to warm for 5-10 minutes.

5   Remove the grill pan from the heat. Lift out the pork and cut
it into thin strips, then return it to the pan and mix with the
onions and capsicums. To serve, pile the pork, onions and
peppers into the tortillas, roll into cone shapes and top with
the avocado and radish salsa.

Chinese-style lemon chicken

PREPARATION: 25 minutes   COOKING: about 25 minutes   SERVES 4

GI estimate LOW

1 tablespoon canola (rapeseed) oil

425 g skinless, boneless chicken breasts (fillets), sliced

1 onion, halved and thinly sliced

1 large green capsicum (pepper), seeded and cut into thin strips

1 garlic clove, chopped

1 tablespoon finely chopped fresh root ginger

2 large carrots, thinly sliced at a slant

1 can water chestnuts, about 220 g, drained and sliced

300 ml salt-reduced chicken stock

3 tablespoons dry sherry

2 tablespoons cornflour

2 teaspoons caster sugar

3 tablespoons salt-reduced soy sauce

1 tablespoon toasted sesame oil

grated zest of 2 large lemons

juice of 1 lemon

150 g fine green beans, cut into 5 cm lengths

3 cups (225 g) bean sprouts

Each serving provides
1487 kJ, 355 kcal, 29 g protein, 16 g fat
(3 g saturated fat), 20 g carbohydrate
(11 g sugars), 6 g fibre

1 Heat the oil in a flameproof casserole dish. Add the chicken and cook for about 1 minute or until the meat is just turning white. Add the onion, capsicum, garlic and ginger, and cook over a moderate heat, stirring often, for 5-6 minutes or until the onion is softened but not browned.

2 Add the carrots and water chestnuts. Pour in the stock and sherry, then heat until simmering, but not boiling rapidly. Cover and simmer for 10 minutes, stirring occasionally.

3 Meanwhile, mix the cornflour and sugar to a smooth paste with the soy sauce, sesame oil and lemon zest and juice. Stir the cornflour mixture into the casserole and bring to the boil, still stirring. Add the green beans, cover the casserole dish and simmer gently for 2 minutes. Stir in the bean sprouts and simmer for a final 2 minutes. Serve at once, before the bean sprouts soften.

SOME MORE IDEAS

● Fresh shiitake mushrooms are good in this casserole - add 1 cup (100 g) sliced shiitake with the green beans so that they will be just lightly cooked.

● Try 2 cups (200 g) chopped baby corn (sweetcorn) instead of water chestnuts and 3 baby bok choy instead of bean sprouts.

HEALTHY EATING

● The large quantity of vegetables in this dish helps to keep the GI low.

● Bean sprouts, along with other sprouted beans and seeds, are rich in B vitamins and vitamin C.

One-pot Japanese chicken

GI estimate MEDIUM

Based on Japanese-style steamboats, in which food is cooked at the table in a simmering broth, this chicken and vegetable casserole makes a satisfying main course. A sharp and savoury citrus sauce adds flavour and lowers the GI of the dish.

PREPARATION: 15 minutes, plus 10 minutes soaking   COOKING: about 30 minutes   SERVES 4

225 g fine rice noodles

600 ml salt-reduced chicken stock

550 g skinless, boneless chicken breasts (fillets), thinly sliced

225 g carrots, sliced

2 cups (200 g) snow peas (mangetout)

1 can sliced bamboo shoots, about 220 g, drained

125 g shiitake mushrooms, sliced

115 g Chinese cabbage, shredded

PONZU SAUCE

3 tablespoons mirin (sweet rice wine)

juice of 1 lemon

juice of 1¹/₂ limes

3 tablespoons rice vinegar

¹/₂ cup (80 ml) salt-reduced soy sauce

FOR LOWER GI

Use glass or cellophane noodles, which are made from mung bean starch.

Each serving provides
2066 kJ, 493 kcal, 38 g protein, 8 g fat
(3 g saturated fat), 60 g carbohydrate
(10 g sugars), 5 g fibre

1 The ponzu sauce can be made a day or more in advance. Pour the mirin into a small saucepan, bring to the boil over a high heat and boil for 30 seconds so that the alcohol evaporates. Stir in all the remaining sauce ingredients and remove from the heat. Pour into a dish, cover and set aside.

2 Place the noodles in a bowl and pour in cold water to cover. Leave to soak for 10 minutes, then drain and set aside. Bring the chicken stock to the boil in a large flameproof casserole dish. Reduce the heat so that the stock simmers, then add the chicken pieces and simmer for 10 minutes.

3 Stir in the carrots and bring back to simmering point, then cook for 5 minutes. Add the snow peas and bamboo shoots and simmer for a further 2-3 minutes. Stir in the mushrooms with the shredded Chinese cabbage, bring back to simmering point and cook for 2-3 minutes. Finally, stir in the rice noodles, bring back to simmering point and cook for a few minutes until the noodles are cooked.

4 Divide the ponzu sauce among 4 small bowls. Ladle the casserole into warm serving bowls. Serve at once, offering the ponzu sauce with the casserole, so that bite-sized pieces can be dipped before they are eaten.

COOK'S TIP

● If you can't find fresh shiitake mushrooms, look for the dried kind in health food shops. Soak before use.

SOME MORE IDEAS

● Replace the Chinese cabbage with the leaves from a bunch of watercress and 1¹/₂ cups (125 g) young spinach leaves.

● Tofu works well in this dish to make a vegetarian casserole. Replace the chicken with 450 g firm tofu, cut into 3.5 cm cubes, adding it with the carrots, and use salt-reduced vegetable stock.

HEALTHY EATING

● Snow peas are an excellent source of vitamin C and they also provide beta-carotene, potassium and fibre.

● Soy sauce is a popular condiment in Chinese and Japanese cooking. It is a concentrated source of sodium, so it is diluted for this sauce with fresh citrus juice, rice wine and rice vinegar.

● The vinegar helps to lower the GI of this dish.

HEALTHY EATING

● Using tortillas instead of pastry lowers the fat content of this dish. Tortillas, whether they are made from cornmeal or wheat, are a better source of low-GI carbohydrates than most white breads. When you are at the sandwich bar, a tortilla wrap is generally a better choice than a sandwich (unless the bread is stoneground wholemeal or rye).

● There is little nutritional difference between canned red kidney beans and cooked dried ones.

Aztec chicken pie

Instead of pastry this unusual pie is made with layers of wheat tortillas filled with diced chicken in a spicy sauce. Serve with a green salad and a dish of diced avocado sprinkled with lime juice for a meal with a Mexican flavour.

GI estimate LOW

PREPARATION: 35-40 minutes   COOKING: 25 minutes   SERVES 6

1 First make the filling. Heat the oil in a large pan, add the onion and cook for 10 minutes or until softened. Stir in the garlic, capsicum, corn and chilli, and cook for 5 minutes.

2 Add the tomatoes with their juice, the ground coriander, cumin and sugar. Season to taste and stir well. Bring to the boil, then reduce the heat and simmer for 10 minutes.

3 Stir in the chicken, beans and half the fresh coriander. Heat through gently for 5 minutes. Preheat the oven to 200°C (Gas 6).

4 Lightly oil a large china flan dish, measuring about 28 cm in diameter and 5 cm deep. Place a tortilla on the bottom and spoon over one-fifth of the filling. Cover with a second tortilla, then spread over another fifth of the filling. Continue layering, finishing with the last tortilla on top. The stack will be slightly higher than the side of the dish.

5 Mix the yogurt with the sour cream, most of the cheese and 2 tablespoons of the remaining coriander. Spoon over the top of the pie. Sprinkle with the remaining cheese. Bake for 25 minutes or until the top is golden. Sprinkle with the rest of the coriander and serve hot, cut into wedges.

ANOTHER IDEA

● To make a borlotti bean tortilla pie, soften the onion, then add the crushed garlic, 1 seeded and chopped yellow capsicum, 3 chopped zucchini (courgettes) and a medium-sized chopped fennel bulb. Cook for 5 minutes, then stir in the tomatoes, ground coriander, sugar and seasoning to taste. Simmer for 10 minutes. Add 1 can borlotti beans, about 410 g, drained and rinsed, stir well and heat through. Layer the bean mixture with the flour tortillas, top with the yogurt and sour cream mixture and bake as in the main recipe.

2 tablespoons olive oil

1 large, mild onion, chopped

2 garlic cloves, crushed

1 green capsicum (pepper), seeded and chopped

200 g baby corn (sweetcorn), chopped into 3

1 red chilli, seeded and chopped

2 cans chopped tomatoes, about 400 g each

1 teaspoon ground coriander

1 teaspoon ground cumin

1 teaspoon caster sugar

300 g cooked skinless, boneless chicken breasts (fillets), diced

1 can red kidney beans, about 410 g, drained and rinsed

6 tablespoons chopped fresh coriander

freshly ground pepper

6 large wheat tortillas

$2/3$ cup (160 g) low-fat natural yogurt

$1/3$ cup (90g) light sour cream

$1/2$ cup (60 g) finely grated mature cheddar

Each serving provides
1659 kJ, 396 kcal, 25 g protein, 19 g fat
(7 g saturated fat), 30 g carbohydrate
(11 g sugars), 8 g fibre

Stuffed turkey rolls with lentils

GI estimate LOW

PREPARATION: 40 minutes   COOKING: 1¹/₂ hours   SERVES 4

4 skinless, boneless turkey breasts
    (fillets), about 500 g in total
1 tablespoon olive oil
1 onion, finely chopped
1 parsnip, cut into 1 cm dice
2 carrots, cut into 1 cm dice
1 tablespoon plain flour
600 ml salt-reduced chicken stock
2 teaspoons Dijon mustard
1 can whole peeled chestnuts, about
    240 g, drained
1 cup (200 g) French-style green (puy)
    lentils
2 teaspoons balsamic vinegar
freshly ground pepper
sprigs of fresh flat-leaf parsley
    to garnish

APRICOT STUFFING
1 onion, finely chopped
¹/₃ cup (60 g) dried apricots, finely
    chopped
2 garlic cloves, crushed
1 cup (80 g) fresh wholemeal
    breadcrumbs
3 tablespoons chopped parsley
1 egg yolk
grated zest and juice of 1 orange

Each serving provides
2213 kJ, 529 kcal, 49 g protein, 14 g fat
(3 g saturated fat), 55 g carbohydrate
(20 g sugars), 13 g fibre

1 Preheat the oven to 180°C (Gas 4). One at a time, lay the turkey fillets between 2 pieces of cling film and pat out with a rolling pin into a rectangle measuring about 15 x 12 cm.

2 For the stuffing, put the onion, apricots, garlic, breadcrumbs, parsley, egg yolk, a third of the orange zest and 1 tablespoon of the orange juice in a bowl. Season to taste and mix well. Divide the stuffing among the turkey slices and use a fork to spread it over them, pressing it down evenly. Roll up each slice from a narrow edge and secure with wooden cocktail sticks to keep the rolls in shape.

3 Heat the oil in a flameproof casserole dish. Add the turkey rolls and fry over a moderate heat for 5 minutes, turning occasionally to brown them evenly. Use a draining spoon to transfer the rolls from the casserole dish to a plate.

4 Add the onion to the casserole dish and cook for about 5 minutes or until it is softened. Stir in the parsnip and carrots, then sprinkle in the flour and stir until it is evenly distributed. Pour in the stock and stir in the mustard. Add the chestnuts, and bring to the boil, stirring. Replace the turkey rolls in the casserole, cover and transfer to the oven to cook for about 1¹/₄ hours or until the turkey is tender.

5 About 30 minutes before the turkey rolls are ready, place the lentils in a large saucepan with plenty of cold water. Bring to the boil and cook for 20 minutes or until the lentils are tender. Drain the lentils and return them to the pan. Add the rest of the orange zest and juice, and the vinegar.

6 Transfer the turkey rolls to a board and mix the vegetables with the lentils. Remove the cocktail sticks from the turkey rolls and slice them neatly. Serve them on a bed of lentils.

Chicken liver mousse

PREPARATION and COOKING: 15 minutes, plus at least 4 hours chilling   SERVES 4

1   Place the chicken livers, onion and garlic in a saucepan and add stock or water to cover. Tie the parsley, thyme and bay leaf into a bouquet garni and add to the pan. Slowly bring to the boil, skimming the surface as necessary, then reduce the heat and simmer gently for 5–8 minutes or until the livers are cooked through but still slightly pink in the centre when you cut into one.

2   Drain, and discard the bouquet garni. Tip the livers, onions and garlic into a food processor. Add 1 tablespoon of ricotta, the vinegar and brandy, and process until smooth, adding the remaining 1/2 tablespoon ricotta if it is necessary for a lighter texture. Season to taste, then stir in the peppercorns.

3   Spoon the mousse into a serving bowl, or individual ramekins, and smooth the top. Sprinkle with a layer of finely chopped parsley. Cover with cling film and chill for at least 4 hours, but preferably overnight.

4   Before serving, allow the mousse to return to room temperature. Serve with slices of hot toasted grainy wholemeal or other low-GI bread.

COOK'S TIP

● If you can't find pink or green peppercorns, substitute finely chopped drained capers.

ANOTHER IDEA

● Replace the brandy with orange juice and add the finely grated zest of 1/2 orange.

HEALTHY EATING

● Chicken livers are one of the richest sources of iron – each serving of this mousse provides more than half of the recommended daily intake. They are, of course, a great source of healthy lean protein, too.

● Poaching the chicken livers with vegetables and herbs, instead of frying them, gives them lots of flavour without adding fat.

250 g chicken livers, well trimmed

1 onion, finely chopped

1 garlic clove, crushed

600 ml salt-reduced vegetable stock or water

several sprigs parsley

several sprigs thyme

1 bay leaf

1–1 1/2 tablespoons ricotta or plain low-fat fromage frais

2 teaspoons garlic vinegar or white wine vinegar

2 teaspoons brandy or Calvados

1 tablespoon pink or green peppercorns in brine, drained and patted dry

2 tablespoons finely chopped parsley

Each serving provides
508 kJ, 122 kcal, 13 g protein, 4 g fat
(2 g saturated fat), 7 g carbohydrate
(4 g sugars), 1 g fibre

Chicken satay

Gingery cubes of chicken and colourful crunchy vegetables are grilled on wooden skewers and served with a peanut sauce in this version of the Indonesian starter. It becomes a main dish with extra chicken and a serving of basmati rice.

PREPARATION: 40 minutes, plus at least 2 hours marinating   COOKING: 10-15 minutes   SERVES 4

2 x 3 cm piece fresh root ginger, peeled and finely chopped

2 tablespoons salt-reduced soy sauce

juice of $^1/_2$ lime

1 tablespoon canola (rapeseed) oil

340 g skinless, boneless chicken breasts (fillets), cut into 2 cm cubes

1 lime, cut into 8 wedges

8 cherry tomatoes, about 100 g in total

1 yellow capsicum (pepper), seeded and cut into chunky pieces

1 zucchini (courgette), about 150 g, thickly sliced

sprigs of fresh coriander to garnish

PEANUT SAUCE

2 tablespoons canola (rapeseed) oil

1 small onion, finely chopped

$^1/_3$ cup (50 g) unsalted peanuts, finely chopped

1 garlic clove, chopped

1 teaspoon green Thai curry paste

1 tablespoon salt-reduced soy sauce

$^1/_2$ teaspoon caster sugar

25 g coconut cream

Each serving provides
1639 kJ, 392 kcal, 24 g protein, 29 g fat
(7 g saturated fat), 10 g carbohydrate
(4 g sugars), 3 g fibre

1 To make the marinade, mix the ginger, soy sauce, lime juice and oil together in a bowl. Add the chicken and toss to coat. Cover with cling film and leave to marinate in the refrigerator for at least 2 hours, turning once or twice. Soak 8 wooden or bamboo skewers in cold water for 30 minutes.

2 To make the peanut sauce, heat the oil in a small saucepan, add the onion and cook over a moderate heat, stirring, for 3 minutes. Add the peanuts and cook for 3-5 minutes or until both the nuts and onion are lightly browned, stirring occasionally. Add the garlic, curry paste, soy sauce, sugar and 150 ml of water. Bring to the boil. Add the coconut cream and mix well. Simmer gently for 5 minutes or until thickened, stirring occasionally. Purée the sauce in a blender or food processor to make a thick cream. Return to the saucepan and set aside.

3 Preheat the grill to high. Lift the chicken out of the marinade; reserve the marinade. Thread the chicken, lime wedges and vegetables onto the soaked skewers. Arrange the skewers on the grill rack and brush with the marinade. Place under the grill and cook for 10-15 minutes, turning once or twice, until the chicken is cooked thoroughly.

4 While the chicken is cooking, reheat the sauce. Arrange the skewers on 4 serving plates, garnish with sprigs of coriander and serve with the sauce.

SOME MORE IDEAS

● A 400 g pack of firm tofu or tempeh could be used to replace the chicken and make a vegetarian dish. Drain the tofu well, cut it into large cubes and marinate instead of the chicken.

● Try other vegetable combinations, such as 1 red onion, cut into 8 wedges, 8 medium-sized button mushrooms, about 100 g in total, and $^1/_2$ cup (50 g) snow peas (mangetout).

HEALTHY EATING

● In common with most other nuts, peanuts are high in fat, although much of the fat they contain is of the unsaturated variety. Research suggests that diets that contain a daily intake of peanuts, peanut butter or peanut (groundnut) oil may help to lower total cholesterol, particularly harmful LDL cholesterol, and help to protect against coronary heart disease.

HEALTHY EATING

● Cashew nuts are a low-GI source of protein and fibre. They also provide minerals such as iron, magnesium and selenium. Although cashews are high in fat, the majority of it is the 'healthy' monounsaturated type.

● Stir-frying is a healthy way to cook, because only a little oil is needed, any meat or poultry used is very lean, and cooking is done quickly over quite a high heat so that the vegetables retain the maximum amount of nutrients.

Chicken and cashew pancakes

GI estimate LOW

Chicken stir-fried with carrots, celery and cabbage, then lightly flavoured with orange and sesame, makes a delicious filling for pancakes. This dish is sure to meet with your family's approval.

PREPARATION: 15-20 minutes   COOKING: about 30 minutes   SERVES 4

1 To make the pancakes, sift the flour into a bowl and add a little pepper to taste. Make a well in the centre. Mix the egg with the milk and pour into the well. Gradually whisk the flour into the egg and milk to form a smooth batter.

2 Use a little of the oil to lightly grease a 20 cm non-stick frying pan, and place it on a moderate heat. Pour in a little of the batter and swirl it evenly across the surface, then cook for 2 minutes to form a pancake. Toss the pancake or flip it over with a palette knife and cook on the other side for about 30 seconds. Slide out onto a warm heatproof plate and cover with a sheet of greaseproof paper.

3 Cook the remaining batter in the same way, making a total of 8 pancakes and stacking them up, interleaved with greaseproof paper. Grease the pan with more oil between pancakes as necessary. When all the pancakes have been made, cover the pancake stack with foil, sealing it well. Place the plate over a pan of gently simmering water to keep the pancakes warm while you prepare the filling.

4 Heat a wok or large frying pan. Add the cashew nuts and stir-fry them over a moderate heat for a few minutes or until golden. Remove to a plate and set aside.

5 Add the oil to the wok or frying pan and swirl it around, then add the chicken, garlic, ginger and chilli, if using. Stir-fry for 3 minutes.

6 Add the carrot and celery sticks, and stir-fry for a further 2 minutes. Add the orange zest and cabbage and stir-fry for 1 minute. Sprinkle over the soy sauce and sesame oil and stir-fry for another minute. Return the cashews to the pan and toss to mix with the other ingredients.

7 Divide the stir-fry filling among the warm pancakes and fold them over or roll up. Serve immediately, with a little extra soy sauce to sprinkle.

$3/4$ cup (110 g) plain flour

1 egg, beaten

300 ml lite or low-fat milk

1 teaspoon canola (rapeseed) oil

pepper

CHICKEN AND CASHEW NUT FILLING

$1/3$ cup (50 g) cashew nuts

1 tablespoon canola (rapeseed) oil

300 g skinless, boneless chicken breasts (fillets), cut into strips

1 garlic clove, crushed

1 teaspoon finely chopped fresh root ginger

1 red chilli, seeded and finely chopped (optional)

2 carrots, cut into thin sticks

2 celery sticks, cut into thin sticks

grated zest of $1/2$ orange

205 g Savoy cabbage, shredded

1 tablespoon salt-reduced soy sauce, plus extra for serving

1 teaspoon toasted sesame oil

FOR EVEN LOWER GI
Replace half the flour with stoneground wholemeal flour.

Each serving provides
1698 kJ, 406 kcal, 28 g protein, 19 g fat
(3 g saturated fat), 31 g carbohydrate
(9 g sugars), 5 g fibre

Indian-style grilled chicken breasts

PREPARATION: about 15 minutes   COOKING: 15 minutes   SERVES 4

4 skinless, boneless chicken breasts
    (fillets), about 140 g each
canola (rapeseed) oil for brushing
lemon or lime wedges to serve
sprigs of fresh coriander to garnish

YOGURT MARINADE

1 garlic clove, crushed
1 tablespoon finely chopped fresh root
    ginger
1^1/$_2$ teaspoons tomato purée
1^1/$_2$ teaspoons garam masala
1 teaspoon ground coriander
1^1/$_2$ teaspoons ground cumin
^{1}/$_2$ teaspoon dried turmeric
pinch of cayenne pepper, or to taste
^{1}/$_3$ cup (90 g) low-fat natural yogurt

RAITA

1^1/$_3$ cup (340 g) low-fat natural yogurt
1 cucumber, about 300 g, peeled, cut
    into quarters lengthwise and
    seeded
100 g tomatoes, very finely chopped
^{1}/$_2$ teaspoon ground coriander
^{1}/$_2$ teaspoon ground cumin
pinch of cayenne pepper

FOR EVEN LOWER GI

Omit the yogurt from the marinade,
double all the other ingredients and stir
in 1 tablespoon white distilled vinegar.
Vinegar lowers the GI of food and this
version will also create a crispier
texture on the grilled breasts.

Each serving provides
1295 kJ, 309 kcal, 36 g protein, 13 g fat
(4 g saturated fat), 12 g carbohydrate
(10 g sugars), 1 g fibre

1   Preheat the grill to high. To make the marinade, put all the
    marinade ingredients into a large bowl and whisk together
    well. If you prefer, put the ingredients in a blender or food
    processor and process until well blended. Transfer to a bowl
    large enough to hold all the chicken breasts.

2   Score 2 slits on each side of the chicken breasts. Place them
    in the marinade, turning to coat and rubbing the marinade
    into the slits. (If you have time, leave the chicken to marinate
    in the refrigerator overnight.)

3   Brush the grill rack with oil, then place the chicken breasts
    on top. Grill for 12-15 minutes, turning and basting with the
    remaining marinade, until the juices run clear when the
    chicken is pierced with a knife and the marinade looks
    slightly charred.

4   Meanwhile, make the raita. Place the yogurt in a bowl.
    Coarsely grate the cucumber, then squeeze to remove as
    much moisture as possible. Add the cucumber to the yogurt
    together with the tomatoes, ground coriander, cumin and
    cayenne. Stir well to mix. Spoon the raita into a serving dish.

5   Transfer the chicken breasts to a serving plate. Add lemon
    or lime wedges and garnish with coriander sprigs. Serve
    with the raita on the side.

ANOTHER IDEA

● A quick alternative to raita is to serve the chicken breasts with
a simple salad of chopped tomatoes and onions on lettuce leaves
with finely chopped coriander sprinkled over the top.

Turkey and lentil pâté

GI estimate LOW

PREPARATION and COOKING: 1¹/₄ hours, plus about 2 hours chilling   SERVES 6

1   Put the lentils in a saucepan, cover generously with water and bring to the boil. Simmer for about 45 minutes or until tender. Drain well and set aside to cool.

2   Heat the oil in a large frying pan and fry the shallots and garlic over a moderately high heat for 2 minutes or until they have softened. Reduce the heat to moderate and add the minced turkey and the livers. Cook, stirring, for 8-10 minutes.

3   Pour in the Marsala or sherry, bring to the boil and allow the mixture to bubble for 1-2 minutes. Season to taste.

4   Transfer the mixture to a food processor. Add the coriander leaves and cooked lentils, and process for a few seconds to form a coarse paste. Alternatively, chop the coriander finely, and mash all the ingredients together thoroughly using a fork.

5   Spoon into 6 ramekins, pressing down well with the back of the spoon. Cover and chill for about 2 hours before serving, garnished with fresh coriander sprigs.

¹/₃ cup (60 g) brown lentils
1¹/₂ tablespoons canola (rapeseed) oil
4 French shallots, finely chopped
1 garlic clove, crushed
450 g minced turkey
115 g turkey (or chicken) livers, chopped
3 tablespoons dry Marsala wine or
    sherry
freshly ground pepper
30 g fresh coriander leaves
sprigs of fresh coriander to garnish

Each serving provides
1115 kJ, 266 kcal, 34 g protein, 11 g fat
(2 g saturated fat), 6 g carbohydrate
(2 g sugars), 2 g fibre

HEALTHY EATING

● Turkey livers are a rich source of iron, zinc, vitamin A and many of the B vitamins, especially B12.

● Like all pulses and beans, lentils are a GI 'superfood': they are low GI and a source of fibre and vitamins.

Spicy turkey chilli with spaghetti

GI estimate LOW

Sweet capsicums and warm spices flavour this chilli, made with minced turkey rather than the traditional beef for a lower fat content, and served on wholemeal spaghetti for a low GI score.

PREPARATION: 10 minutes   COOKING: about 25 minutes   SERVES 4

²/₃ cup (160 g) low-fat natural yogurt

1 spring onion, finely chopped

4 tablespoons finely chopped mixed fresh herbs, such as parsley, coriander and chives

1 tablespoon canola (rapeseed) oil

1 large garlic clove, crushed

1 onion, finely chopped

2 red or green capsicums (peppers), seeded and finely chopped

1¹/₂ teaspoons cayenne pepper, or to taste

2 teaspoons ground cumin

1 teaspoon dried oregano

500 g minced turkey

2 cans chopped tomatoes, about 400 g each

1 can red kidney beans, about 400 g, drained and rinsed

240 g wholemeal spaghetti

freshly ground pepper

Each serving provides
2715 kJ, 649 kcal, 63 g protein, 16 g fat
(4 g saturated fat), 62 g carbohydrate
(15 g sugars), 14 g fibre

1 First make the topping. Mix the yogurt with the spring onion and herbs. Cover and chill until required.

2 Heat the oil in a large frying pan or a saucepan. Add the garlic and fry, stirring, for 30 seconds. Add the onion and red or green capsicums, and fry, stirring occasionally, for 5 minutes or until softened.

3 Stir in the cayenne pepper, ground cumin and oregano and continue to cook, stirring occasionally, for about 2 minutes. Add the turkey and cook, stirring occasionally, until it is browned and crumbly.

4 Stir in the tomatoes and kidney beans and add seasoning to taste. Bring to the boil, then reduce the heat and simmer for 15 minutes.

5 Meanwhile, cook the spaghetti in boiling water for about 10-12 minutes, or according to the packet instructions, until al dente. Drain well.

6 Divide the spaghetti among 4 plates and spoon an equal amount of turkey chilli over each serving. Season to taste. Serve with the herb-flavoured yogurt.

HEALTHY EATING

● Turkey is a healthy source of protein. It contains zinc and many B vitamins, particularly thiamin, B12 and niacin. It also provides iron.

● Red kidney beans are low in fat and rich in low-GI carbohydrate. They provide good amounts of thiamin and niacin, and useful amounts of iron. They are also a good source of soluble fibre. When eaten with pasta, rice or other grains, kidney beans and other pulses supply good amounts of high-quality protein.

Turkey and celery casserole

GI estimate LOW

PREPARATION: 30 minutes   COOKING: 40-45 minutes   SERVES 4

2 tablespoons olive oil

4 boneless turkey (or chicken) breasts
   (fillets), about 400 g in total

1 onion, finely chopped

3 sweet red or green apples

2 celery hearts, halved lengthwise

strip of pared orange zest

juice of 1 orange

1 teaspoon juniper berries, lightly
   crushed

400 ml salt-reduced chicken stock

3/4 cup (75 g) walnut halves

freshly ground pepper

VEGETABLE MASH

4 carrots, cut into chunks

1 medium sweet potato (kumara), about
   450 g, peeled and cut into chunks

2 large parsnips, cut into chunks

100 ml lite or low-fat milk

Each serving provides
2244 kJ, 536 kcal, 32 g protein, 27 g fat
(3 g saturated fat), 45 g carbohydrate
(32 g sugars), 9 g fibre

1 Preheat the oven to 180°C (Gas 4). Heat the oil in a flameproof casserole dish. Add the turkey breasts and cook over a high heat for 1-2 minutes, turning to brown both sides. Remove them from the pan and set aside.

2 Add the onion to the casserole dish, reduce the heat to low and cook gently for about 5 minutes or until softened but not browned. Peel, core and dice 2 of the apples and add to the casserole dish (reserve the third apple for garnishing). If the celery is too long to fit in the casserole dish, cut it across in half, then add with the orange zest and juice, juniper berries, stock and walnuts. Season lightly and bring to the boil over a moderate heat.

3 Return the turkey breasts to the casserole, tucking them under the celery. Cover tightly and transfer to the oven to cook for 20-25 minutes or until the turkey is tender. The celery should still be quite firm. Do not overcook or the turkey will become dry and the celery too soft.

4 Meanwhile, prepare the mash. Put the vegetables in a large saucepan and pour in just enough boiling water to cover. Bring back to the boil, reduce the heat, cover the pan and simmer for about 20 minutes or until the vegetables are tender. Alternatively steam the vegetables.

5 Tip the cooked vegetables into a colander to drain. Pour the milk into the pan and place over a high heat. When the milk is hot, remove from the heat and return the vegetables to the pan. Mash the vegetables with the milk and seasoning to taste until smooth. Cover the pan to keep the mash hot while you finish the casserole.

6 Transfer the turkey, celery, apples and walnuts to a warm dish. Cover and keep hot. Discard the orange zest, then bring the cooking liquid to the boil over a high heat. Boil hard for about 5 minutes or until the liquid is reduced and slightly syrupy in consistency.

7 Meanwhile, quarter and core the remaining apple for the garnish, then cut it into neat slices. Divide the mash among 4 plates and top with the celery, apples and walnuts. Slice the turkey and arrange on the celery. Taste the sauce for seasoning, then spoon it over the turkey and celery. Garnish with the apple slices and serve.

Turkey kebabs with relish

PREPARATION: 20 minutes, plus marinating   COOKING: 15 minutes   SERVES 4

1   Cut the turkey breasts into 24 pieces, each about 5 x 2 cm. Combine the turkey pieces with 2 of the chopped garlic cloves, 1 tablespoon lemon juice, the wine, sage, rosemary, thyme, fennel seeds, 2 tablespoons of the olive oil and seasoning. Toss so that all the turkey pieces are covered with the herb mixture. Leave to marinate for at least 10 minutes, or up to 1 hour if you have the time.

2   Meanwhile, make the relish. Put the red capsicum, diced fennel and olive paste or diced olives in a bowl together with the remaining garlic, 1/2 tablespoon lemon juice and 1/2 tablespoon oil. Season to taste. Mix well, then set aside.

3   Preheat the grill to high, or prepare a charcoal fire in the barbecue. Thread the marinated turkey pieces onto the rosemary stalks if using, or onto skewers, and top each one with a shallot.

4   Grill or barbecue the kebabs for about 15 minutes or until cooked through and the turkey pieces are lightly browned. Turn the kebabs and baste with the remaining marinade frequently. Serve the kebabs hot, with the relish.

ANOTHER IDEA

● Instead of making a vegetable relish, add the red capsicum and fennel to the kebabs as 2.5 cm chunks. Alternate with pieces of turkey on the skewers, and brush with the turkey marinade.

450 g skinless, boneless turkey breasts (fillets)

3 garlic cloves, chopped

1 1/2 tablespoons lemon juice

2 tablespoons dry white wine

1 tablespoon chopped fresh sage or 2 teaspoons dried sage, crumbled

1 tablespoon chopped fresh rosemary

1 1/2 teaspoons fresh thyme leaves or 1/2 teaspoon dried thyme

1 teaspoon fennel seeds, lightly crushed

2 1/2 tablespoons extra virgin olive oil

freshly ground pepper

1 red capsicum (pepper), seeded and finely diced

1 bulb of fennel, finely diced

1 tablespoon black olive paste (tapenade) or 10 black Kalamata olives, pitted and finely diced

8 stalks of fresh rosemary (optional)

8 French shallots

Each serving provides
1217 kJ, 291 kcal, 27 g protein, 18 g fat
(3 g saturated fat), 6 g carbohydrate
(4 g sugars), 3 g fibre

HEALTHY EATING

● Red capsicums are an excellent source of vitamin C and they are rich in beta-carotene. Both of these nutrients are powerful antioxidants that can help to counteract the damaging effects of free radicals and protect against many diseases including cancer and heart disease.

Oat-crusted fish with orange **116**

Fish en papillote **119**

Malay-style braised fish **120**

Trout with green beans and pesto **121**

Swordfish with Mexican salad **123**

Spinach and smoked trout roulade **124**

Sardine open sandwich **126**

Lemon mackerel pâté **127**

Fish with spicy lentils **129**

Baked whole fish with grapefruit **130**

Spaghetti with clams **132**

Skate with citrus-honey sauce **133**

Steamed fish with black beans **134**

Chinese-style whole fish **137**

Tunisian tuna and egg briks **138**

Grilled polenta and tuna pizza **139**

Fish and seafood

Oat-crusted fish with orange

GI estimate LOW–MED

Here is a low-GI version of breaded fish, using porridge oats instead of breadcrumbs. The crisp coating seals in the flavour of the fish and adds beneficial fibre; the oranges help to lower the GI of the dish. Serve with a large mixed salad or seasonal vegetables.

PREPARATION: 15 minutes   COOKING: about 15 minutes   SERVES 4

2 oranges

140 g instant porridge oats or oatmeal

2 teaspoons Dijon mustard

freshly ground pepper

8 small white fish fillets, such as bream, whiting or sardines, about 75 g each

2 eggwhites, lightly beaten with a fork

2 tablespoons olive oil

Each serving provides
1723 kJ, 411 kcal, 37 g protein, 16 g fat
(2 g saturated fat), 31 g carbohydrate
(6 g sugars), 4 g fibre

1 Preheat the oven to 220°C (Gas 7). Finely grate the zest from one of the oranges. Cut away all the peel and white pith from both the oranges, then cut out the segments from the surrounding membrane. Set the orange segments aside.

2 Mix together the oats, mustard, orange zest and a little seasoning to taste on a plate, stirring to incorporate the mustard evenly.

3 Brush each fish fillet with eggwhite, then press into the oat mixture to coat thoroughly on both sides. Place the fillets on a lightly greased baking tray and drizzle with the olive oil.

4 Bake for about 15 minutes, depending on the thickness of the fish, until it flakes easily when tested with a fork. Serve hot, topped with the orange segments.

COOK'S TIP

● A baked potato (as shown in the picture) is a healthier accompaniment than chips, but for the lowest GI score it is better to serve the fish with boiled new potatoes.

SOME MORE IDEAS

● Instead of orange segments, serve the fish with a tomato and orange salsa. Dice the orange flesh and mix with 1 large diced tomato, a little chopped red onion, and chopped fresh mint, crushed garlic and seasoning to taste.

● For a more zesty and chunkier crust, mix together 1/2 cup (50 g) rolled oats, 1 tablespoon finely chopped fresh sage, 1 teaspoon grated or creamed horseradish, the grated zest of 1 lemon and seasoning to taste. Tuck sprigs of fresh sage into the cavities of 4 small white fish such as whiting or garfish. Brush the fish with eggwhite and coat all over with the oat mixture. Drizzle with 1 tablespoon olive oil, and bake as in the main recipe for about 15 minutes.

HEALTHY EATING

● Oats and oatmeal have a low GI. They are also a good source of soluble fibre, which can help to lower blood cholesterol levels.

● All types of oily fish are an excellent source of omega-3 fats, which are great for the heart and for boosting the immune system.

HEALTHY EATING

● As well as a lean type of protein, fish is a good source of phosphorus, which together with calcium is needed for the hardening of bones and teeth.

● Burghul wheat is made from whole wheat grains. It is a good source of low-GI carbohydrate, dietary fibre and B vitamins.

● Bok choy has a nutritional content similar to cabbage, and is a particularly good source of folate and beta-carotene.

Fish en papillote

Laying a piece of fish on a bed of greens, seasoning with a few aromatics and then wrapping up tightly into a parcel is a simple and trouble-free way to cook fish. It seals in all the nutrients, too.

GI estimate LOW

PREPARATION: 20 minutes   COOKING: 10 minutes   SERVES 4

1. Preheat the oven to 240°C (Gas 9). Cut out four 30 cm squares of foil or baking paper. Arrange one-quarter of the chopped Asian greens in the middle of each foil or paper square. Top with a fish steak, and sprinkle over the orange zest and juice, basil, garlic, wine, olive oil, fennel, carrot and seasoning to taste. Fold over the foil or paper to form a parcel, leaving a little air inside so the ingredients can steam, and twist the edges to seal. Set the parcels on a baking tray. Set aside.

2. Combine the burghul wheat with 900 ml water in a large saucepan and bring to the boil. Reduce the heat to moderately low, cover and cook for 12–15 minutes or until the grain is just tender. Drain the burghul if necessary.

3. While the burghul is cooking, put the fish parcels into the oven and bake for 10 minutes. Open one of the parcels to check that the fish is cooked and will flake easily.

4. Fork through the cooked grain and mix in the olive oil, lemon juice, garlic, basil, coriander and spring onions. Season to taste. Serve a fish parcel to each person, letting them open it at the table. Serve the burghul pilaf alongside in a bowl.

SOME MORE IDEAS
- Kingfish or tuna can be used instead of blue eye or hake.
- Replace the dry white wine with orange juice.
- For salmon en papillote, divide 4 large tomatoes, sliced, among 4 foil or baking paper squares and lay 4 pieces of skinless salmon fillet, about 140 g each, on top. Sprinkle with 2 garlic cloves, finely chopped, 1 red chilli, seeded and sliced, 4 spring onions, sliced, 3 tablespoons chopped fresh coriander, 1/2 teaspoon ground cumin and 2 tablespoons lemon juice. Wrap and bake for 10 minutes, and serve with the burghul pilaf.

280 g mixed Asian greens, such as bok choy and Chinese cabbage, chopped

4 fish steaks, such as blue eye or hake, about 140 g each

grated zest and juice of 1/2 small orange

3 tablespoons shredded fresh basil

2 garlic cloves, finely chopped

1/2 cup (125 ml) dry white wine

1 tablespoon olive oil

1/2 medium-sized bulb of fennel, thinly sliced

1 carrot, cut into thin strips

freshly ground pepper

BURGHUL AND HERB PILAF

200 g burghul (bulgur) wheat

1 tablespoon olive oil

juice of 1/2 lemon

1 garlic clove, finely chopped

2 tablespoons shredded fresh basil

2 tablespoons chopped fresh coriander

3 spring onions, sliced

Each serving provides
1638 kJ, 391 kcal, 30 g protein, 13 g fat
(2 g saturated fat), 34 g carbohydrate
(5 g sugars), 11 g fibre

FISH AND SEAFOOD

119

Malay-style braised fish

PREPARATION: 10 minutes   COOKING: about 20 minutes   SERVES 4

GI estimate LOW

1 tablespoon canola (rapeseed) oil

4 spring onions, chopped

1 red chilli, seeded and thinly sliced

2 celery sticks, thinly sliced

1 red capsicum (pepper), seeded and
    thinly sliced

1 garlic clove, crushed

$1/2$ teaspoon fennel seeds

2 teaspoons ground coriander

$1/2$ teaspoon ground cumin

$1/4$ teaspoon turmeric

$1/2$ can chopped tomatoes, about 230 g

$1/2$ cup (125 ml) coconut milk

300 ml salt-reduced fish stock

2 tablespoons fish sauce or salt-
    reduced soy sauce

1 can sliced bamboo shoots, about
    220 g, drained

675 g thick skinless white fish fillets,
    such as ling, hoki or cod, cut into
    chunks

16 raw tiger prawns, peeled

juice of $1/2$ lime

2 spring onions, chopped

1 tablespoon chopped fresh coriander

Each serving provides
1697 kJ, 405 kcal, 54 g protein, 17 g fat
(7 g saturated fat), 9 g carbohydrate
(7 g sugars), 4 g fibre

1 Heat the oil in a large frying pan. Add the spring onions, chilli, celery and capsicum, and fry, stirring constantly, for 5 minutes.

2 Stir in the garlic, fennel seeds, coriander, cumin and turmeric, and cook for 1 minute. Add the tomatoes with their juice, the coconut milk, stock and fish sauce or soy sauce. Bring to the boil, then reduce the heat and cover the pan. Simmer for 5 minutes.

3 Stir in the bamboo shoots, white fish and prawns. Cover the pan again and simmer for 5-7 minutes or until the pieces of fish are just cooked and the prawns have turned pink. Stir in the lime juice.

4 Serve the braised fish at once, garnished with a sprinkle of chopped spring onions and coriander.

ANOTHER IDEA

● Chicken can be used instead of fish. Heat the oil and brown 4 halved, skinless, boneless chicken breasts (fillets) for 4 minutes on each side. Remove from the pan. Add the vegetables and soften as in step 1, then add 150 g sliced mushrooms and cook for about 2 minutes. Return the chicken to the pan with the garlic and spices. Finish cooking, using salt-reduced chicken stock (instead of fish stock), and replacing the bamboo shoots with 1 can sliced water chestnuts, about 220 g, drained.

Trout with green beans and pesto

GI estimate LOW–MED

PREPARATION: 10 minutes   COOKING: about 15 minutes   SERVES 4

8 trout fillets, about 100 g each
4 sprigs of fresh dill
2¹/₂ cups (250 g) green beans, halved
2 tablespoons capers
200 ml dry white wine
300 ml hot salt-reduced fish stock
4 teaspoons plain flour
2 teaspoons pesto
freshly ground pepper
sprigs of fresh dill to garnish

FOR LOWER GI

The dish is shown served on a bed of mashed potatoes, but to keep the GI low, serve with boiled wild rice.

Each serving provides
1254 kJ, 300 kcal, 41 g protein, 9 g fat
(2 g saturated fat), 5 g carbohydrate
(3 g sugars), 2 g fibre

1   Check the trout fillets for bones by running your fingers over the flesh. (Tweezers are useful for removing any stray bones, if necessary.) Lay the fillets skin side down and season them. Pull the fronds off the dill sprigs and sprinkle them over the fish. Roll up the fillets from tail to head end, with the skin on the outside, and set aside.

2   Put the beans in a large, fairly shallow pan with a lid. Arrange the fish rolls, joins down, on top of the beans. Sprinkle on the capers and pour in the wine and stock. Bring the liquid almost to the boil, then reduce the heat and cover the pan. Simmer for 12–15 minutes or until the fish and beans are just tender.

3   Mix the flour and pesto to a smooth paste. Use a draining spoon to transfer the fish rolls and beans to warm plates. Bring the cooking liquid to the boil. Whisk in half the pesto and flour paste until thoroughly combined, then whisk in the remaining paste. Continue boiling, still whisking, for about 2-3 minutes or until the sauce is slightly thickened.

4   Taste the sauce and adjust the seasoning if necessary, then spoon it over the fish and beans. Garnish with sprigs of dill and serve.

HEALTHY EATING

● Trout is rich in omega-3 fatty acids, shown to help reduce the risk of heart attacks and stroke. Omega-3 fatty acids also have an anti-inflammatory effect, which can help to relieve rheumatoid arthritis and the skin condition psoriasis.

FISH AND SEAFOOD

121

Swordfish with a Mexican salad

GI estimate LOW

Lively Mexican flavours combine in this quick and easy dish of spicy swordfish steaks paired with a salsa-style kidney bean salad based on the famous avocado dip, guacamole. Serve with boiled basmati rice or warm wheat tortillas.

PREPARATION: 15 minutes   COOKING: 6-10 minutes   SERVES 4

1 Mix the olive oil with the garlic and ground coriander, and season with a little pepper, to taste. Brush this mixture over both sides of the swordfish steaks.

2 Heat a ridged cast-iron grill pan or non-stick frying pan until hot. Fry the fish for 3-5 minutes on each side until just cooked - they should still be very slightly translucent in the centre, as swordfish becomes dry if overcooked.

3 Meanwhile, make the salad. Peel, stone and chop the avocados, and mix with the tomatoes, onion, chilli, coriander and lime juice. Stir in the kidney beans and season to taste.

4 Serve the spicy swordfish steaks with the salad and a garnish of mixed salad leaves.

SOME MORE IDEAS

● To make spicy swordfish wraps, after cooking the fish, flake it into bite-sized pieces. While still hot, toss with 1 red capsicum (pepper), seeded and finely chopped, and the salad, made without the beans. Add some fresh salad leaves and sprigs of watercress and wrap the mixture in 8 warmed wheat tortillas.

● As an alternative to swordfish, try marlin steaks, which are similar in appearance.

● Use canned chickpeas instead of kidney beans.

2 tablespoons olive oil

1 garlic clove, crushed

1/2 teaspoon ground coriander

freshly ground pepper

4 swordfish steaks, about 500 g in total

2 avocados

6 ripe roma (plum) tomatoes, chopped

1 red onion, finely chopped

1 red chilli, seeded and chopped

6 tablespoons chopped fresh coriander

juice of 2 limes

1 can red kidney beans, about 400 g, drained

4 cups (100 g) mixed salad leaves to garnish

Each serving provides
2277 kJ, 544 kcal, 32 g protein, 40 g fat (8 g saturated fat), 16 g carbohydrate (6 g sugars), 8 g fibre

HEALTHY EATING

● As well as providing healthy, lean protein, swordfish is an excellent source of niacin. This B vitamin is involved in the release of energy in cells.

● Although avocados contain large amounts of fat, most of it is monounsaturated - the same heart-healthy kind found in olive oil. They are also rich in vitamin E.

Spinach and smoked trout roulade

GI estimate LOW–MED

This light spinach roll is easier to make than it looks - just make sure that the spinach is squeezed really dry before adding to the sauce base. Serve with a tomato salad and grainy wholemeal rolls.

PREPARATION and COOKING: 40 minutes   SERVES 6

¹/₄ cup (35 g) polenta

3 cups (200 g) baby spinach, stalks trimmed, blanched

25 g non-hydrogenated margarine

25 g plain flour

300 ml lite or low-fat milk

4 eggs, separated

pinch of freshly grated nutmeg

freshly ground pepper

SMOKED TROUT FILLING

¹/₂ cup (125 g) low-fat cream cheese

4 tablespoons creamed cottage cheese (or plain low-fat fromage frais)

2 tablespoons chopped fresh dill

140 g skinless smoked trout fillet

2 teaspoons lemon juice

TOMATO SALAD

1 tablespoon extra virgin olive oil

2 teaspoons sherry vinegar

pinch of caster sugar

1 small onion, chopped

14 (about 170 g) baby roma (plum) tomatoes, halved

Each serving provides
1092 kJ, 261 kcal, 19 g protein, 15 g fat (5 g saturated fat), 13 g carbohydrate (6 g sugars), 2 g fibre

1 Lightly oil a 23 x 33 cm Swiss roll tin and line with baking paper. Sprinkle evenly with the polenta. Preheat the oven to 200°C (Gas 6).

2 Squeeze the excess water out of the spinach, then chop finely. Melt the margarine in a heavy-based saucepan, stir in the flour and cook for a few seconds. Off the heat, gradually whisk in the milk, then put back on a low heat and cook, whisking constantly, until the sauce bubbles and thickens. Remove from the heat and stir in the spinach, followed by the egg yolks, nutmeg and seasoning to taste.

3 In a large, clean bowl, whisk the eggwhites until stiff. Fold into the spinach mixture, one-third at a time. Spoon into the prepared tin and gently level the surface.

4 Bake for 12-15 minutes or until slightly risen and firm to the touch. Place the tin on a wire rack, cover with a clean tea towel and leave to cool for 5 minutes.

5 Meanwhile, make the filling. Put the cream cheese in a mixing bowl and mix in the cottage cheese, 1 tablespoon at a time. Stir in the dill, and season to taste. Flake the trout into another bowl, and toss with the lemon juice.

6 Turn out the spinach 'cake' onto the tea towel and carefully peel away the baking paper. Spread evenly with the soft cheese mixture, then arrange the smoked trout on top. Roll up the cake from one of the short ends. Transfer to a serving platter. (If making ahead of time, cover and keep in the refrigerator for up to 1 hour.)

7 For the tomato salad, whisk together the olive oil, vinegar, sugar and seasoning to taste in a bowl. Add the onion and toss to coat, then add the tomatoes and toss again. Cut the roulade into 12 slices. Serve with the tomato salad.

COOK'S TIP

● Use the same amount of cherry tomatoes if you can't get hold of baby roma (plum) tomatoes.

HEALTHY EATING

● Trout is a source of lean protein as well as heart-healthy omega-3 fats.

● Low-fat cream cheese provides essential nutrients such as protein and calcium. Its lower fat content means it has fewer calories than traditional cream cheese.

● Although spinach is a rich source of iron, the body is not able to absorb this iron easily. Serving a vitamin C-rich food such as tomatoes with the spinach helps to increase iron uptake.

Sardine open sandwich

PREPARATION: 10 minutes   SERVES 4

1 carrot, grated

1 cup (30 g) watercress, roughly
   chopped

2 tablespoons chopped fresh chives

$^2/_3$ cup (160 g) low-fat cream cheese

8 thick slices rye bread

2 cans sardines in olive oil, about 120 g
   each, drained

1 small red onion, thinly sliced

a few long fresh chives to garnish

freshly ground pepper

Each serving provides
1482 kJ, 354 kcal, 27 g protein, 15 g fat
(5 g saturated fat), 24 g carbohydrate
(5 g sugars), 12 g fibre

1   Mix the grated carrot, watercress and chives into the cream cheese. Season to taste with pepper.

2   Spread the cheese mixture evenly over one side of each slice of rye bread. Halve the sardines lengthwise, then arrange them, skin side up, on top of the cheese.

3   Arrange the red onion slices over the sardines and top with the chives to garnish. Sprinkle with pepper and serve.

SOME MORE IDEAS

● For a different texture and flavour, try multigrain or wholemeal stoneground bread instead of rye bread.

● To reduce the fat content of this dish, use sardines canned in springwater rather than in oil, and cottage cheese instead of low-fat cream cheese.

● Try smoked mackerel and apple open sandwiches. Mix the cream cheese with 1 grated sweet red apple, 2 tablespoons finely chopped cucumber and the chives. Spread over low-GI bread and top with 175 g flaked smoked mackerel fillet. Garnish with thin slices of radish.

HEALTHY EATING

● Sardines are rich in heart-healthy omega-3 fatty acids and contain the type of iron easily absorbed by the body. In addition, eating the bones of canned fish such as sardines will boost your calcium intake.

● The orange colour of carrots is due to beta-carotene, an antioxidant that helps to protect against free radical damage.

Lemon mackerel pâté

PREPARATION: 10–15 minutes, plus 30 minutes chilling   SERVES 4

1 Using a fork, break up the mackerel fillets into large pieces and place in a bowl. Add the cream cheese, lemon zest, half of the lemon juice, the peppercorns, chives and parsley. Mash all the ingredients together with a fork. This will make a coarse-textured pâté. For a smooth version, combine the ingredients in a food processor and process. Taste the pâté and stir in more lemon juice if necessary.

2 Spoon the pâté into 4 ramekins, cover with cling film and chill for 30 minutes. Just before serving, top each with a sprig of parsley and serve with lemon wedges.

SOME MORE IDEAS

● For a smoked trout pâté, substitute smoked trout fillets for the mackerel and add 1 tablespoon creamed horseradish instead of the green peppercorns.

● Add a crushed garlic clove and use fresh dill instead of chives.

● Toast ¹/₂ cup (50 g) shelled walnuts or hazelnuts, chop coarsely and fold into the finished pâté. Season with freshly ground black pepper or a small pinch of cayenne pepper.

● Chill the pâté in a bowl, then scoop out using an ice cream scoop or a spoon and serve in cup-shaped lettuce leaves. Offer crudités for dipping such as celery, fennel and carrot sticks, strips of red capsicum (pepper) and whole radishes.

HEALTHY EATING

● Oily fish like mackerel is rich in heart-healthy omega-3 fats. It is also a good source of vitamin D.

● Lemons contain excellent levels of vitamin C.

2 smoked mackerel fillets, or other smoked fish, about 125 g each, skinned

200 g low-fat cream cheese (or plain low-fat fromage frais)

finely grated zest and juice of 1 small lemon

2 teaspoons bottled soft green peppercorns, drained, rinsed and chopped, or 1 teaspoon dried green peppercorns, coarsely crushed

1 tablespoon finely snipped fresh chives

1 tablespoon finely chopped parsley

sprigs of parsley

lemon wedges

Each serving provides
1185 kJ, 283 kcal, 18 g protein, 22 g fat (7 g saturated fat), 4 g carbohydrate (3 g sugars), <1 g fibre

HEALTHY EATING

● White fish such as cod is low in calories and high in healthy protein. Frying it in batter more than doubles the calorie content, whereas brushing it with a little olive oil and grilling it keeps the fat, and therefore calories, at healthy levels.

● Lentils, like all pulses, are a GI 'superfood', providing hunger-satisfying protein, dietary fibre and low-GI carbohydrate. They make a handy store-cupboard ingredient as they do not need to be soaked before cooking.

Fish with spicy lentils

GI estimate LOW

Green puy lentils, grown in the south of France, have a unique, nutty flavour that is enhanced by chilli. Their firm texture is a perfect complement for the flakiness of fresh blue eye or other white fish. Serve this satisfying dish with a mixed salad.

PREPARATION and COOKING: about 35 minutes   SERVES 4

1 Preheat the grill to moderately high. Heat 1 tablespoon of the olive oil in a saucepan, add the onion, celery, leeks and chillies, and cook gently for 2 minutes. Stir in the lentils. Add the stock, thyme and bay leaf and bring to the boil. Lower the heat and simmer for about 20 minutes or until the lentils are tender. If at the end of this time the lentils have not absorbed all the stock, drain them (you can use the excess stock to make a soup).

2 While the lentils are cooking, mix together the remaining 1 tablespoon oil, the lemon juice and cayenne pepper. Lay the fish on the grill pan, skinned side up, season to taste, and brush with the oil mixture. Grill for 6-7 minutes or until the fish flake easily. There is no need to turn the fish.

3 Spread the lentils in a warmed serving dish and arrange the pieces of fish on top. Serve immediately, with lemon wedges.

COOK'S TIP

● If you can't find puy lentils, use ordinary brown lentils.

SOME MORE IDEAS

● For fish with mustard lentils, cook the lentils as in the main recipe, omitting the chillies. Mix $1/2$ cup (125 g) crème fraîche with 1-2 tablespoons Dijon mustard and stir into the cooked lentils. Spread a thin layer of Dijon mustard over the seasoned white fish fillets, drizzle with olive oil and grill. Serve the fish on top of the lentils, garnished with grilled cherry tomatoes.

● Try the dish with salmon.

2 tablespoons olive oil

1 onion, chopped

2 celery sticks, chopped

2 medium-sized leeks, chopped

1-2 red chillies, seeded and finely chopped

170 g French-style green (puy) lentils, rinsed and drained

3 cups (750 ml) salt-reduced vegetable stock

1 sprig of fresh thyme

1 bay leaf

juice of 1 lemon

pinch of cayenne pepper

4 pieces of skinless white fish fillet, such as blue eye, hoki or cod, about 140 g each

freshly ground pepper

lemon wedges to serve

Each serving provides
1597 kJ, 381 kcal, 41 g protein, 14 g fat
(3 g saturated fat), 24 g carbohydrate
(7 g sugars), 8 g fibre

Baked whole fish with grapefruit

This colourful recipe offers an intriguing combination of citrus and fennel flavours that taste wonderful together. Serve with new potatoes and steamed mixed vegetables.

GI estimate LOW

PREPARATION: 20 minutes   COOKING: 25 minutes   SERVES 4

2 large pink grapefruit

2 tablespoons olive oil

2 large onions, halved through the stalk and sliced crossways

1 large bulb of fennel, thinly sliced

2 garlic cloves, crushed

1 tablespoon fresh thyme leaves

$1/2$ cup (125 ml) dry white wine or vermouth

freshly ground pepper

4 bay leaves

4 whole red mullet or trevally, about 225 g each, cleaned

juice of 2 oranges

$1/2$ teaspoon chilli paste, or to taste

Each serving provides
2061 kJ, 492 kcal, 47 g protein, 23 g fat
(7 g saturated fat), 19 g carbohydrate
(16 g sugars), 4 g fibre

1 Preheat the oven to 200°C (Gas 6). Working over a bowl to catch the juices, peel the grapefruit and slice between the membranes to cut out the segments, dropping them into the bowl. Squeeze the juice from the membranes into the bowl.

2 Heat the olive oil in a large frying pan over a moderate heat. Add the onions and fennel and cook for about 4 minutes, stirring frequently, until the onion has softened and started to brown. Reduce the heat and add the garlic, thyme and wine or vermouth. Cook for 2-3 minutes, stirring frequently, until the wine has reduced by half. Season to taste.

3 Turn the vegetables into an ovenproof dish large enough to hold the fish. Put a bay leaf in the cavity of each fish and season well. Lay the fish on top of the vegetables and scatter over the grapefruit segments, reserving the juice.

4 Put the grapefruit juice into a measuring jug with the orange juice. If needed, top up with water to make 300 ml; if there is more juice than this, it can all be used. Stir in the chilli paste and pour the juice over the fish and vegetables. Cover with foil and bake for about 25 minutes or until the fish flakes easily. Serve hot.

SOME MORE IDEAS

● Use barramundi, coral trout or monkfish fillets instead of whole fish.

● For salmon baked on asparagus, use 4 pieces of skinless salmon fillet, about 140 g each. Remove the woody ends from 300 g (about 16) asparagus spears. Sauté 1 red onion, sliced, in 2 tablespoons olive oil until soft and golden, then turn into a baking dish. Lay the asparagus spears on the onion and then place the salmon fillets on top, season with pepper to taste and arrange the grapefruit segments over them. Mix together the fruit juice and chilli paste and pour over the fish. Cover with foil and bake for 20 minutes.

HEALTHY EATING

● As well as providing lean protein, red mullet is a good source of phosphorus and calcium, both of which are involved in maintaining healthy bones and teeth.

● Grapefruit is an excellent source of vitamin C, and pink and ruby grapefruit also contain the antioxidant beta-carotene.

Spaghetti with clams

PREPARATION: 15 minutes   COOKING: 20 minutes   SERVES 4

1 tablespoon olive oil

1 onion, chopped

2 garlic cloves, chopped

1 small red chilli, seeded and chopped

$1^2/_3$ cup (150 g) sliced chestnut or
    Swiss brown mushrooms

1 can tomatoes, about 400 g

1 tablespoon chopped fresh basil

1 tablespoon chopped parsley

$^1/_2$ teaspoon raw (demerara) sugar

240 g spaghetti

48 clams (vongole) in their shells,
    about 900 g in total, rinsed

4 tablespoons red or white wine

FOR EVEN LOWER GI
Use wholemeal spaghetti.

Each serving provides
2025 kJ, 484 kcal, 40 g protein, 8 g fat
(1 g saturated fat), 59 g carbohydrate
(5 g sugars), 3 g fibre

1 Heat the olive oil in a medium-sized saucepan, add the onion, garlic and chilli, and cook over a moderate heat for 5 minutes. Stir in the mushrooms and cook for 2 minutes, then add the tomatoes with their juice, crushing them down with a wooden spoon. Sprinkle in the basil, parsley and sugar and stir. Cover and simmer for 10 minutes.

2 Meanwhile, cook the spaghetti in boiling water for about 10-12 minutes, or according to the packet instructions, until al dente. Drain the pasta in a colander.

3 Put the empty pasta pan back on the heat, add the clams and splash in the wine. Tip the pasta back in. Cover and cook for 3 minutes, shaking the pan occasionally. All the shells should have opened; discard any clams that remain shut.

4 Pour the tomato sauce into the spaghetti and clam mixture, and stir and toss over the heat for 1-2 minutes or until it is all bubbling. Season to taste and serve.

SOME MORE IDEAS
- Use plain or spinach-flavoured tagliatelle instead of spaghetti.
- Pipis, cockles and mussels also work well in this dish.

HEALTHY EATING

● Clams are a healthy source of protein and an excellent source of phosphorus. This mineral is needed for healthy bones and teeth.

● Unlike white bread and potatoes, pasta is a low-GI food. It is low fat, too, and only becomes fattening when excessive amounts of oil, cream or butter are added to the accompanying sauces. Keep a close eye on your portions, though: allow 60 g uncooked pasta per person.

Skate with citrus-honey sauce

GI estimate MEDIUM

PREPARATION and COOKING: 45 minutes   SERVES 4

1 Preheat the oven to 200°C (Gas 6). Put the potatoes in a roasting pan, drizzle over the olive oil and season to taste. Toss well. Roast on the top shelf of the oven for 25–30 minutes or until tender.

2 Meanwhile, arrange the skate in a single layer in a large shallow ovenproof dish and pour over the stock. Cover tightly with foil and poach in the oven for about 25 minutes or until the fish flakes easily.

3 While the fish and potatoes are cooking, make the sauce. Squeeze the juice from 2 of the oranges and pour into a small pan. Add the lemon juice, margarine and honey. Cut the peel and pith from the remaining orange with a sharp knife. Working over the saucepan to catch the juice, cut in between the membranes to release the segments. Set the segments aside.

4 When the skate is cooked, carefully lift it from the stock and arrange on plates. Gently warm the sauce, but don't allow it to boil. Add the orange segments and season to taste. Pour over the fish, sprinkle with the parsley and serve immediately, with the roast potatoes.

COOK'S TIP
● If you can't get skate, use ling, leather jacket or john dory.

SOME MORE IDEAS
● For scallops with citrus and chive sauce, use 12 large scallops (without their corals). Heat 1 tablespoon olive oil in a large non-stick frying pan, add the scallops and sear over a high heat for about 1 minute on each side or until caramelised on the outside, but still moist inside. Keep warm while you make the sauce as in the main recipe, replacing the parsley with about 1¹/₂ tablespoons snipped fresh chives.

● Instead of roast potatoes, make a wild rice and lemongrass pilaf to serve with the skate. Fry 4 chopped French shallots in 1 tablespoon olive oil, then add 250 g mixed long-grain and wild rice. Pour in 600 ml of hot salt-reduced vegetable stock and stir in 1 teaspoon finely chopped lemongrass. Cover and simmer for 20 minutes, until the rice is tender and the stock has been absorbed. Add 3 tablespoons chopped fresh coriander and serve.

675 g even-sized new potatoes, scrubbed and halved
1 tablespoon olive oil
freshly ground pepper
4 pieces of skate wing, about 600 g in total
1 cup (250 ml) salt-reduced fish stock
3 oranges
juice of 1 lemon
30 g non-hydrogenated soft margarine
4 tablespoons pure floral honey
1 tablespoon finely chopped parsley to garnish

FOR LOWER GI
Instead of roast potatoes, serve with a wild rice and lemongrass pilaf (see recipe under 'Some more ideas').

Each serving provides
2053 kJ, 490 kcal, 36 g protein, 14 g fat (2 g saturated fat), 54 g carbohydrate (33 g sugars), 5 g fibre

Steamed fish with black beans

GI estimate LOW

In this fragrant, fresh-tasting dish, white fish fillets are sprinkled with rice wine and steamed, then served with a Chinese-style black bean sauce flavoured with ginger, garlic and soy. Serve with brown rice.

PREPARATION and COOKING: 1¼ hours, plus 8 hours soaking   SERVES 4

115 g dried black beans, soaked for at least 8 hours

4 barramundi or sea bass fillets, about 550 g in total, skin on

1 tablespoon rice wine

1 tablespoon canola (rapeseed) oil

1 garlic clove, crushed

2 French shallots, finely chopped

2 x 3 cm piece of fresh root ginger, finely chopped

4 tablespoons salt-reduced vegetable stock

2 tablespoons salt-reduced soy sauce

2 tablespoons dry sherry

2 teaspoons soft light brown sugar

1 teaspoon cornflour

chopped fresh coriander or flat-leaf parsley, plus sprigs to garnish

Each serving provides
1301 kJ, 311 kcal, 36 g protein, 7 g fat
(1 g saturated fat), 23 g carbohydrate
(3 g sugars), 5 g fibre

1 Drain the soaked beans and rinse under cold running water. Put them in a saucepan, cover with plenty of fresh cold water and bring to the boil. Boil rapidly for 10 minutes, then reduce the heat and simmer for 45–60 minutes or until tender. Drain well and set aside.

2 Arrange the fish fillets, in one layer, in a steamer. Sprinkle with the rice wine and season with a little pepper to taste. Cover and steam for about 10 minutes, depending on the thickness of the fillets; they should be firm, opaque and just able to be flaked with the tip of a knife.

3 Meanwhile, heat the oil in a frying pan or wok, add the garlic, shallots and ginger, and stir-fry for 3–4 minutes or until softened. Add the black beans, stock, soy sauce, sherry and sugar, and stir-fry until hot and bubbling.

4 Mix the cornflour to a smooth paste with 2 tablespoons water and add to the pan or wok. Bring to the boil, stirring until the sauce thickens, then simmer for 1–2 minutes, stirring frequently.

5 Put the steamed fish fillets on 4 serving plates. Spoon over the black bean sauce, garnish with fresh herbs and serve.

SOME MORE IDEAS

● Sprinkle the fish with dry sherry, or lemon or lime juice, instead of rice wine.

● For butterflied prawns with black beans, use 340 g peeled raw king prawns. To butterfly them, simply cut a deep slit along the back of each prawn without cutting all the way through, then open the prawn out flat, like a book. Lightly brush the prawns all over with 2 teaspoons canola (rapeseed) oil and cook under a preheated hot grill for 3–4 minutes or until pink. Alternatively, stir-fry the butterflied prawns in 1 tablespoon olive oil for 2–3 minutes. Add the hot black bean sauce to the prawns and toss briefly to mix, then serve with rice noodles.

HEALTHY EATING

● Traditional versions of this Chinese-style dish are high in sodium because they use black beans that have been fermented and salted. Here, dried black beans are used instead, producing a healthier version without salt.

● Barramundi and sea bass are a rich source of protein with very little fat. They are also a good source of vitamin B12 and the heart-healthy omega-3 fats.

● Ginger aids digestion.

Chinese-style whole fish

GI estimate MEDIUM

A whole fish cooked with ginger, garlic and spring onions is a traditional centrepiece of a Chinese meal. Here it is served with a mixture of noodles and bean sprouts to make a very special dish.

PREPARATION: 15 minutes   COOKING: 30-35 minutes   SERVES 4

1 Preheat the oven to 200°C (Gas 6). Brush a large sheet of thick foil with the oil and place the fish on top. Place the lime slices inside the fish and scatter over the spring onions, carrot, ginger and garlic. Drizzle over the soy sauce and sesame oil, and sprinkle over the coriander leaves. Bring the ends of the foil together and fold and twist to seal in the fish. Place on a baking tray. Bake for 30-35 minutes or until the fish flakes easily (open the parcel to check).

2 Meanwhile, place the noodles in a saucepan of boiling water, return to the boil and simmer for 3 minutes. Or cook them according to the packet instructions. Drain well. Heat the oil in a wok, add the onions and garlic, and cook over a high heat for 30 seconds. Add the bean sprouts and cook for about 1 minute or until they begin to soften. Add the noodles together with the soy sauce. Cook over a high heat for 2-3 minutes, stirring and tossing well.

3 Remove the fish from the oven, unwrap and transfer to a hot serving platter. Garnish with coriander leaves and lime halves. Serve the fish cut into slices, with the noodles.

ANOTHER IDEA
● The Chinese flavours in this dish also work well with a whole red mullet, which takes about 20 minutes to cook.

HEALTHY EATING

● It is the egg noodles that raise the GI of this dish to medium, yet they are low in fat and perfectly permissible once in a while.

● Canola (rapeseed) oil is a good choice of cooking oil as it contains a high proportion of monounsaturated fats as well as omega-3 fats, both of which lower cholesterol and so are good for your heart.

1 teaspoon canola (rapeseed) oil
1 barramundi or sea bass, about 800 g, cleaned and scaled
1 lime, cut into 4 slices
6 spring onions, cut into fine shreds
1 carrot, cut into fine matchsticks
2 x 3 cm piece fresh root ginger, cut into fine matchsticks
2 garlic cloves, thinly sliced
2 tablespoons salt-reduced soy sauce
1 teaspoon toasted sesame oil
1 tablespoon fresh coriander leaves
fresh coriander leaves to garnish
lime halves to serve

NOODLES
250 g Chinese egg noodles
1 tablespoon canola (rapeseed) oil
2 small red onions, cut into very thin wedges
1 garlic clove, thinly sliced
300 g bean sprouts
3 tablespoons salt-reduced soy sauce

FOR LOWER GI
Replace the egg noodles with glass or cellophane noodles.

Each serving provides
2206 kJ, 527 kcal, 55 g protein, 11 g fat (2 g saturated fat), 52 g carbohydrate (4 g sugars), 6 g fibre

Tunisian tuna and egg briks

PREPARATION: 30 minutes   COOKING: 12-15 minutes   SERVES 4 (makes 8 briks)

2 1/2 tablespoons olive oil

8 spring onions, thinly sliced

200 g baby spinach leaves, roughly torn

4 sheets filo pastry, 30 x 50 cm each, about 120 g in total

1 can tuna in springwater, about 200 g, drained and flaked

2 eggs, hard-boiled and finely chopped

dash of hot pepper sauce

freshly ground pepper

4 ripe tomatoes, chopped

1/2 cucumber, chopped

1 tablespoon lemon juice

4 tablespoons mango or apricot chutney

FOR LOWER GI

Omit the fruit chutney and serve with low-fat natural yogurt plus a large mixed salad.

Each serving provides
1683 kJ, 402 kcal, 28 g protein, 17 g fat
(3 g saturated fat), 33 g carbohydrate
(16 g sugars), 5 g fibre

1 Heat 2 teaspoons of the olive oil in a large saucepan and cook the spring onions over a low heat for 3 minutes or until beginning to soften. Add the spinach, cover with a tight-fitting lid and cook for a further 2–3 minutes or until tender and wilted, stirring once or twice. Tip the mixture into a sieve or colander and leave to drain and cool.

2 Using a saucer as a guide, cut out 24 rounds about 12.5 cm in diameter from the filo pastry, cutting 6 rounds from each sheet. Stack the filo rounds in a pile, then cover with cling film to prevent them from drying out.

3 When the spinach mixture is cool, squeeze out as much excess liquid as possible, then transfer to a bowl. Add the tuna, eggs, hot pepper sauce and seasoning to taste. Mix together well.

4 Preheat the oven to 200°C (Gas 6). Take one filo round and very lightly brush with some of the remaining olive oil. Top with a second round and brush with a little oil, then place a third round on top and brush with oil.

5 Place a heaped tablespoon of the filling in the middle of the round, then fold the pastry over to make a half-moon shape. Fold in the edges, twisting them to seal, and place on a non-stick baking tray. Repeat with the remaining pastry and filling to make 8 briks in all.

6 Lightly brush the briks with the remaining olive oil. Bake for 12-15 minutes or until the pastry is crisp and golden brown.

7 Meanwhile, combine the tomatoes and cucumber in a bowl and sprinkle with the lemon juice and seasoning to taste. Serve the briks hot with this salad and the chutney.

Grilled polenta and tuna pizza

GI estimate LOW–MED

PREPARATION: 30 minutes   COOKING: 10-12 minutes   SERVES 4

2$\frac{1}{4}$ cups (335 g) polenta

1 tablespoon chopped fresh thyme

3 tablespoons chopped parsley

freshly ground pepper

1 tablespoon olive oil

1 can chopped tomatoes, about 400 g

1 yellow capsicum (pepper), halved and seeded

1 can tuna in springwater, about 200 g, drained and flaked

1 cup (250 g) ricotta

12 black olives, pitted and halved

1-2 teaspoons fresh thyme leaves to garnish

Each serving provides
2154 kJ, 515 kcal, 24 g protein, 17 g fat
(6 g saturated fat), 65 g carbohydrate
(5 g sugars), 4 g fibre

1 Cook the polenta in 5 cups (1.25 litres) boiling water for about 5 minutes, or according to the packet instructions, until thick and smooth.

2 Remove from the heat and stir in the chopped thyme, parsley, and seasoning to taste. Spoon the polenta onto a greased baking tray or pizza tin and spread out to make a smooth 30 cm round with slightly raised edges. Brush the edges with the olive oil. Set aside.

3 Preheat the grill to high. Put the tomatoes in a saucepan with their juice and bring to the boil. Simmer over a moderate heat for 6-8 minutes, stirring occasionally, until most of the liquid has evaporated, leaving a fairly thick sauce. Season to taste.

4 Meanwhile, grill the capsicum, skin side up, until blistered and blackened all over. Put the capsicum in a plastic bag and leave until it is cool enough to handle, then peel off the skin. Slice the capsicum.

5 Spread the tomato sauce over the polenta base and top with the capsicum strips, tuna, crumbled ricotta and olive halves. Turn the grill down to moderately hot and grill the pizza for 10-12 minutes or until bubbling and golden brown. Sprinkle with the thyme leaves and serve.

HEALTHY EATING

● Polenta is low in fat and has a moderate GI, making it a useful substitute for the traditional bread pizza base with its high GI rating. The vegetable topping gives the dish a low GI score overall.

● When tuna is canned, it retains vitamins and minerals, and some omega-3 fatty acids. Tuna canned in springwater or brine contains half the calories of tuna in oil.

● Capsicums are rich in vitamin C and their naturally waxy skin helps to prevent the loss of this vitamin during storage.

FISH AND SEAFOOD

139

Wholewheat and tofu stir-fry **142**

Spiced lentil dal **145**

Moroccan-style pumpkin **146**

Eggplant casserole with polenta **147**

Braised vegetables with falafel **148**

Poached eggs with asparagus **150**

Dal with cauliflower and carrots **151**

Chunky vegetable crumble **153**

Spaghetti with brie and tomato **154**

Chakchouka **155**

Bean hot pot with orange salad **156**

Scrunch-top filo pie **158**

Garlicky bean terrine **159**

Chickpea and vegetable frittata **161**

Roast vegetable and pasta bake **162**

Cannellini bean burgers **164**

Refried bean burritos **165**

Spaghetti with a chickpea sauce **167**

Bean and lentil lasagne **168**

Millet with spinach and pine nuts **170**

Speedy two-bean chilli **171**

Tuscan-style baked polenta **172**

Oaty red lentil gratin **175**

Tagliatelle with broccoli **176**

Pasta with sage and fetta **177**

Spicy vegetable tagine **178**

Penne primavera **181**

Egyptian lentils with macaroni **183**

Couscous pilaf with tahini yogurt **184**

Vegetarian dishes

Wholewheat and tofu stir-fry

Here pre-cooked wholewheat grains are simmered in stock, then tossed with fresh ginger and mixed vegetables to make the perfect partner for Japanese-style marinated tofu. The result is a delicious and low-GI dish that can be thrown together in minutes.

PREPARATION and COOKING: 30 minutes   SERVES 4

600 ml salt-reduced vegetable stock

200 g pre-cooked wholewheat grains (wheat berries)

2 garlic cloves, crushed

1 tablespoon finely grated fresh root ginger

2 tablespoons salt-reduced soy sauce

1 tablespoon mirin (sweet rice wine)

1 tablespoon canola (rapeseed) oil

1 tablespoon pure floral honey

1 teaspoon Chinese five-spice

285 g tofu, cut into bite-sized triangles

VEGETABLE PAN-FRY

2 tablespoons canola (rapeseed) oil

2 garlic cloves, crushed

1 tablespoon finely grated fresh root ginger

1 large red capsicum (pepper), seeded and cut into long matchsticks

1 leek, cut into long matchsticks

250 g bean sprouts

Each serving provides
1533 kJ, 366 kcal, 15 g protein, 20 g fat (2 g saturated fat), 32 g carbohydrate (12 g sugars), 8 g fibre

1 Pour the stock into a saucepan and bring to the boil. Add the cooked wholewheat grains and simmer for 15–20 minutes or until they are tender.

2 Meanwhile, mix together the garlic, ginger, soy sauce, mirin, oil, honey and five-spice in a bowl. Add the tofu and turn until all the pieces are coated in the mixture. Set aside to marinate while cooking the vegetables.

3 Heat the oil in a wok or large frying pan, add the garlic and ginger, and stir-fry for a few seconds. Add the capsicum and leek strips, and stir-fry for 3–4 minutes or until softened. Stir in the bean sprouts and stir-fry for 3 minutes.

4 Add the wholewheat grains to the wok. Hold a sieve over the wok and tip the tofu mixture into it, straining the marinade into the wok. Toss until the wholewheat grains and marinade are mixed with the vegetables. Gently toss in the tofu and cook for 2 minutes until heated through. Serve immediately.

COOK'S TIP

● Wholewheat grains (or wheat berries) are available from health food shops. They take up to 2 hours to cook, so for a speedy alternative use burghul (bulgur) wheat instead (simmered in twice the volume of boiling water for 15 minutes).

ANOTHER IDEA

● To make a Mediterranean wholewheat and vegetable stir-fry, mix together 2 crushed garlic cloves, 8 chopped sun-dried tomatoes packed in oil, drained, 1 tablespoon oil from the jar and 10 shredded fresh basil leaves. Add the tofu and set aside to marinate. In step 3, omit the ginger, leek and bean sprouts, and stir-fry 1 thinly sliced onion and 2 zucchini (courgettes), cut into strips, with the capsicum and garlic. Add the wholewheat grains, 55 g black olives and the tofu and tomato mixture. Heat through, stirring and tossing, and serve.

HEALTHY EATING

● Wholewheat grains are the entire grain of the wheat plant, minus the hull. Because the whole of the grain is eaten, they are a good source of dietary fibre and have a low GI.

● Tofu is a low-fat healthy source of protein. Evidence is beginning to suggest that including products made from soybeans, such as tofu, in the diet regularly may help to reduce the risk of heart disease and certain cancers.

Spiced lentil dal

Potatoes and cauliflower are a favourite combination for curry, and they are delicious cooked with lentils in a mildly spiced sauce. With a refreshing carrot chutney, and fruit and nut raita served on the side, even confirmed meat-eaters will be impressed.

PREPARATION: 25 minutes   COOKING: about 55 minutes   SERVES 4

1   Heat the oil in a large saucepan. Add the onion, garlic and ginger, and cook for 5 minutes. Stir in the curry powder and stir for a further 2 minutes over a gentle heat.

2   Stir in the lentils, cumin, turmeric and 4 cups (1 litre) water. Bring to the boil, then cover the pan and simmer gently for 10 minutes. Stir in the potatoes and cook for 10 minutes, then add the cauliflower and cook for a further 10 minutes. Add the capsicum and tomatoes, and simmer for 5 minutes.

3   Meanwhile, prepare the side dishes. Mix together the carrots, chilli, lime juice and coriander for the chutney. Transfer to a serving dish. For the raita, slice the bananas into a serving bowl. Stir in the yogurt and sprinkle with the almonds.

4   Stir the spinach into the curry and cook for 2 minutes or until just wilted. Stir in the coriander and serve, with the chutney and raita.

ANOTHER IDEA

● Additional pulses can be added. Black-eyed beans and chickpeas are particularly good. If using dried pulses, soak them overnight, then drain and cook them in boiling water for up to 60 minutes until almost tender before adding them to the curry.

HEALTHY EATING

● Like all pulses, lentils are a GI 'superfood': they provide hunger-satisfying protein, soluble fibre and low-GI carbohydrate.

● This curry is packed full of vegetables. Together with the lentils they provide valuable dietary fibre, vitamins and minerals.

2 tablespoons canola (rapeseed) oil

1 large onion, coarsely chopped

1-2 garlic cloves, crushed

2 tablespoons finely chopped fresh root ginger

1 tablespoon mild curry powder

3/4 cup (185 g) red lentils

1 teaspoon ground cumin

1 teaspoon turmeric

400 g small new potatoes, halved

1 small cauliflower, broken into florets

1 red capsicum (pepper), seeded and coarsely chopped

4 tomatoes, skinned and quartered

3 carrots, coarsely grated

1 green chilli, seeded and finely chopped

juice of 1 lime

2 tablespoons chopped fresh coriander

2 firm bananas

280 g low-fat natural yogurt

1/2 cup (45 g) flaked almonds, toasted

2 1/2 cups (225 g) baby spinach leaves

generous handful of fresh coriander leaves, coarsely chopped

Each serving provides
2283 kJ, 545 kcal, 27 g protein, 21 g fat (2 g saturated fat), 61 g carbohydrate (26 g sugars), 17 g fibre

VEGETARIAN DISHES

145

Moroccan-style pumpkin

PREPARATION: about 10 minutes   COOKING: about 20 minutes   SERVES 4

600 ml hot salt-reduced vegetable
    stock
$1/2$ teaspoon turmeric
$1/2$ teaspoon ground coriander
pinch of ground cumin
200 g leeks, halved lengthwise
    and sliced
225 g parsnips, cut into 1 cm dice
600 g piece of pumpkin, peeled,
    seeded and cut into 1 cm dice
400 g yellow or green zucchini
    (courgettes), sliced
1 red capsicum (pepper), seeded and
    chopped
$1/2$ cup (90 g) dried apricots, chopped
1 can butter beans, about 400 g,
    drained
pinch of crushed dried chillies, or to
    taste (optional)
$1/4$ cup (40 g) pine nuts
chopped parsley or fresh coriander to
    garnish

Each serving provides
1417 kJ, 339 kcal, 16 g protein, 10 g fat
(1 g saturated fat), 45 g carbohydrate
(28 g sugars), 9 g fibre

1 Pour the stock into a flameproof casserole dish. Stir in the
turmeric, ground coriander and cumin. Add the leeks and
parsnips and bring to the boil. Reduce the heat to moderate,
cover the pan and simmer the vegetables for 5 minutes.

2 Add the pumpkin, zucchini and capsicum to the pan, then
bring the stock back to the boil. Stir in the apricots, butter
beans and chilli, if using, adding more to taste for a spicier
result. Reduce the heat, cover the pan and simmer for
10 minutes or until all the vegetables are tender.

3 Meanwhile, toast the pine nuts in a non-stick frying pan over
a moderate heat, stirring constantly, until just beginning to
brown and give off their nutty aroma. Tip the pine nuts onto
a board and chop them coarsely.

4 Taste the casserole and adjust the seasoning, if necessary,
then ladle it into deep bowls. Sprinkle with the chopped pine
nuts and parsley or fresh coriander and serve.

HEALTHY EATING

● Pumpkin is a rich source of
beta-carotene, an antioxidant that
helps to protect against free radical
damage. Save and toast the seeds as
a healthy low-GI snack, providing
good amounts of protein and zinc.

Eggplant casserole with polenta

GI estimate LOW–MED

PREPARATION: about 20 minutes   COOKING: about 45 minutes   SERVES 4

1. Heat the olive oil in a flameproof casserole dish. Add the onion and baby corn and fry over a moderate heat for 5 minutes. Preheat the oven to 180°C (Gas 4).

2. Add the slices of butternut pumpkin to the casserole dish, toss them in the oil and then stir in the eggplant and capsicum. Cover and leave the vegetables to sweat over a low heat for 10 minutes, turning them twice, until they are lightly tinged golden brown. Pour in the wine and then stir in the stock. Bring to the boil and add seasoning to taste. Cover and cook in the oven for 30 minutes.

3. Meanwhile, make the topping. Preheat the grill to high. Spread the flaked almonds on a baking tray and toast under the grill until they are lightly browned. Place in a small bowl and mix in the garlic, lemon zest and parsley.

4. To prepare the polenta, bring 4 cups (1 litre) water to the boil in a large saucepan over a high heat. Gradually whisk in the polenta and continue whisking until the polenta absorbs all the liquid. Reduce the heat to moderate and cook for 5-10 minutes, stirring, until the polenta is thick. Beat in the parmesan and oregano with seasoning to taste.

5. To serve, spoon the polenta onto plates or into large individual bowls. Ladle the vegetable casserole on top and sprinkle with the topping.

COOK'S TIP

- If you can't find fresh baby corn, used canned instead.

1 tablespoon olive oil

1 large onion, cut into 8 wedges

12 baby corn (sweetcorn)

1 small or 1/2 large butternut pumpkin, about 600 g, peeled, quartered lengthwise, seeded and cut across into thick slices

1 eggplant (aubergine), halved lengthwise and cut across into thick slices

1 red capsicum (pepper), seeded and cut into 1 cm dice

100 ml dry white wine

2 cups (500 ml) hot salt-reduced vegetable stock

freshly ground pepper

2 tablespoons flaked almonds

1 garlic clove, finely chopped

finely shredded or coarsely grated zest of 1 lemon

5 tablespoons chopped parsley

1 1/3 cups (200 g) polenta

1/2 cup (50 g) freshly grated parmesan

2 tablespoons chopped fresh oregano

FOR LOWER GI

Instead of polenta, serve with pearl barley that has been cooked with a sprinkling of dried sage.

Each serving provides
1921 kJ, 459 kcal, 15 g protein, 15 g fat
(4 g saturated fat), 64 g carbohydrate
(11 g sugars), 10 g fibre

Braised vegetables with falafel

As a change from rice or pasta, why not try some falafel? Canned chickpeas that are baked rather than deep-fried are used in this quick and healthy version of the Mediterranean classic.

PREPARATION: 30 minutes   COOKING: about 1 hour   SERVES 4

2 cans chickpeas, about 400 g each,
    drained and rinsed

8 spring onions, chopped

6 tablespoons chopped parsley

2 tablespoons chopped fresh coriander

2 tablespoons ground coriander

freshly ground pepper

2 tablespoons olive oil

1 garlic clove, crushed

500 g onions, sliced

2 large yellow, red or orange capsicums
    (peppers), seeded and sliced

250 g zucchini (courgettes)

300 ml salt-reduced vegetable stock

340 g cherry tomatoes, halved

$1/2$ cucumber, grated

85 g watercress leaves, finely
    shredded

85 g rocket, finely shredded

3 tablespoons chopped fresh mint

grated zest of 1 lime

200 g low-fat natural yogurt

fresh mint sprigs to garnish

Each serving provides
1410 kJ, 337 kcal, 17 g protein, 13 g fat
(2 g saturated fat), 38 g carbohydrate
(17 g sugars), 14 g fibre

1 Brush a shallow baking dish with a little oil. Put the chickpeas in a bowl and use a potato masher to mash them, then mix in the spring onions, parsley, fresh and ground coriander, and seasoning to taste. Alternatively, mix the ingredients in a food processor. With your hands, shape the mixture into 24 balls slightly larger than walnuts, placing them in the greased dish. Set aside.

2 Preheat the oven to 200°C (Gas 6). Heat the olive oil in a flameproof casserole dish. Add the garlic, onions and capsicums. Stir well, then cover and cook gently, stirring frequently, for 15 minutes, or until the vegetables are soft but not browned.

3 Stir in the zucchini and stock. Bring to the boil, then cover the casserole dish and transfer it to the oven. Place the falafel in the oven at the same time. Cook for 20 minutes.

4 Add the tomatoes to the casserole and stir. Cover and return it to the oven. Use a spoon and fork to turn the falafel, taking care not to break them. Cook the casserole and falafel for a further 20 minutes or until the vegetables are tender and the falafel lightly browned.

5 Meanwhile, to make the yogurt sauce, squeeze the cucumber in handfuls to remove excess moisture. Put it into a bowl. Stir in the watercress, rocket, mint, lime zest and yogurt. Add seasoning to taste and transfer to a serving dish. Cover and chill until ready to serve.

6 Transfer the falafel to a serving dish. Taste the casserole for seasoning, garnish with mint sprigs and serve with the falafel and yogurt sauce.

SOME MORE IDEAS

● To turn the casserole into a ratatouille, use 250 g onions and add 1 diced eggplant (aubergine) with the zucchini.

● For a stronger flavour add 2 crushed garlic cloves and the grated zest of 1 lemon to the falafel in step 1.

HEALTHY EATING

● Chickpeas are a good source of dietary fibre, particularly the soluble fibre that can help reduce high blood cholesterol levels. They have a low GI and also provide protein.

● Watercress provides good amounts of several antioxidants, including vitamins C and E. It also contributes substantial amounts of folate, niacin and vitamin B6.

Poached eggs with asparagus

PREPARATION and COOKING: about 25 minutes   SERVES 4

125 g lamb's lettuce (mâche)

2 heads witlof (Belgian endive/chicory),
    about 170 g in total

¹/₄ cup (15 g) snipped fresh chives

2 tablespoons extra virgin olive oil

2 teaspoons red wine vinegar

1 garlic clove, crushed

¹/₂ teaspoon wholegrain mustard

freshly ground pepper

750 g young asparagus spears

1 teaspoon vinegar

12 quail's eggs, or 8 small hen's eggs

¹/₂ cup (50 g) finely shaved parmesan

Each serving provides
918 kJ, 219 kcal, 14 g protein, 17 g fat
(5 g saturated fat), 4 g carbohydrate
(3 g sugars), 4 g fibre

1 Break up any large bunches of lamb's lettuce, then put into a mixing bowl. Thinly slice the witlof on the diagonal, discarding the last 1 cm of the base. Add to the lamb's lettuce together with the chives and toss together. Set aside.

2 Put all the olive oil, red wine vinegar, garlic and mustard in a screw-top jar and season to taste. Shake together to mix.

3 Steam the asparagus for about 4 minutes or until barely tender. Alternatively, cook the asparagus in a wide pan of simmering water for 3-4 minutes. To test, pierce the thickest part of the stalk with a thin, sharp knife.

4 While the asparagus is cooking, half fill a frying pan with water and bring to the boil. Add the vinegar, then reduce the heat so the water is just simmering. Carefully crack a couple of the eggs, one at a time, and slip into the water. Cook for 1 minute until the yolks have just set. Remove the poached eggs from the water and drain on a kitchen towel. Keep warm while poaching the rest of the eggs.

5 Pour the dressing over the salad and toss together. Spread out on a large serving platter. Arrange the asparagus on the salad and place the poached eggs on top. Scatter over the parmesan shavings and grind a little pepper over the top. Serve immediately.

COOK'S TIP

● Quail's eggs make this meal an extra special treat, although it works perfectly well with small hen's eggs.

HEALTHY EATING

● Although much smaller in size, quail's eggs have a very similar nutritional composition to hen's eggs. They are a good source of protein and contain vitamins A, E, riboflavin, B12 and niacin.

● Asparagus is a good source of many of the B vitamins, including folate.

Dal with cauliflower and carrots

GI estimate LOW

PREPARATION: 15 minutes   COOKING: about 45 minutes   SERVES 4

1 Heat the oil in a saucepan over a moderate heat, add the onion and garlic, and cook, stirring occasionally, for about 5 minutes or until just starting to soften. Stir in the ginger and cook for a further 3 minutes.

2 Add the lentils and stir to coat with the onion mixture. Pour in the stock, then cover the pan and bring to the boil. Reduce the heat and simmer for about 15 minutes.

3 Add the carrots and cauliflower. Cover the pan again and simmer for 12-15 minutes or until the lentils are tender and the vegetables are cooked.

4 Season to taste. Stir in the coriander and lemon juice, and serve immediately.

ANOTHER IDEA

● To make spicy split pea dal, sauté the onion, garlic and ginger in the oil as in the main recipe, adding 1 tablespoon curry powder and 1 small red chilli, seeded and finely chopped, with the ginger. Add 1 cup (220 g) yellow split peas with 200 g new potatoes, peeled and cut into dice. Stir, then pour in 3 cups (750 ml) salt-reduced vegetable stock and bring to the boil. Cover and simmer for 40-45 minutes or until the split peas are tender. Just before serving, stir in 2 finely chopped tomatoes along with 3 tablespoons low-fat natural yogurt. Season to taste and serve.

2 tablespoons canola (rapeseed) oil

1 onion, chopped

1 large garlic clove, finely chopped

5 cm piece fresh root ginger, finely chopped

1 cup (185 g) yellow lentils

2 cups (500 ml) salt-reduced vegetable stock

100 g carrots, cut into small sticks

170 g cauliflower, cut into small florets

3 tablespoons chopped fresh coriander

1 tablespoon lemon juice

Each serving provides
1083 kJ, 259 kcal, 14 g protein, 11 g fat (1 g saturated fat), 28 g carbohydrate (7 g sugars), 9 g fibre

HEALTHY EATING

● Like all pulses, lentils are a GI 'superfood': they provide hunger-satisfying protein, soluble fibre and low-GI carbohydrate.

● Unlike most vegetables, which are more nutritious when eaten raw, the nutritional value of carrots increases when they are cooked.

● Cauliflower is a member of the cruciferous family of vegetables. It provides useful amounts of vitamin C and dietary fibre and also contains phytochemicals thought to help protect against cancer.

HEALTHY EATING

● Together, parsnips and turnips provide fibre, B vitamins and potassium and are a surprisingly useful source of vitamin C.

● New potatoes, scrubbed but not peeled, have one-third more dietary fibre than peeled potatoes. The nutrients found just under the skin will also be preserved.

● Sunflower seeds are rich in vitamin E. They also offer thiamin, iron and phosphorus.

Chunky vegetable crumble

A tasty mixture of root vegetables and creamy butter beans topped with a savoury cheese crumble makes a nourishing vegetarian dish. Sunflower seeds add texture and protein to the crumble topping.

PREPARATION: 40 minutes   COOKING: 20 minutes   SERVES 4

1　Heat the oil in a large saucepan, add the onion and cook gently for 10 minutes or until softened. Add the garlic and cook for a further minute.

2　Add the carrots, parsnips, turnips and potatoes. Stir in the stock, Worcestershire sauce, tomato purée and bay leaves. Bring to the boil, then reduce the heat, cover and simmer for 20 minutes, stirring occasionally.

3　Meanwhile, make the crumble topping. Put the flour in a bowl and rub in the margarine. Sprinkle on 1^1/$_2$ tablespoons cold water and mix together using a fork to make large crumbs. Stir in the cheese and sunflower seeds. Set aside.

4　Preheat the oven to 190°C (Gas 5). Stir the butter beans into the vegetables and cook for a further 5-7 minutes or until the vegetables are just tender. Remove the bay leaves.

5　Remove a large ladleful of the vegetables and stock, and mash until smooth or purée in a blender or processor. Stir the purée into the vegetable mixture in the pan. Stir in the parsley, and season to taste.

6　Spoon the vegetable mixture into a lightly greased 1.7 litre ovenproof dish. Sprinkle the crumble mixture evenly over the top. Bake for 20 minutes or until golden brown.

SOME MORE IDEAS

● Replace 1 of the carrots with 250 g quartered kohlrabi (German turnip).

● For an oaty vegetable crumble, use ^{1}/$_3$ cup (35 g) freshly grated parmesan instead of cheddar, and replace the sunflower seeds with 30 g rolled oats. Bake as in the main recipe.

1 tablespoon canola (rapeseed) oil

1 onion, sliced

2 garlic cloves, crushed

3 carrots, cut into 2 cm chunks

2 parsnips, cut into 2 cm chunks

250 g baby turnips, quartered

350 g waxy new potatoes, scrubbed and cut into 2 cm chunks

450 ml salt-reduced vegetable stock

generous dash of Worcestershire sauce, or salt-reduced soy sauce

1 tablespoon tomato purée

2 bay leaves

1 can butter beans, about 400 g, drained and rinsed

3 tablespoons chopped parsley

freshly ground pepper

CRUMBLE TOPPING

^{1}/$_2$ cup (100 g) stoneground wholemeal flour

30 g non-hydrogenated soft margarine

^{2}/$_3$ cup (85 g) coarsely grated mature cheddar

^{1}/$_4$ cup (30 g) sunflower seeds

FOR LOWER GI

Substitute orange sweet potatoes (kumara) for the new potatoes and add a chopped zucchini (courgette) with the butter beans in step 4.

Each serving provides
2493 kJ, 596 kcal, 27 g protein, 24 g fat (6 g saturated fat), 62 g carbohydrate (15 g sugars), 10 g fibre

Spaghetti with brie and tomato

PREPARATION and COOKING: 30 minutes   SERVES 4

240 g spaghetti

2 tablespoons olive oil

2 plump garlic cloves, finely chopped

9 young asparagus spears, about 170 g,
    cut into 5 cm pieces

300 g cherry tomatoes, halved

large handful of fresh basil leaves,
    roughly torn

170 g brie, cut into cubes

freshly ground pepper

FOR EVEN LOWER GI
Use wholemeal spaghetti.

Each serving provides
1918 kJ, 458 kcal, 17 g protein, 23 g fat
(9 g saturated fat), 47 g carbohydrate
(3 g sugars), 2 g fibre

1 Cook the spaghetti in a large pan of boiling water for about 10-12 minutes, or according to the packet instructions, until al dente. Meanwhile, make the sauce.

2 Heat the oil in a large frying pan, add the garlic and cook for about 30 seconds. Don't let it brown. Tip in the asparagus and add 4 tablespoons of water. Cook over a moderate heat for 3-5 minutes, stirring frequently, until the asparagus is just tender and most of the water has evaporated.

3 Add the cherry tomatoes and basil, and cook for a further 2 minutes or until the tomatoes start to soften but still hold their shape.

4 Drain the spaghetti in a colander, then pour it into a large serving bowl. Add the vegetable mixture and the brie, and toss gently to mix. Serve hot, with the brie beginning to melt, sprinkled with a grinding of pepper.

SOME MORE IDEAS
● For a stronger flavour, replace the brie with camembert.

● For spaghetti with brie, asparagus and fresh tomato salsa, cook the spaghetti as in the main recipe, adding the asparagus to the pan for the last 3 minutes of the cooking time. Meanwhile, finely chop 300 g ripe tomatoes and mix with 1 finely chopped small red onion, 4 tablespoons chopped parsley, 1 crushed garlic clove, 2 tablespoons extra virgin olive oil and seasoning to taste. Drain the spaghetti and asparagus, and tip them into a large serving bowl. Add the salsa and the cheese, and toss gently.

HEALTHY EATING

● Like all cheeses, brie is a good source of calcium and provides hunger-satisfying protein.

● Pasta is a GI 'superfood', providing slow-release, low-GI carbohydrate.

● Basil, a member of the mint family, is believed to aid digestion.

Chakchouka

PREPARATION: 10 minutes   COOKING: 20 minutes   SERVES 2

1 tablespoon olive oil

1 small onion, roughly chopped

2 garlic cloves, crushed

1 red and 1 green capsicum (pepper), seeded and thinly sliced

400 g large ripe tomatoes, roughly chopped

2 tablespoons tomato purée

$1/4$ teaspoon crushed dried chillies (optional)

1 teaspoon ground cumin

pinch of sugar

4 eggs

sprigs of fresh flat-leaf parsley to garnish

Each serving provides
1214 kJ, 290 kcal, 17 g protein, 20 g fat (4 g saturated fat), 11 g carbohydrate (10 g sugars), 5 g fibre

1 Heat the olive oil in a deep, heavy-based frying pan. Add the onion, garlic and capsicums, and cook gently for 5 minutes or until softened.

2 Stir in the tomatoes, tomato purée, chillies, if using, cumin and sugar. Cover and cook gently for about 5 minutes or until the mixture is thick and well combined.

3 Make 4 hollows in the vegetable mixture using the back of a wooden spoon, then break an egg into each hollow. Cover the pan again and cook gently for 6–8 minutes or until the eggs are just set.

4 Serve immediately, straight from the pan, garnishing each plate with sprigs of parsley.

COOK'S TIP
● Serve this dish as a quick lunch for two or a snack for four.

SOME MORE IDEAS
● Add $1/2$ cup (60 g) pitted black olives or chopped sun-dried tomatoes to the vegetable mixture.
● Instead of dried chillies, add 1 teaspoon harissa or chilli sauce.

HEALTHY EATING

● Eggs have a low GI and are a good source of protein, vitamin A and B vitamins.

● Tomatoes are rich in the antioxidants vitamin C, beta-carotene and lycopene. Antioxidants boost the immune system and help to protect the body's cells against the effects of free radicals.

VEGETARIAN DISHES

155

Bean hot pot with orange salad

GI estimate LOW

Creole spices enliven this hearty mixed bean and vegetable casserole. Like the classic French cassoulet, it has a crisp crumb topping. With the accompanying refreshing salad, it makes a tasty, well-balanced and low-GI meal.

PREPARATION: 20 minutes, plus overnight soaking   COOKING: 3^1/$_2$ hours   Serves 4

1 tablespoon canola (rapeseed) oil

1 onion, finely chopped

3 garlic cloves, crushed

1 teaspoon freshly grated nutmeg

1 cinnamon stick

2 bay leaves

1 can chopped tomatoes, about 400 g

1 tablespoon tomato purée

2 celery sticks, thinly sliced

1^2/$_3$ cup (150 g) thickly sliced chestnut or Swiss brown mushrooms

1 tablespoon dark brown sugar

freshly ground pepper

3 cups (750 ml) salt-reduced vegetable stock

^{3}/$_4$ cup (150 g) dried flageolet beans, soaked overnight and drained

^{3}/$_4$ cup (150 g) dried pinto beans, soaked overnight and drained

3 tablespoons chopped parsley

2 cups (160 g) fresh wholemeal breadcrumbs

30 g non-hydrogenated soft margarine, melted

1 cos lettuce

2 oranges

1 tablespoon extra virgin olive oil

3 tablespoons flaked almonds, toasted

Each serving provides
1967 kJ, 470 kcal, 14 g protein, 24 g fat
(3 g saturated fat), 50 g carbohydrate
(19 g sugars), 10 g fibre

1   Preheat the oven to 160°C (Gas 3). Heat the oil in a large pan and add the onion and garlic. Cook for 5 minutes over a low heat to soften the onion slightly. Add the nutmeg, cinnamon stick, bay leaves, tomatoes with their juice, tomato purée, celery, mushrooms, sugar and plenty of pepper. (Do not add salt as it will harden the beans.) Pour in the stock and stir in the flageolet and pinto beans, then bring to the boil. Place in an ovenproof dish, cover and cook in the oven for 2^1/$_2$ hours or until the beans are tender.

2   Remove the cinnamon stick and bay leaves and discard. Stir in 2 tablespoons of the parsley and season to taste. Increase the oven temperature to 180°C (Gas 4). In a bowl, toss the breadcrumbs with the melted margarine until it is evenly distributed. Spoon the breadcrumbs over the beans and return the casserole to the oven, uncovered. Cook for a further 45 minutes or until the liquid has thickened and the breadcrumbs are golden.

3   Just before the bean pot has finished cooking, make the salad. Wash and shred the lettuce and place in a salad bowl. Cut all the peel and pith from the oranges. Holding the oranges over the salad bowl, use a small sharp knife to cut the segments from between the membranes, allowing the juice and segments to drop into the bowl with the lettuce. Drizzle the oil over, add the almonds and toss together.

4   Remove the bean pot from the oven, scatter on the remaining tablespoon of chopped parsley and serve with the salad on the side.

COOK'S TIP

● If you are in a hurry, canned beans, drained, make a handy substitute for the dried beans in this recipe. The 2^1/$_2$ hour cooking time in step 1 can be omitted.

HEALTHY EATING

● Beans are a GI 'superfood': they provide hunger-satisfying protein, soluble fibre, iron and low-GI carbohydrate.

● Oranges are an excellent source of vitamin C, which helps the body to absorb the iron provided by the beans. The acidity of orange juice helps to lower the GI of the dish.

● Almonds provide protein and vitamin E.

Scrunch-top filo pie

PREPARATION: 25 minutes   COOKING: 25-30 minutes   SERVES 4

GI estimate LOW–MED

2 sheets filo pastry, 30 x 50 cm each,
   about 60 g in total

$1/4$ cup (40 g) pine nuts

675 g baby spinach leaves, trimmed of
   any large stalks

200 g soft goat's cheese

2 teaspoons plain flour

2 eggs, lightly beaten

$1/4$ teaspoon freshly grated nutmeg

freshly ground pepper

4 tomatoes, about 300 g in total, diced

1 tablespoon canola (rapeseed) oil

Each serving provides
1713 kJ, 409 kcal, 21 g protein, 30 g fat
(12 g saturated fat), 15 g carbohydrate
(4 g sugars), 4 g fibre

1. Preheat the oven to 180°C (Gas 4). To make the filling, toast the pine nuts in a large saucepan for 2-3 minutes, stirring frequently, until golden brown. Remove and set aside.

2. Add half the spinach to the saucepan, with just the water used for washing still clinging to the leaves. Cover and cook for 3-4 minutes or until wilted and tender. Tip into a colander to drain while you cook the remaining spinach. Press out excess water, then roughly chop the spinach.

3. Put the cheese in a bowl and sprinkle over the flour, then gradually beat in the eggs. Stir in the spinach, pine nuts and nutmeg, and season to taste.

4. Spoon half of the spinach mixture into a 1.4 litre ovenproof dish that is about 5 cm deep. Top with the tomatoes, then cover with the remaining spinach mixture.

5. Cut each sheet of filo pastry into eight 12.5 cm squares, discarding the excess pastry. Brush the squares with the oil, then crumple them up loosely and place oil side up over the filling. Bake for 25-30 minutes or until the filling is lightly set and the pastry topping is golden brown and crisp. Serve hot.

COOK'S TIP

● For a lower-fat but equally tasty version, use ricotta instead of goat's cheese.

HEALTHY EATING

● Filo pastry has a high GI but because so little is used in this recipe, and it is divided among 4 servings, the overall GI of the dish remains low.

● Spinach is a great source of many of the antioxidants that help to protect against cancer, including vitamins C and E and beta-carotene. The beta-carotene content of spinach is 6 times greater than that of broccoli.

● Pine nuts, also called pine kernels, are a good source of vitamin E and potassium.

Garlicky bean terrine

GI estimate LOW

PREPARATION and COOKING: 2 3/4 hours, plus 8 hours soaking and 2 hours chilling   SERVES 8

1 Drain the soaked beans and rinse under cold running water. Put them in a saucepan with the onion, lemon zest, bay leaves and enough cold water to cover generously. Bring to the boil and boil rapidly for 10 minutes, then reduce the heat and simmer for 45–60 minutes or until tender.

2 Meanwhile, drain the vine leaves and rinse them in cold water. Spread out on a paper towel and pat dry. Lightly oil a 900 g terrine dish or loaf tin and line it with the vine leaves, shiny side out, allowing them to hang over the top of the dish. Set aside.

3 Preheat the oven to 180°C (Gas 4). Drain the beans and discard the onion, lemon zest and bay leaves. Tip the beans into a bowl and mash until fairly smooth.

4 Add the cottage cheese, garlic, lemon juice, eggs, parsley and seasoning to taste. Mix together, then fold in the olives. Spoon into the prepared terrine dish or tin, pressing the mixture into the corners. Level the top, then fold over the overhanging leaves. Cover the top with additional leaves, if necessary.

5 Place a piece of oiled foil over the top of the dish or tin, tucking the edges under the rim to seal securely. Set the dish in a roasting pan and pour in enough warm water to come two-thirds of the way up the sides of the dish. Bake for 1 hour or until the top of the terrine feels firm to the touch. Remove the dish from the water, set it on a wire rack and leave to cool. Chill for at least 2 hours before serving.

6 To unmould, run a knife round the edge of the terrine and turn out onto a plate or board. Cut into slices and transfer to plates. Garnish each portion with witlof leaves, orange segments and almonds, and serve.

COOK'S TIP
● If you can't find dried flageolet beans use cannellini or borlotti beans, dry or canned, instead.

225 g dried flageolet beans, soaked for at least 8 hours

1 small onion, halved

strip of lemon zest

2 bay leaves

10 vine leaves preserved in brine (or more if needed), stalks trimmed

115 g creamed cottage cheese (or plain low-fat fromage frais)

2 garlic cloves, crushed

1 tablespoon lemon juice

2 eggs, lightly beaten

2 tablespoons chopped parsley

freshly ground pepper

50 g pimiento-stuffed green olives, sliced

1 small head witlof (Belgian endive/ chicory), leaves separated

2 oranges, peeled and segmented

1/4 cup (40 g) toasted almonds

Each serving provides
761 kJ, 182 kcal, 12 g protein, 6 g fat (1 g saturated fat), 21 g carbohydrate (4 g sugars), 9 g fibre

VEGETARIAN DISHES

159

Chickpea and vegetable frittata

GI estimate LOW

This thick and chunky omelette is served flat, like a cake. It is equally delicious hot or cold and is ideal for a picnic. Serve with a simple tomato and red onion salad.

PREPARATION and COOKING: 30 minutes   SERVES 4

1 Heat 1 tablespoon of the olive oil in a 25 cm non-stick frying pan with a flameproof handle. Add the onion and cook for 2-3 minutes or until starting to soften. Stir in the garlic, cumin, ground coriander and cayenne pepper, and continue cooking for 1 minute, stirring constantly.

2 Add a further 1 tablespoon of the oil to the frying pan, then add the potatoes, red capsicum and eggplant. Continue frying for 5 minutes, stirring frequently, until the vegetables are lightly browned.

3 Add 5 tablespoons of water, cover and steam for 5 minutes. Then remove the lid and continue cooking until all excess liquid has evaporated. Stir in the chickpeas.

4 Lightly beat the eggs in a large mixing bowl. Add the chopped coriander and season to taste. Tip in the vegetable and chickpea mixture from the pan and stir to mix.

5 Preheat the grill to high. Heat the remaining 1 tablespoon of oil in the frying pan over a moderate heat. Pour in the egg mixture, spreading the vegetables out evenly. Cook the frittata for 3-4 minutes or until almost set - there will still be some uncooked egg mixture on the top.

6 Place the pan under the grill for about 2 minutes or until the top looks set. Remove from the heat and allow the frittata to rest in the pan for 2 minutes, then slide it onto a serving plate or board. Serve hot, cut into wedges.

ANOTHER IDEA

● For a salmon and butter bean frittata, omit the cumin, ground coriander and aubergine, and add 2 diced zucchini (courgettes) with the water in step 3. Replace the chickpeas with 1 can butter beans, about 410 g, drained and rinsed. In step 4, add 1 can salmon, about 200 g, drained and flaked, 2 tablespoons chopped fresh dill, 1 tablespoon snipped fresh chives and the finely grated zest of 1 lemon to the beaten eggs with the vegetables and beans.

3 tablespoons olive oil
1 small onion, chopped
1 garlic clove, crushed
1 teaspoon ground cumin
1 teaspoon ground coriander
pinch of cayenne pepper
250 g new potatoes, scrubbed and cut into 1 cm dice
1 small red capsicum (pepper), seeded and diced
1 small eggplant (aubergine), about 200 g, cut into 1 cm dice
1 can chickpeas, about 400 g, drained and rinsed
6 eggs
2 tablespoons chopped fresh coriander
freshly ground pepper

Each serving provides
1453 kJ, 347 kcal, 16 g protein, 23 g fat
(4 g saturated fat), 20 g carbohydrate
(3 g sugars), 6 g fibre

HEALTHY EATING

● New potatoes are acceptable on a low-GI eating plan - they have a moderate GI score (unlike mashed or baked potatoes, which have high GI scores). Make sure you don't overcook them, though, as this will raise the GI.

Roast vegetable and pasta bake

A hearty vegetarian dish packed with flavour, this is ideal for a family meal or casual entertaining. A selection of vegetables – butternut pumpkin, asparagus and leeks – is roasted in garlicky olive oil, then tossed with chunky pasta shapes and a cheesy sauce.

PREPARATION and COOKING: about 1^1/$_4$ hours   SERVES 4

1 small butternut pumpkin, peeled, seeded and cut into 5 cm cubes, about 450 g peeled weight

2 red onions, cut into large chunks

2 garlic cloves, thinly sliced

2 tablespoons olive oil

freshly ground pepper

500 g leeks, thickly sliced

9 asparagus spears, about 170 g, cut across in half

2^2/$_3$ cups (240 g) rigatoni or penne pasta

600 ml lite or low-fat milk

3 tablespoons cornflour

^{2}/$_3$ cup (85 g) extra mature cheddar, grated

2 teaspoons wholegrain mustard

Each serving provides
2407 kJ, 575 kcal, 25 g protein, 18 g fat
(6 g saturated fat), 80 g carbohydrate
(20 g sugars), 10 g fibre

1   Preheat the oven to 220°C (Gas 7). Put the pumpkin and red onions in a large roasting pan and scatter over the sliced garlic. Drizzle with the oil and season to taste. Toss to coat the vegetables with the oil, then place the pan in the oven and roast for 15 minutes.

2   Remove from the oven and add the leeks and asparagus. Toss gently to mix with the other vegetables, then return to the oven. Roast for a further 20 minutes or until all the vegetables are tender and beginning to brown.

3   Meanwhile, cook the pasta in a large saucepan of boiling water for 10-12 minutes, or according to the packet instructions, until al dente.

4   While the pasta is cooking, make the sauce. Measure out 4 tablespoons of the cold milk into a jug, add the cornflour and stir to make a smooth paste. Heat the remaining milk in a saucepan until almost boiling. Stir the hot milk into the cornflour mixture, then return to the saucepan and heat gently, stirring, until the mixture boils and thickens. Simmer for 2 minutes.

5   Remove the sauce from the heat and add about two-thirds of the cheese and the mustard. Season to taste.

6   Take the pan of vegetables from the oven. Drain the pasta well in a colander, then tip on top of the vegetables and stir to combine. Stir in the sauce. Sprinkle the remaining cheese evenly over the top. Return to the oven and bake for 10-15 minutes or until golden and bubbling. Serve hot.

COOK'S TIP

● For a stronger cheesy flavour, use ^{1}/$_3$ cup (35 g) grated parmesan instead of the cheddar.

HEALTHY EATING

● The bright orange flesh of butternut pumpkin is an indicator of its high beta-carotene content. Pumpkin is also a good source of vitamin C and a useful source of vitamin E.

● Milk is one of the best sources of calcium in the diet. Calcium is a vital mineral needed to ensure strong, healthy bones and teeth, and for the proper functioning of muscles and nerves.

Cannellini bean burgers

GI estimate LOW

PREPARATION: 20 minutes   COOKING: 8–10 minutes   SERVES 4

5 teaspoons olive oil

1 small onion, finely chopped

1 carrot, coarsely grated

2 teaspoons sun-dried tomato paste, or tomato purée

2 cans cannellini beans, about 400 g each, drained and rinsed

1/2 cup (50 g) fresh wholemeal breadcrumbs

1/2 cup (60 g) mature cheddar, grated

2 tablespoons chopped parsley

freshly ground pepper

1 tablespoon extra virgin olive oil

1 teaspoon lemon juice

340 g cherry tomatoes, quartered

1 tablespoon torn or shredded fresh basil

4 large grainy wholemeal baps

rocket to garnish

Each serving provides
2087 kJ, 499 kcal, 21 g protein, 19 g fat
(5 g saturated fat), 58 g carbohydrate
(8 g sugars), 15 g fibre

HEALTHY EATING

● Beans such as cannellini beans are a GI 'superfood': they provide hunger-satisfying protein, soluble fibre and low-GI carbohydrate.

● Cheese is high in saturated fat, so you need to limit your portions. Choosing a strongly flavoured type, such as mature cheddar, means that you only need a small amount.

1 Heat 3 teaspoons of the olive oil in a non-stick frying pan, add the onion and cook for 5 minutes, stirring frequently, until softened. Add the grated carrot and cook for a further 2 minutes, stirring. Remove from the heat and stir in the tomato paste.

2 Preheat the grill to moderate. Tip the cannellini beans into a bowl and mash with a potato masher to break them up roughly. Add the cooked vegetables, breadcrumbs, cheese, parsley and seasoning to taste.

3 Use your hands to mix all the ingredients together, then divide into 4 portions. Shape each into a large burger, about 10 cm in diameter and 2.5 cm thick. Lightly brush the burgers on both sides with the remaining olive oil and place on the rack of the grill pan. Cook for 4–5 minutes on each side or until slightly crisp and hot all the way through.

4 Meanwhile, make the salad by whisking together the extra virgin olive oil, lemon juice and seasoning to taste in a bowl. Add the tomatoes and basil.

5 Split the baps in half using a serrated knife. If liked, toast under the grill with the burgers for the last 2–3 minutes of cooking. Place the bean burgers inside and serve, with the tomato salad and a garnish of rocket.

Refried bean burritos

PREPARATION and COOKING: 1³/₄ hours, plus 8 hours soaking   SERVES 6

1 Drain the soaked beans and rinse under cold running water. Put them in a large pan, cover with plenty of fresh water and add the quartered onion, 2 peeled garlic cloves and the bay leaves. Bring to the boil and boil rapidly for 10 minutes, then reduce the heat, partly cover and simmer gently for about 45-60 minutes or until tender.

2 Meanwhile, make the salsa by mixing together the tomatoes, chilli, lime zest and juice, sugar and coriander in a bowl. Cover and leave at room temperature until ready to serve.

3 When the beans have finished cooking, spoon out 150 ml of the cooking liquid and reserve. Drain the beans, discarding the onion and bay leaves.

4 Heat the oil in a large frying pan, add the finely chopped onion and garlic, and cook gently for 10 minutes or until soft. Add the reserved whole garlic cloves, a ladleful of the beans and a few spoonfuls of the reserved cooking liquid. Mash with a fork to break up the beans and garlic cloves.

5 Continue adding the beans a ladleful at a time with a little of the liquid, cooking over a low heat and mashing, to make a dryish purée. Season to taste. Meanwhile, heat the tortillas in the oven or in a microwave.

6 Spoon the refried beans into the middle of the tortillas. Sprinkle with the cheese followed by the shredded lettuce, then add the yogurt. Roll up the tortillas and serve immediately, with the tomato and chilli salsa.

1¹/₄ cup (250 g) dried pinto beans, soaked for at least 8 hours
2 onions (1 quartered and 1 finely chopped)
3 garlic cloves (2 whole and 1 finely chopped)
2 bay leaves
450 g firm, ripe tomatoes, diced
1 green chilli, seeded and finely chopped
finely grated zest and juice of 1 lime
pinch of caster sugar
3 tablespoons chopped fresh coriander
1¹/₂ tablespoons canola (rapeseed) oil
freshly ground pepper
8 large wheat tortillas
³/₄ cup (105 g) grated cheddar
1 cos lettuce, shredded
¹/₂ cup (125 g) Greek-style yogurt

Each serving provides
1286 kJ, 307 kcal, 11 g protein, 16 g fat (6 g saturated fat), 30 g carbohydrate (7 g sugars), 4 g fibre

HEALTHY EATING

● Tortillas, a part of the staple diet in Mexico and other countries in Central and South America, may be made from wheat or from masa harina, a form of maize. Both types have a moderate GI score, and make a great alternative to white bread.

● Vitamin C from the tomatoes and lime juice in the salsa helps the absorption of iron from the beans.

Spaghetti with a chickpea sauce

GI estimate LOW

Here's a colourful and easy vegetarian dish that makes a satisfying main course all on its own. It's a delicious way to mix pasta and beans for a good balance of protein and low-GI carbohydrate.

PREPARATION and COOKING: 20-25 minutes   SERVES 4

1   Heat the olive oil in a heavy-based saucepan, add the onion and garlic, and cook over a moderate heat for 3-4 minutes, stirring occasionally, until softened.

2   Add the celery and fry, stirring, for 1-2 minutes, then stir in the tomatoes with their juice and bring to the boil. Reduce the heat and simmer gently, stirring occasionally, for about 15 minutes or until thick.

3   Meanwhile, cook the spaghetti in a large pan of boiling water for 10-12 minutes, or according to the packet instructions, until al dente.

4   When the sauce is cooked, stir in the chickpeas and hot chilli sauce. Add the spinach leaves and simmer for 1-2 minutes, stirring, until the spinach wilts. Season to taste.

5   Drain the spaghetti and toss with the chickpeas and tomato sauce. Scatter over the parsley leaves, and serve immediately, sprinkled with the pecorino cheese.

SOME MORE IDEAS

● For tagliatelle with cannellini beans, use tagliatelle or fettuccine instead of spaghetti, and replace the chickpeas with canned cannellini or haricot beans. Instead of spinach, add 200 g cooked asparagus spears, cut into 2.5 cm lengths, to the sauce. Just before serving, stir in 85 g thin strips of trimmed prosciutto; omit the pecorino cheese.

● Grill 4 lean slices of back bacon until crisp and golden, then drain well and chop roughly. Stir into the tomato sauce with the chickpeas. Reduce the pecorino cheese to 1/4 cup (25 g).

---

2 tablespoons olive oil

1 onion, chopped

1 garlic clove, crushed

1 celery stick, finely chopped

1 can chopped tomatoes, about 400 g

240 g wholemeal spaghetti

2 cans chickpeas, about 410 g each, drained and rinsed

1/2 teaspoon hot chilli sauce, or to taste

2 cups (170 g) baby spinach leaves

freshly ground pepper

fresh flat-leaf parsley leaves to garnish

1/2 cup (45 g) freshly grated pecorino cheese or parmesan

Each serving provides
2049 kJ, 489 kcal, 20 g protein, 16 g fat
(4 g saturated fat), 67 g carbohydrate
(6 g sugars), 8 g fibre

HEALTHY EATING

● Like all beans and pulses, chickpeas are a GI 'superfood': they provide hunger-satisfying protein, soluble fibre and low-GI carbohydrate.

● Pasta, especially wholemeal pasta, is a GI 'superfood', providing slow-release, low-GI carbohydrate.

Bean and lentil lasagne

GI estimate LOW

This colourful main dish is built up with layers of red capsicum, lentil and bean sauce, sheets of lasagne and sliced artichoke hearts. The creamy topping is a combination of ricotta and parmesan.

PREPARATION: 45 minutes, plus 5 minutes standing   COOKING: 40 minutes   SERVES 6

1 tablespoon canola (rapeseed) oil

1 large red onion, thinly sliced

$^1/_2$ cup (125 g) split red lentils

2 large red capsicums (peppers), seeded and diced

1 large carrot, thinly sliced

2 celery sticks, thinly sliced

2$^1/_4$ cups (560 ml) salt-reduced vegetable stock

1 bay leaf

2 cans cannellini beans, about 400 g each, drained and rinsed

freshly ground pepper

200 g instant lasagne sheets, about 12

1 can artichoke hearts in water, about 400 g, drained, rinsed and sliced

$^2/_3$ cup (160 g) ricotta

100 ml lite or low-fat milk

3 tablespoons freshly grated parmesan

FOR EVEN LOWER GI
Use wholemeal lasagne sheets.

Each serving provides
1499 kJ, 358 kcal, 22 g protein, 8 g fat
(3 g saturated fat), 48 g carbohydrate
(9 g sugars), 12 g fibre

1 To make the sauce, heat the oil in a saucepan, add the onion and cook gently for 10 minutes or until softened. Add the lentils, capsicums, carrot, celery, stock and bay leaf. Bring to the boil, then reduce the heat and simmer for about 25 minutes or until the lentils and vegetables are tender.

2 Remove the bay leaf, then purée in a blender or food processor, or using a hand-held blender in the pan, until smooth. Stir in the cannellini beans and season to taste.

3 Preheat the oven to 190°C (Gas 5). Spoon about one-quarter of the sauce over the bottom of a greased large ovenproof dish. Cover with one-third of the lasagne sheets, then top with half of the remaining sauce. Arrange half the sliced artichoke hearts over the sauce. Repeat with another layer of pasta, then the rest of the sauce and the rest of the artichokes. Finish with the last of the pasta sheets.

4 Put the ricotta into a bowl and stir in the milk until smooth. Season with pepper to taste. Spoon it over the lasagne, then scatter the parmesan on top.

5 Bake for 40 minutes or until bubbling and the top is golden. Remove from the oven and leave to stand for 5 minutes before serving.

SOME MORE IDEAS

● Replace the artichoke hearts with 400 g baby spinach leaves, steamed for about 1 minute or until wilted.

● For a mixed bean and lentil lasagne, replace the cannellini beans with 2 cans mixed beans (usually haricot, pinto, kidney, chickpea), about 410 g each, drained and rinsed. Use either artichoke hearts or steamed spinach.

HEALTHY EATING

● Red lentils cook quickly to a purée and so are particularly good in soups and sauces such as this one. Lentils provide B vitamins and iron and, like all pulses, they have a low GI.

● Pasta is an excellent source of low-fat, low-GI carbohydrate and contains valuable vitamins, particularly the B vitamins.

Millet with spinach and pine nuts

PREPARATION: 10 minutes   COOKING: 20-25 minutes   SERVES 4

1 cup (185 g) millet
1/4 cup (45 g) dried apricots, roughly chopped
3 cups (750 ml) salt-reduced vegetable stock
1/3 cup (50 g) pine nuts
250 g baby spinach leaves
juice of 1/2 lemon
freshly ground pepper

Each serving provides
1254 kJ, 300 kcal, 9 g protein, 11 g fat
(1 g saturated fat), 40 g carbohydrate
(10 g sugars), 6 g fibre

1 Put the millet and dried apricots into a large saucepan and stir in the stock. Bring to the boil, then lower the heat. Simmer for 15-20 minutes or until all the stock has been absorbed and the millet is tender.

2 Meanwhile, toast the pine nuts in a small frying pan until they are golden brown and fragrant. Set aside.

3 Add the spinach and lemon juice to the millet, with seasoning to taste. Cover the pan and leave over a very low heat for 4-5 minutes to wilt the spinach.

4 Stir the millet and spinach mixture gently, then spoon into a serving bowl. Scatter the toasted pine nuts on top and serve immediately.

ANOTHER IDEA

● Try eggplant (aubergine) with millet and sesame seeds. Cut 2 medium-sized eggplants into dice. Heat 2 tablespoons olive oil in a large frying pan, add the eggplant and brown over a high heat, stirring constantly. Remove from the heat and stir in 1 cup (185 g) millet and 3 cups (750 ml) vegetable stock. Return to the heat and bring to the boil. Stir, then reduce the heat and simmer for 15-20 minutes or until the stock has been absorbed and the millet is tender. Season to taste. Transfer to a serving bowl and scatter over 2 tablespoons chopped fresh coriander and 2 tablespoons toasted sesame seeds.

HEALTHY EATING

● Millet provides useful amounts of protein, iron, calcium and B vitamins and, as has a low GI.

● Pine nuts are a good source of vitamin E and potassium.

VEGETARIAN DISHES

Speedy two-bean chilli

GI estimate LOW

PREPARATION: 5 minutes   COOKING: 25 minutes   SERVES 4

1. Heat the oil in a large frying pan. Add the onion and chilli, and fry over a moderate heat for 5 minutes, stirring occasionally, until the onion is lightly browned.

2. Stir in the tomatoes with their juice, the chilli sauce, tomato sauce, stock, parsley and oregano. Bring to the boil, then reduce the heat and simmer for 10 minutes, stirring occasionally.

3. Add the kidney and cannellini beans and the corn. Simmer for a further 10 minutes.

4. Meanwhile, mix the creamed cottage cheese with the snipped chives. Taste the chilli for seasoning and adjust if necessary. Serve the chilli sprinkled with the oregano leaves and offer the cheese mixture separately.

HEALTHY EATING

● Beans are a GI 'superfood': they provide hunger-satisfying protein, soluble fibre and low-GI carbohydrate.

● Cottage cheese is a healthy low-fat source of protein. It also provides calcium and has a low GI.

2 tablespoons olive oil

1 large onion, halved and sliced

1 red chilli, seeded and chopped

1 can chopped tomatoes, about 400 g

1 tablespoon hot chilli sauce

2 tablespoons tomato ketchup

600 ml hot salt-reduced vegetable stock

1 tablespoon chopped parsley

1 tablespoon chopped fresh oregano

1 can red kidney beans, about 400 g, drained and rinsed

1 can cannellini beans, about 400 g, drained and rinsed

200 g frozen corn (sweetcorn)

150 g creamed cottage cheese (or plain low-fat fromage frais)

2 tablespoons snipped fresh chives

fresh oregano leaves to garnish

Each serving provides
1730 kJ, 413 kcal, 16 g protein, 23 g fat (4 g saturated fat), 34 g carbohydrate (16 g sugars), 11 g fibre

VEGETARIAN DISHES

171

Tuscan-style baked polenta

Polenta is a much-loved staple of northern Italy. In this recipe, parmesan-flavoured 'soft' polenta - polenta that hasn't been left to set - provides the topping for a mixture of borlotti beans and a creamy wild mushroom sauce.

PREPARATION: 45 minutes   COOKING: 20 minutes   SERVES 4

25 g dried porcini mushrooms

400 ml lite or low-fat milk

1$\frac{1}{2}$ tablespoons olive oil

15 g non-hydrogenated soft margarine

2 celery sticks, thinly sliced

2$\frac{2}{3}$ cups (245 g) sliced chestnut or
    Swiss brown mushrooms

3 tablespoons plain flour

squeeze of lemon juice

freshly ground pepper

1 can borlotti beans, about 400 g,
    rinsed and drained

170 g polenta

2 eggs, lightly beaten

$\frac{1}{3}$ cup (35 g) freshly grated parmesan

Each serving provides
1972 kJ, 471 kcal, 23 g protein, 17 g fat
(4 g saturated fat), 57 g carbohydrate
(10 g sugars), 8 g fibre

1 Place the dried mushrooms in a small saucepan and add 1 cup (250 ml) of the milk. Bring just to the boil, then remove from the heat and set aside to soak.

2 Heat the olive oil and margarine in a wide saucepan over a moderate heat. Add the celery and cook gently, stirring occasionally, for 3-4 minutes or until softened. Raise the heat, add the mushrooms and cook, stirring, for about 3 minutes or until softened.

3 Add the flour and cook, stirring, for 2 minutes. Gradually mix in the remaining 150 ml milk and cook, stirring well, until the mixture just comes to the boil and thickens.

4 Strain the milk from the porcini mushrooms and add it to the mushroom and celery sauce. Bring back to the boil, stirring. Coarsely chop the porcini and add to the pan. Simmer for 2 minutes, then add the lemon juice and season to taste.

5 Pour the mushroom sauce into a shallow ovenproof dish and spread out in an even layer. Scatter the borlotti beans on top. Set aside.

6 Preheat the oven to 200°C (Gas 6). In a heavy-based saucepan, cook the polenta in 3 cups (750 ml) boiling water, or according to the packet instructions, until it is thick. Remove from the heat and briskly stir in the eggs and about half of the parmesan. Season to taste.

7 Pour the polenta mixture over the mushrooms and beans. Sprinkle the remaining parmesan over the top. Bake for about 20 minutes or until the filling is bubbling and the top is lightly browned. Serve hot.

COOK'S TIP

● If dried porcini mushrooms are not available at the supermarket, you should be able to find them at gourmet grocers, food markets, delicatessens and health food shops.

HEALTHY EATING

- Polenta is low in fat and has a moderate GI score and so it is a reasonable source of carbohydrate. It can be served 'soft' with fish, meat and vegetable dishes as a GI-friendly alternative to mashed potatoes, or it can be left to set, then cut up and grilled or fried. It is particularly useful for those who need to follow a wheat- or gluten-free diet.

Oaty red lentil gratin

GI estimate LOW

Red lentils, mushrooms and celery form the base of this hearty gratin. The cheese and oat topping becomes lightly browned and crunchy during the few minutes in the oven. Serve with a tomato salad and green vegetables, such as broccoli and zucchini.

PREPARATION: 45 minutes   COOKING: 10 minutes   SERVES 4

1   Heat the olive oil in a saucepan, add the onion and celery, and cook, stirring occasionally, for 5 minutes.

2   Add the sliced mushrooms and stir well to combine. Cook for a further 5 minutes or until softened.

3   Stir in the lentils and add 2 cups (500 ml) of the stock. Bring to the boil, then reduce the heat and cover. Simmer for about 20 minutes or until the lentils are tender, adding the rest of the stock if the lentils appear to be drying out.

4   Preheat the oven to 220°C (Gas 7). Mix the oats with the grated cheese and cayenne pepper. When the lentils are cooked, season with pepper to taste. Transfer them to a shallow ovenproof dish and spread out evenly.

5   Spread the oat and cheese mixture over the top. Place the dish in the oven and bake for about 10 minutes or until the topping is crisp and golden brown. Serve hot.

2 tablespoons olive oil

1 onion, chopped

2 celery sticks, chopped

2^1/$_4$ cups (200 g) sliced chestnut or Swiss brown mushrooms

1 cup (250 g) red lentils

600 ml salt-reduced vegetable stock

1 cup (100 g) rolled oats

100 g gouda cheese or mature cheddar, grated

pinch of cayenne pepper

Each serving provides
1965 kJ, 469 kcal, 27 g protein, 21 g fat
(7 g saturated fat), 44 g carbohydrate
(5 g sugars), 13 g fibre

SOME MORE IDEAS

● Cook the onion and celery with 2 finely chopped garlic cloves and 1 tablespoon chopped fresh oregano.

● In step 2, add a pinch each of curry powder and ground cumin with the mushrooms.

● To make a mixed lentil gratin, cook the onion with 1 chopped garlic clove (omit the celery). Instead of mushrooms, add 1 chopped fennel bulb and 2 sliced small leeks, and cook for about 5 minutes or until softened. Add ^{1}/$_2$ cup (125 g) red lentils, ^{1}/$_2$ cup (125 g) French-style green (puy) lentils and the stock, and cook as in the main recipe. Transfer to a shallow ovenproof dish and top with a mixture of 1^1/$_4$ cups (100 g) fresh wholemeal breadcrumbs, ^{1}/$_2$ cup (50 g) freshly grated parmesan and ^{1}/$_2$ cup (60 g) grated cheddar. Bake as in the main recipe.

HEALTHY EATING

● Lentils, like all pulses, are a GI 'superfood': they provide hunger-satisfying protein, soluble fibre and low-GI carbohydrate.

● Oats are another GI 'superfood', with a low GI that produces a gentle, sustained rise in blood glucose levels. They have other health benefits too, including lowering cholesterol.

● All mushrooms provide useful amounts of B vitamins.

Tagliatelle with broccoli

PREPARATION: 10 minutes   COOKING: about 15 minutes   SERVES 2

120 g spinach (green) tagliatelle
150 g broccoli florets
150 g cauliflower florets
200 g mild blue cheese such as
   roquefort or dolcelatte
freshly grated nutmeg
freshly ground pepper

Each serving provides
2517 kJ, 601 kcal, 33 g protein, 32 g fat
(19 g saturated fat), 45 g carbohydrate
(4 g sugars), 6 g fibre

1   Cook the tagliatelle in boiling water for 10-12 minutes, or according to the packet instructions, until al dente.

2   Meanwhile, cut the broccoli and cauliflower florets into bite-sized pieces. Add them to the simmering pasta for the last 2-3 minutes of the cooking time. Drain the pasta and vegetables in a large colander.

3   Return the rinsed out pan to the stove and add the cheese. Turn the heat to the lowest setting and melt the cheese gently, stirring frequently to make a smooth sauce. As soon as the cheese has melted, add the cooked pasta and vegetables. Turn the pasta and vegetables in the cheese sauce until coated and heated through. Season to taste with nutmeg and pepper. Serve immediately.

COOK'S TIP

● Use brie or camembert instead of blue cheese for a milder-tasting dish. Add 1 tablespoon finely chopped fresh basil just before serving.

SOME MORE IDEAS

● For a peppery flavour, and a good source of iron, add 50 g roughly chopped watercress. Stir in the watercress when adding the pasta and vegetables to the melted cheese.

● For a stronger flavour, use gorgonzola cheese.

HEALTHY EATING

● All pasta is a healthy, low-GI source of carbohydrate.

● Broccoli and cauliflower belong to the cruciferous family of vegetables, which contain various phytochemicals that are thought to protect against cancers.

Pasta with sage and fetta

PREPARATION: 10 minutes   COOKING: about 20 minutes   SERVES 4

GI estimate LOW

1 Cook the pasta in boiling water for 10-12 minutes, or according to the packet instructions, until al dente.

2 While the pasta is cooking, heat a large frying pan over a moderately high heat. Add the pancetta, garlic, if using, shallots and sage, and cook, stirring frequently, for 6-8 minutes or until the pancetta is golden brown and the shallots are soft.

3 Add the chickpeas, tomatoes with their juice and the sugar, and bring to the boil. Reduce the heat and simmer for 10 minutes or until the sauce has thickened slightly. Season with pepper (there is no need to add extra salt as fetta is quite salty).

4 Drain the pasta and stir into the sauce so that it is well coated. Add the rocket and stir in lightly, then sprinkle with the fetta and serve.

$2^2/_3$ cups (240 g) tubular pasta, such as casarecce, penne or macaroni

50 g pancetta, finely chopped

2 garlic cloves, finely chopped (optional)

2 French shallots, finely chopped

8 fresh sage leaves, shredded

1 can chickpeas, about 400 g, drained

1 can chopped tomatoes, about 400 g

pinch of sugar

$1^1/_2$ cups (50 g) rocket leaves, stalks removed if preferred

$2/_3$ cup (100 g) crumbled fetta

freshly ground pepper

FOR EVEN LOWER GI
Use wholemeal pasta.

Each serving provides
1588 kJ, 379 kcal, 19 g protein, 10 g fat (5 g saturated fat), 54 g carbohydrate (4 g sugars), 7 g fibre

HEALTHY EATING

● Fetta is high in fat and salt, but because it has such a strong flavour, a little goes a long way. Like all cheese, it is a good source of protein, calcium and phosphorus. It also provides useful amounts of various B vitamins and vitamin E.

● Pasta is a low-fat and low-GI source of carbohydrate.

VEGETARIAN DISHES

177

Spicy vegetable tagine

PREPARATION: 25 minutes   COOKING: 30 minutes   SERVES 4

2 tablespoons olive oil

1 large red onion, roughly chopped

4 garlic cloves, sliced

1 tablespoon shredded fresh root ginger

550 g butternut pumpkin, peeled, seeded and cubed

1 teaspoon ground cinnamon

1 teaspoon ground cumin

1 teaspoon ground coriander

6 green cardamom pods, split open and seeds lightly crushed

3 bay leaves

2 cans chopped tomatoes, about 400 g each

225 g large carrots, very thickly sliced

300 ml boiling salt-reduced vegetable stock

$^1/_3$ cup (40 g) raisins

$^1/_3$ cup (30 g) dried cherries

125 g okra, sliced lengthwise into 3

1 large red capsicum (pepper), chopped

1 can chickpeas, about 300 g, drained

$^1/_3$ cup (30 g) toasted flaked almonds

3 tablespoons chopped flat-leaf parsley

SPICY COUSCOUS

340 g instant couscous

450 ml boiling salt-reduced vegetable stock

1 tablespoon olive oil

1 teaspoon chilli sauce such as harissa

$^1/_2$ teaspoon coriander

$^1/_2$ teaspoon cumin

Each serving provides
2259 kJ, 540 kcal, 15 g protein, 21 g fat
(3 g saturated fat), 79 g carbohydrate
(31 g sugars), 14 g fibre

1 Heat the olive oil in a large pan and stir-fry the onion over a high heat for 2-3 minutes or until beginning to soften and colour. Toss in the garlic and ginger and cook for a few more seconds. Tip in the pumpkin and stir-fry for about 1 minute.

2 Turn down the heat. Add all of the spices, the bay leaves, tomatoes with their juice and carrots. Pour in the boiling stock. Stir in the raisins and cherries, then cover and simmer for 10 minutes.

3 Meanwhile, prepare the couscous. Tip the couscous into a large bowl and pour in the boiling stock. Add the olive oil, chilli sauce and spices. Leave until the liquid has been absorbed, then fork the mixture through to separate the grains. Tip into a colander lined with baking paper.

4 Stir the okra and capsicum into the stew, then cover and leave to simmer for 5 minutes. Add the chickpeas and stir. Set the colander containing the couscous over the pan and simmer for a further 5-10 minutes or until all the vegetables are tender but still retain their shape and texture and the couscous is hot.

5 Tip the couscous onto a platter. Pile the vegetable stew on top of the couscous and scatter over the toasted almonds and chopped parsley.

COOK'S TIP

● If you can't find dried cherries, use dried or frozen cranberries instead, available from most health food shops.

SOME MORE IDEAS

● For an apricot and coriander tagine, replace the cherries and raisins with dried apricots, use halved French beans instead of the okra, and substitute fresh coriander for the parsley. Add 2 tablespoons chopped fresh coriander to the tagine at the end of the cooking time and scatter some over the finished dish.

● Red kidney beans can be used as an alternative to the chickpeas, or instead of adding them to the tagine toss them into the couscous for added texture.

HEALTHY EATING

● Beans and chickpeas are GI 'superfoods': they provide hunger-satisfying protein, soluble fibre and low-GI carbohydrate. As a protein source, they are even better when eaten with grains such as couscous or basmati rice. Canned versions are a convenient way of including them in the diet.

● Although raisins have a high GI, the small amount used in this recipe will not affect the overall GI of the dish.

Penne primavera

This well-known Italian dish is designed to make the most of young spring produce, but you can adapt it using whatever seasonal vegetables are available, including good-quality frozen vegetables.

PREPARATION: 15 minutes   COOKING: 15 minutes   SERVES 4

1 Cook the pasta in boiling water for 10-12 minutes, or according to the packet instructions, until al dente.

2 While the pasta is cooking, cut the asparagus into 3 cm lengths, keeping the tips separate. Drop the pieces of asparagus stalk, the green beans and peas into a saucepan of boiling water. Bring back to the boil and cook for 5 minutes. Add the asparagus tips and cook for a further 2 minutes. Drain thoroughly.

3 Heat the olive oil in a saucepan. Add the onion and cook for 3-4 minutes or until softened. Add the garlic, pancetta and mushrooms, and continue to cook, stirring occasionally, for a further 2 minutes.

4 Stir in the flour, then gradually pour in the wine and bring to the boil, stirring. Simmer until the sauce is thickened. Stir in the cream and herbs with seasoning to taste. Add the vegetables to the sauce and heat gently for 1-2 minutes, without boiling.

5 Drain the pasta and divide among 4 serving bowls. Spoon the sauce over the top. Serve immediately.

COOK'S TIP
● Use frozen peas instead of fresh, adding them with the asparagus tips.

2$^2/_3$ cups (240 g) wholemeal penne pasta or other pasta shapes

8 young asparagus spears (150 g)

1$^3/_4$ cups (175 g) green beans, trimmed and cut into 3 cm lengths

170 g shelled fresh peas

1 tablespoon olive oil

1 onion, chopped

1 garlic clove, chopped

85 g pancetta, chopped

1$^1/_4$ cups (115 g) sliced button mushrooms

1 tablespoon plain flour

1 cup (250 ml) dry white wine

4 tablespoons pouring cream

2 tablespoons chopped mixed fresh herbs, such as parsley and thyme

freshly ground pepper

Each serving provides
1964 kJ, 469 kcal, 17 g protein, 17 g fat
(7 g saturated fat), 51 g carbohydrate
(5 g sugars), 8 g fibre

HEALTHY EATING

● Asparagus is a good source of many of the B vitamins, especially folate.

● Peas are a GI 'superfood': they provide hunger-satisfying protein, soluble fibre and low-GI carbohydrate. Peas also contain useful amounts of thiamin, niacin and B6, folate and vitamin C.

VEGETARIAN DISHES

181

HEALTHY EATING

● Like all pulses, lentils are a GI 'superfood': they provide
hunger-satisfying protein, soluble fibre and low-GI carbohydrate.
They also provide useful amounts of many B vitamins and iron.

● The onion topping is traditionally deep fried, but here it is
fried in a small amount of canola (rapeseed) oil in a non-stick
pan to reduce the fat content.

Egyptian lentils with macaroni

GI estimate LOW

For Egypt's vegetarians this highly spiced dish is a protein staple. It takes a bit of time to cook – but couldn't be simpler. Any leftovers can be eaten as a cold side dish.

PREPARATION: 10-15 minutes   COOKING: about 1 hour   SERVES 4

1 Put the lentils in a heavy-based saucepan and pour in enough water to cover them by 8 cm. Bring to the boil and boil vigorously for about 10 minutes, skimming the surface as necessary. Reduce the heat and simmer for about 30-40 minutes or until tender. Drain well and keep warm.

2 Meanwhile, heat 1 tablespoon of the oil in a large non-stick frying pan over a high heat. Add the onion and stir to coat with the oil, then reduce the heat and cook for about 20 minutes, stirring frequently, until soft. Stir in the sugar, raise the heat and continue cooking, stirring, until the onion becomes dark brown and crisp. Immediately pour onto a paper towel to drain, and set aside.

3 Heat $1/2$ tablespoon of the remaining oil in a large saucepan. Add the garlic and fry for 30 seconds, stirring. Stir in the turmeric and continue frying for a further 30 seconds. Pour in the tomatoes with their juice and add a pinch of sugar. Bring to the boil, stirring. Reduce the heat and simmer for 10-15 minutes, stirring occasionally, until the sauce thickens a little. Season to taste.

4 Heat the remaining oil in a frying pan. Stir in the cumin, ground coriander and cayenne pepper, and fry for about 30 seconds, stirring. Add the cooked lentils and stir in seasoning to taste. Keep warm over a very low heat.

5 Cook the macaroni in boiling water for 10-12 minutes, or according to the packet instructions, until al dente. Drain well. Spoon onto a serving platter, and top with the spiced lentils and the tomato sauce. Sprinkle with the chopped coriander and top with the crisp onions. Serve at once.

SOME MORE IDEAS
● Use red or green lentils instead of puy lentils. Cook them according to the packet instructions.
● Add 1 seeded and thinly sliced red capsicum (pepper), softening it in the oil before adding the spices in step 4.

$1^1/4$ cups (245 g) French-style green (puy) lentils, rinsed
$2^1/2$ tablespoons canola (rapeseed) oil
1 large onion, very thinly sliced
1 teaspoon raw (demerara) sugar
1 large garlic clove, crushed
$1/2$ teaspoon turmeric
2 cans chopped tomatoes, about 400 g each
pinch of sugar
2 teaspoons ground cumin
2 teaspoons ground coriander
$1/4$ teaspoon cayenne pepper
freshly ground pepper
$1^1/4$ cups (200 g) macaroni
2 tablespoons finely chopped fresh coriander or parsley

FOR EVEN LOWER GI
Use wholemeal pasta twists instead of macaroni.

Each serving provides
2039 kJ, 487 kcal, 23 g protein, 14 g fat (1 g saturated fat), 69 g carbohydrate (10 g sugars), 14 g fibre

Couscous pilaf with tahini yogurt

GI estimate LOW

This vegetable-rich couscous is lower in fat than most pilafs and it makes a healthy low-GI meal. You can also serve it as a side dish with cooked meat or poultry, when it will serve 8 or more.

PREPARATION: 25 minutes   COOKING: 35 minutes   SERVES 6

1 tablespoon olive oil

1 medium onion, chopped

4 garlic cloves, chopped

1 small carrot, diced

1 teaspoon mild chilli powder

1 teaspoon ground coriander

1 teaspoon garam masala

2$^{1}/_{2}$ teaspoons paprika

$^{1}/_{2}$ teaspoon ground ginger

$^{1}/_{2}$ teaspoon ground cinnamon

2$^{1}/_{2}$ teaspoons ground cumin

4 green cardamom pods

85 g orange sweet potato (kumara)

85 g turnip

1 zucchini (courgette)

75 g runner or French beans, trimmed

1 can chopped tomatoes, about 400 g

900 ml salt-reduced vegetable stock

1 can borlotti beans, about 400 g, drained

250 g cabbage, roughly chopped

85 g broccoli, cut into small florets

340 g instant couscous

3 tablespoons sultanas

freshly ground pepper

2 tablespoons tahini (sesame paste)

4 tablespoons low-fat natural yogurt

1 tablespoon lemon juice

sprigs of fresh coriander to garnish

Each serving provides
1153 kJ, 276 kcal, 12g protein, 9 g fat
(1 g saturated fat), 38 g carbohydrate
(16 g sugars), 9 g fibre

1. Heat the olive oil in a 4.5 litre stockpot, flameproof casserole dish or saucepan and add the onion. Reserve the equivalent of about 1 garlic clove, then add the rest to the pan. Cook for about 3 minutes or until the onion has softened. Add the carrot and cook for a further 3 minutes.

2. Sprinkle in the chilli powder, coriander, garam masala, paprika, ginger, cinnamon and 2 teaspoons cumin (reserve the remaining cumin for the tahini yogurt). Split the cardamom pods and scrape the tiny black seeds into the pan and stir for a few seconds. Cut the sweet potato, turnip and zucchini into bite-sized chunks and add to pan. Cut the beans into bite-sized lengths and add to the pan. Cook the vegetables for 5 minutes or until softened slightly.

3. Pour in the tomatoes with their juice and the stock, and stir in the borlotti beans. Bring to the boil, then reduce the heat, cover and simmer for 10–15 minutes. Add the cabbage and broccoli, and cook, covered, for a further 5 minutes.

4. Reduce the heat to the lowest setting. Add the couscous and sultanas with a little seasoning to taste. Fork through the vegetables and stock. Cover and cook very gently for 5 minutes. The couscous should have absorbed all the liquid and plumped up.

5. Meanwhile, make the tahini yogurt. (Stir the tahini in the jar to ensure it is smooth before measuring out the quantity for the recipe.) Mix the tahini with the reserved garlic and the yogurt, then stir in 4 tablespoons water, the lemon juice, the reserved $^{1}/_{2}$ teaspoon cumin and seasoning to taste. Sprinkle with fresh coriander to garnish. Serve the pilaf with the tahini yogurt offered separately.

COOK'S TIP

● Use any leftovers, gently mashed, as a delicious stuffing for chicken or other poultry.

HEALTHY EATING

● Borlotti beans are low in fat and rich in low-GI carbohydrate. They provide good amounts of B vitamins (thiamin, niacin and B6) and useful amounts of iron. In common with other beans and pulses, they are a good source of fibre, particularly soluble fibre, which can help to reduce high blood cholesterol levels.

● Broccoli is an excellent source of beta-carotene and vitamins C and E. It also provides good amounts of the B vitamins niacin, folate and B6.

Roquefort and pear salad **189**

Smoked fish and lentil salad **190**

Gruyère and ham salad **192**

Fetta and couscous salad **193**

Corn and wholewheat salad **195**

Burghul wheat and prawn salad **196**

Minted barley and beans **197**

Buckwheat and seafood salad **198**

Marinated duck with buckwheat **200**

Chinese-style broccoli salad **201**

Lamb and wholewheat salad **203**

Sweet and spicy lentil salad **204**

Avocado and prawn cups **205**

Soused fresh sardine salad **207**

Snow pea, grape and fetta salad **208**

Crab and avocado salad **210**

Fennel, apple and trout salad **211**

Tabouleh with goat's cheese **213**

Cajun-style ham and beans **214**

Chicken liver and raspberry salad **215**

Lentil and sausage salad **217**

Salads

Roquefort and pear salad

GI estimate LOW

The ingredients of this fresh and vibrant salad are perfectly complemented by the subtle walnut oil dressing. Lightly toasted walnut pieces strengthen the walnut flavour, making a tempting lunch. Serve with grainy wholemeal rolls or other low-GI bread.

PREPARATION: 15 minutes   SERVES 4

1 First make the dressing. Stir the mustard and vinegar together in a salad bowl with pepper to taste, then gradually whisk in the canola and walnut oils. Stir in the poppy seeds. Set aside while preparing the salad.

2 Lightly toast the walnut pieces in a small frying pan, stirring them frequently until fragrant. Leave to cool.

3 Add the onion to the salad bowl and mix with the dressing. Quarter, core and slice the pears, leaving the skins on. Add to the bowl and toss gently so that they are well coated with the dressing.

4 Add the watercress and most of the cheese and walnuts to the pears. Toss together gently, then scatter over the remaining cheese and nuts and serve immediately.

SOME MORE IDEAS

● Other blue cheeses, such as Stilton or Danish blue, work equally well here. As most blue cheeses are fairly salty, it isn't necessary to season the dressing with salt.

● For a ricotta and witlof (Belgian endive/chicory) salad, separate the leaves of 2 small heads of witlof, about 170 g in total. Cut each leaf in half lengthwise and arrange on a serving platter. In a small jug, mix together 1 teaspoon Dijon mustard, 1/2 teaspoon finely grated orange zest, 1 tablespoon orange juice and seasoning to taste. Whisk in 1 tablespoon canola (rapeseed) oil and 1 tablespoon walnut or hazelnut oil to make a creamy dressing. Cook 170 g snow peas (mangetout) in boiling water for about 3 minutes or until just tender, then drain and refresh under cold running water. Put into a mixing bowl and add 1 avocado, sliced horizontally into half moons, 4 roma (plum) tomatoes, cut into very thin wedges, and 75 g toasted pecan halves. Drizzle over the dressing and toss gently to coat. Spoon on top of the witlof, add spoonfuls of ricotta, about 200g in total, and serve.

1/2 teaspoon Dijon mustard
2 teaspoons red wine vinegar
1 tablespoon canola (rapeseed) oil
1 tablespoon walnut oil
2 teaspoons poppy seeds
1/2 cup (60 g) walnut pieces
1 red onion, thinly sliced
3 large, ripe pears, preferably red-skinned
3 3/4 cups (115 g) watercress
115 g roquefort, or other blue cheese, crumbled
freshly ground pepper

Each serving provides
1630 kJ, 389 kcal, 10 g protein, 29 g fat (7 g saturated fat), 24 g carbohydrate (17 g sugars), 7 g fibre

HEALTHY EATING

● Pears are a GI 'superfood' because of their high natural sweetness yet low GI. They are also a good source of potassium.

● Cheese contains valuable nutrients, including protein and calcium. Many cheeses are high in fat, but strongly flavoured varieties such as roquefort need only be used in small quantities.

SALADS

Smoked fish and lentil salad

GI estimate LOW

Large flakes of smoked fish, sprigs of watercress and thick slices of juicy, sweet pear make an exciting combination, and they work well with nutty-textured puy lentils. Serve with low-GI bread for a starter that will set tastebuds tingling.

PREPARATION and COOKING: 25–30 minutes   SERVES 6

$^2/_3$ cup (140 g) French-style green (puy) lentils

2 tablespoons extra virgin olive oil

grated zest and juice of 1 lime

1 teaspoon Dijon mustard

1 tablespoon pure floral honey

freshly ground pepper

150 g peppered smoked fish fillet such as mackerel or haddock, skinned and flaked into large pieces

3 spring onions, thinly sliced on the diagonal

2 $^3/_4$ cups (85 g) watercress

1 large, firm pear, preferably red-skinned, cored and thickly sliced

Each serving provides
759 kJ, 181 kcal, 12 g protein, 7 g fat
(1 g saturated fat), 18 g carbohydrate
(8 g sugars), 5 g fibre

1   Put the lentils into a saucepan, cover with cold water and bring to the boil. Reduce the heat and simmer for 15–20 minutes or until they are tender but slightly firm to the bite.

2   Meanwhile, make the dressing. Put the olive oil, lime zest and juice, mustard and honey in a mixing bowl, and add some pepper to taste. Whisk together well.

3   Drain the lentils and tip into the mixing bowl. Toss to coat with the dressing, then fold in the flakes of smoked fish and the spring onions.

4   Arrange the watercress and pear slices on 6 serving plates. Spoon the lentil and mackerel mixture on top and serve immediately.

ANOTHER IDEA

● To make a smoked trout and green lentil salad with raspberry vinaigrette, replace the puy lentils with large brown lentils, cooking them for 20–30 minutes. In the dressing, replace the lime zest and juice with 2 tablespoons raspberry vinegar. Fold in large flakes of smoked trout. Spoon the lentil mixture onto a bed of 2 $^3/_4$ cups (85 g) watercress tossed with 45 g rocket and garnish with $^1/_2$ cup (60 g) raspberries.

HEALTHY EATING

● Like all pulses, lentils are a GI 'superfood': they provide hunger-satisfying protein, soluble fibre and low-GI carbohydrate. Although lentils contain iron, the absorption of this mineral from them is normally poor. Adding ingredients rich in vitamin C, such as limes and watercress, improves the absorption of iron.

Gruyère and ham salad

PREPARATION and COOKING: 25 minutes   SERVES 4

200 g fine green beans

3 tablespoons canola (rapeseed) oil

grated zest and juice of 1 lemon

1 tablespoon dried green peppercorns, crushed

2 teaspoons pure floral honey

115 g gruyère, any rind removed

85 g thickly sliced lean smoked ham, trimmed of fat

125 g cherry tomatoes, halved

2^1/$_2$ cups (225 g) sliced baby button mushrooms

2^3/$_4$ cups (85 g) watercress

1 cup (45 g) baby spinach leaves

1 cup (45 g) rocket

2 tablespoons snipped fresh chives

Each serving provides
1344 kJ, 321 kcal, 17 g protein, 24 g fat
(7 g saturated fat), 8 g carbohydrate
(5 g sugars), 5 g fibre

1 Trim the beans then cook in a saucepan of boiling water for 4 minutes or until just tender. Drain and refresh under cold running water.

2 To make the dressing, place the oil, lemon zest and juice, peppercorns and honey in a screw-top jar. Put the lid on and shake well to mix.

3 Cut the cheese and ham into strips about 5 x 2 cm. Place in a large salad bowl and add the beans, tomatoes, mushrooms, watercress, spinach and rocket. Toss together to combine evenly.

4 Just before serving, shake the dressing again and sprinkle it over the salad. Toss well, scatter over the chives and serve.

COOK'S TIP
● You can use edam or gouda in place of gruyère.

SOME MORE IDEAS
● If you prefer, omit the ham and increase the cheese to 150 g.
● Peaches work well with gruyère, and could be added in thick slices to the salad in place of the tomatoes.

HEALTHY EATING

● As well as protein and calcium, cheese is a good source of zinc.

● The combination of green beans, tomatoes, watercress and salad leaves ensures a good intake of beta-carotene, B vitamins and vitamin C.

● Ham is a good source of protein as well as thiamin.

Fetta and couscous salad

PREPARATION and COOKING: 30-35 minutes   SERVES 4

1 Put the couscous into a large bowl and pour over the hot stock. Set aside to soak for 15-20 minutes or until all the liquid has been absorbed.

2 Meanwhile, steam the asparagus for 3 minutes. Add the zucchini and continue steaming for 2 minutes or until the vegetables are just tender but still retain some crunch. Tip the vegetables into a colander and refresh under cold running water. Drain well.

3 Combine the olive oil, lemon zest and juice, garlic, chillies and seasoning to taste in a screw-top jar. Shake to blend.

4 Fluff up the couscous with a fork, then fold in the capsicum strips, almonds, mint, and steamed asparagus and zucchini. Pour over the dressing and stir gently. Crumble the fetta over the top and serve.

SOME MORE IDEAS

● If you can get yellow zucchini (courgettes), use 1 yellow and 1 green for even more colour.

● Try using other herbs such as chopped fresh coriander.

1¼ cups (230 g) instant couscous

300 ml hot salt-reduced vegetable stock

9 young asparagus spears, about 170 g, halved

2 zucchini (courgettes), cut into thin sticks

3 tablespoons extra virgin olive oil

grated zest of 1 lemon

1 tablespoon lemon juice

1 garlic clove, finely chopped

½ teaspoon crushed dried chillies

freshly ground pepper

1 red capsicum (pepper), seeded and cut into thin strips

⅓ cup (30 g) toasted flaked almonds

handful of fresh mint leaves, finely chopped

170 g fetta

FOR LOWER GI

Instead of the couscous, use burghul (bulgur) wheat, which needs to be simmered for 10 minutes and drained.

Each serving provides
1612 kJ, 385 kcal, 14 g protein, 28 g fat (9 g saturated fat), 20 g carbohydrate (4 g sugars), 3 g fibre

HEALTHY EATING

● Couscous is a miniature pasta made from semolina and is low in fat. The instant variety has a moderate GI score.

SALADS

SALADS

HEALTHY EATING

● Wholewheat grains are the entire grain of the wheat plant,
minus the hull. Because the whole of the grain is eaten, they are
a good source of dietary fibre and have a low GI. They are an
excellent source of B vitamins and beta-carotene as well as the
essential minerals iron, selenium and zinc.

● Canola oil contains a large proportion of monounsaturated
and polyunsaturated fats – the 'good' fats. It also contains large
amounts of vitamin E.

Corn and wholewheat salad

GI estimate LOW

Grains of wholewheat have a distinctive sweet, nutty flavour. Here they are mixed with grilled corn, toasted walnuts and crisp vegetables in a fragrant dressing to make a nutritious salad that is substantial enough to serve as a well-balanced main course.

PREPARATION and COOKING: 35 minutes, plus cooling   SERVES 4

1 Put 900 ml water in a saucepan and bring to the boil. Add the wholewheat grains and the bay leaf. Simmer for about 15-20 minutes or until the wholewheat is tender and all the liquid has been absorbed. (While the wholewheat grains are cooking, preheat the grill to moderately high.) Discard the bay leaf and tip the wholewheat grains into a mixing bowl.

2 Brush the corn cobs all over with $1/2$ tablespoon of canola oil, then put them on the preheated grill rack. Grill for about 10 minutes, turning frequently, until tender and lightly charred in places. Set aside.

3 Meanwhile, lightly toast the walnut pieces in a small frying pan, stirring them frequently until fragrant. Leave to cool.

4 When the corn is cool enough to handle, cut the kernels off the cobs with a sharp knife. Add them to the wholewheat grains in the mixing bowl.

5 To make the dressing, whisk together the mustard, orange zest and juice, the rest of the canola oil and the walnut oil. Season to taste. Drizzle the dressing over the warm wholewheat grains and corn, and toss well to mix. Leave to cool completely.

6 Add the capsicum, mushrooms, cucumber, mint and toasted walnuts to the wholewheat mixture and toss gently together. Taste and add more seasoning, if needed. Serve at room temperature, garnished with slices of hard-boiled egg and sprigs of fresh mint.

COOK'S TIP

● Wholewheat grains (or wheat berries) are available from health food shops. They need pre-soaking and take up to 2 hours to cook, so for a quicker alternative use pearl barley instead (which needs to be simmered in boiling water for 30-40 minutes).

300 g pre-cooked wholewheat grains (wheat berries)

1 bay leaf

2 corn (sweetcorn) cobs

$1^1/2$ tablespoons canola (rapeseed) oil

$2/3$ cup (85 g) walnut pieces

1 teaspoon Dijon mustard

$1/2$ teaspoon finely grated orange zest

1 tablespoon orange juice

1 tablespoon walnut oil

freshly ground pepper

1 red capsicum (pepper), seeded and diced

$1^1/4$ cups (115 g) sliced button mushrooms

$1/2$ cucumber, cut into small chunks

1 tablespoon chopped fresh mint

1 egg, hard-boiled to garnish

sprigs of fresh mint to garnish

Each serving provides
1854 kJ, 443 kcal, 11 g protein, 29 g fat (2 g saturated fat), 38 g carbohydrate (4 g sugars), 8 g fibre

Burghul wheat and prawn salad

PREPARATION and COOKING: 20-25 minutes   SERVES 4

250 g burghul (bulgur) wheat

1 small red onion, very thinly sliced

1 carrot, coarsely grated

1 tomato, diced

6 baby corn (sweetcorn), sliced into rounds

1/2 cucumber, diced

200 g cooked prawns, peeled (thawed if frozen)

4 tablespoons extra virgin olive oil

2 tablespoons lime juice

1 garlic clove, crushed

1/4 teaspoon crushed dried chillies

freshly ground pepper

Each serving provides
1766 kJ, 423 kcal, 19 g protein, 20 g fat
(3 g saturated fat), 41 g carbohydrate
(3 g sugars), 12 g fibre

HEALTHY EATING

● Burghul is coarsely ground wheat grains that have been parboiled, so it's quick and easy to prepare. It is a good source of low-GI carbohydrate, dietary fibre, iron, magnesium and many of the B vitamins.

● Prawns are a good source of protein. Like all seafood, they contain iodine, which is needed for the healthy functioning of the thyroid gland.

● The inclusion of raw vegetables in this salad adds texture, colour and vitamins. The vegetables also help the dish to have a low GI.

1 Put the burghul wheat in a saucepan and pour over 650 ml water. Bring to the boil, then simmer for 10 minutes or until the grain is tender and all the water has been absorbed. Tip into a flat dish, spread out and allow to cool slightly.

2 Combine the onion, carrot, tomato, corn, cucumber and prawns in a large salad bowl. Stir in the burghul wheat.

3 For the dressing, put the olive oil, lime juice, garlic, chillies and seasoning to taste in a small bowl. Whisk with a fork until combined. Stir the dressing into the salad, tossing to coat all the ingredients evenly. If not serving the salad immediately, cover and keep in the refrigerator.

COOK'S TIP
● If you can't find fresh baby corn, use canned.

ANOTHER IDEA
● For a burghul wheat and fetta salad, replace the prawns with 200 g diced fetta.

Minted barley and beans

GI estimate LOW

PREPARATION and COOKING: 1¹/₂ hours   SERVES 4

1. Put the stock in a saucepan with the lemon zest and bay leaf. Bring to a rapid boil, then add the leeks and cook for 2-3 minutes or until just tender. Remove, drain and refresh briefly in cold water. Cut on the diagonal into 2.5 cm lengths. Set aside.

2. Add the oil to the stock in the pan and bring back to the boil. Add the pearl barley, then cover and simmer for about 30-40 minutes or until tender. Spoon out 2 tablespoons of the stock and reserve, then drain the barley. Discard the lemon zest and bay leaf. Tip the barley into a bowl and leave to cool.

3. Add the leeks, canned beans, tomato wedges, spinach and spring onions to the barley and stir gently to mix together.

4. To make the dressing, put the sun-dried tomatoes, oil, vinegar, garlic, mint, chervil, reserved stock and seasoning to taste into a screwtop jar. Shake well until combined.

5. Drizzle the dressing over the barley and vegetables and toss to coat thoroughly. Serve at room temperature, garnished with a sprig of fresh mint.

1.4 litres salt-reduced vegetable stock
strip of lemon zest
1 bay leaf
225 g baby leeks
1 teaspoon canola (rapeseed) oil
1 cup (220 g) pearl barley
1 can black-eyed or cannellini beans, about 400 g, drained and rinsed
6 firm, ripe roma (plum) tomatoes, 500 g in total, cut into thin wedges
140 g baby spinach leaves, shredded
1 bunch spring onions, about 85 g, halved lengthwise and shredded
2 sun-dried tomatoes packed in oil, drained and finely chopped
2 tablespoons oil from the sun-dried tomatoes
1 tablespoon red wine vinegar
1 garlic clove, crushed
2 tablespoons chopped fresh mint
1 tablespoon chopped fresh chervil
freshly ground pepper
sprig of fresh mint to garnish

Each serving provides
1789 kJ, 427 kcal, 17 g protein, 13 g fat
(2 g saturated fat), 68 g carbohydrate
(14 g sugars), 19 g fibre

HEALTHY EATING

● Both barley and beans are GI 'superfoods': they are rich in the kind of carbohydrate that is broken down slowly. They also provide B vitamins and protein.

SALADS

197

Buckwheat and seafood salad

GI estimate LOW

Buckwheat grain is an unusual base for a main dish salad and makes a pleasant change from rice and pasta. Heaps of fresh raw vegetables add colour, flavour and valuable nutrients.

PREPARATION and COOKING: 1¹/2 hours   SERVES 4

3 cups (750 ml) salt-reduced chicken stock

1¹/4 cups (230 g) plain buckwheat kernels

2 tablespoons extra virgin olive oil

1 tablespoon white wine vinegar

1 teaspoon Dijon mustard

2 tablespoons chopped mixed fresh herbs

freshly ground pepper

1 tablespoon canola (rapeseed) oil

400 g mixed seafood or marinara mix, thawed if frozen

1 cucumber, diced

200 g snow peas (mangetout), sliced

1 bulb of fennel, about 250 g, halved and thinly sliced

115 g radishes, thinly sliced

1 sheet nori seaweed to garnish

Each serving provides
2202 kJ, 526 kcal, 37 g protein, 18 g fat
(3 g saturated fat), 51 g carbohydrate
(9 g sugars), 5 g fibre

1 Bring the stock to the boil in a saucepan, then stir in the buckwheat kernels. Bring back to the boil. Reduce the heat, cover and cook over a low heat for 10-15 minutes or until the stock has been absorbed and the grain is tender. Remove from the heat and set aside, still covered.

2 Meanwhile, make the dressing. Put the olive oil, vinegar, mustard and herbs in a bowl and whisk together until thoroughly mixed. Season to taste.

3 Heat 1 tablespoon canola oil in a wok or large frying pan. Add the seafood and stir-fry over a moderate heat for 2-3 minutes or until hot. Add the hot seafood to the buckwheat, together with the cucumber, snow peas, fennel and radishes. Drizzle over the dressing and toss gently.

4 Toast the sheet of seaweed by passing it over the flame of a gas burner, once on each side of the sheet, until it darkens and becomes crisp. Alternatively, use a chef's blowtorch to toast the seaweed. Snip into fine strips with scissors, sprinkle over the salad and serve.

COOK'S TIP
● You may be able to buy toasted buckwheat kernels, known as 'kasha', in a health food shop. These can be used in the same way as the plain kernels to give a nuttier flavour.

ANOTHER IDEA
● Instead of mixed seafood, use 400 g skinless, boneless chicken or turkey breasts (fillets), or lean beef or lamb, cut into thin strips. Stir-fry until cooked and lightly browned, then toss with the dressed buckwheat and vegetables.

HEALTHY EATING

● Despite its name, buckwheat is not a true grain, but a plant that produces cereal-like seeds. It is gluten-free, so it is suitable for anyone with gluten intolerance. It also has a low GI and so is a good substitute for rice. It contains useful amounts of B vitamins, zinc and iron.

● Snow peas provide hunger-satisfying protein and low-GI carbohydrate. They are a good source of vitamin C and contain more fibre than ordinary peas due to the edible pod.

Marinated duck with buckwheat

GI estimate LOW

PREPARATION and COOKING: 50 minutes   SERVES 4

450 g boneless duck breasts

2 garlic cloves, chopped

juice of 1 lemon

12 sprigs fresh thyme

1 tablespoon chopped fresh rosemary

3 tablespoons olive oil

1¼ cups (230 g) plain buckwheat kernels

3 cups (750 ml) salt-reduced chicken stock

125 g fine green beans

200 g mixed salad leaves

5 sprigs fresh basil, finely shredded

½ red onion, thinly sliced

8 green olives, pitted

8 black olives, pitted

2 medium-sized zucchini (courgettes), thinly sliced lengthwise

12 small spring onions

12 cherry tomatoes

1½ tablespoons red wine vinegar, or a mix of sherry and balsamic vinegars

freshly ground pepper

Each serving provides
2402 kJ, 574 kcal, 34 g protein, 25 g fat
(5 g saturated fat), 54 g carbohydrate
(9 g sugars), 7 g fibre

1 Remove all the fat and skin from the duck breasts. With a sharp knife, score the flesh on both sides in a criss-cross pattern. Put the breasts in a bowl and add about two-thirds of the garlic, the lemon juice, half of the thyme sprigs, the rosemary and 1 tablespoon of the olive oil. Leave to marinate while you prepare the rest of the ingredients.

2 Toast the buckwheat kernels in a heavy frying pan over a moderate heat, stirring and tossing, for 4-5 minutes or until they are darker in colour. Remove from the heat.

3 Bring the stock to the boil in a saucepan, then stir in the toasted kernels. Bring back to the boil. Reduce the heat, cover and cook over a low heat for 10-15 minutes or until the stock has been absorbed and the grain is tender. Remove from the heat and set aside, still covered.

4 Heat a ridged cast-iron grill pan for 10 minutes. Meanwhile, drop the green beans into a saucepan of boiling water and blanch for 1-2 minutes. Drain and refresh under cold running water. Cut the beans in half and put into a salad bowl. Add the salad leaves, basil, onion and olives, and toss to mix.

5 Remove the duck breasts from the marinade and place on the hot grill pan. Cook for 3 minutes, then turn the breasts over and cook for a further 3 minutes (the meat will be rare, so cook longer if you prefer it well done). Remove the duck to a board. Place the zucchini, whole spring onions and whole tomatoes on the grill pan and cook for 1-2 minutes or until lightly charred all over.

6 Combine the remaining garlic and 2 tablespoons oil with the vinegar in a small bowl and add the leaves from the remaining thyme sprigs. Whisk together, then drizzle over the salad. Spoon on the buckwheat kernels, and arrange the hot griddled zucchini, spring onions and tomatoes on top. Season with a little pepper to taste. Slice the duck breasts, place over the vegetables and serve.

COOK'S TIP

● You may be able to buy toasted buckwheat kernels, known as 'kasha', in a health food shop. If so, omit step 2.

Chinese-style broccoli salad

GI estimate LOW

PREPARATION and COOKING: about 25 minutes   SERVES 4

1 Toast the buckwheat kernels in a heavy frying pan over a moderate heat, stirring and tossing, for 4-5 minutes or until they are slightly darker in colour. Remove from the heat.

2 Drop the broccoli florets, snow peas and baby corn into a saucepan of boiling water and blanch for about 2 minutes or until the vegetables are slightly softened, but still crisp. Drain and refresh under cold running water.

3 Place the blanched vegetables in a salad bowl together with the spring onions, capsicum, bok choy and bean sprouts.

4 Whisk all the dressing ingredients together and add to the salad, tossing well. Serve immediately, with the toasted buckwheat sprinkled over the top.

HEALTHY EATING

● Peanuts have a low GI, but are high in fat, so you should limit your portions. Shop for the healthier types of peanut butter – without added sugar or palm oil. Peanuts are composed mainly of monounsaturated fats, but palm oil, which is often added to bulk out the product, contains unhealthy saturated fats. Make your own peanut butter by whizzing roasted unsalted peanuts in a food processor for 5 minutes.

2 tablespoons plain buckwheat kernels

300 g small broccoli florets

200 g snow peas (mangetout)

125 g baby corn (sweetcorn), halved lengthwise

1 bunch of spring onions, shredded

1 red capsicum (pepper), seeded and diced

100 g young, tender bok choy leaves

85 g bean sprouts

SALAD DRESSING

4 tablespoons crunchy peanut butter

5 tablespoons warm water

juice of 1 lemon

2 tablespoons salt-reduced soy sauce

$1/4$ teaspoon caster sugar

1 teaspoon finely grated fresh root ginger

Each serving provides
1067 kJ, 255 kcal, 14 g protein, 14 g fat (2 g saturated fat), 17 g carbohydrate (7 g sugars), 7 g fibre

SALADS

Lamb and wholewheat salad

GI estimate LOW

Wholewheat has a deliciously chewy texture and nutty flavour, similar to brown rice. It makes an excellent base for this highly nutritious salad of quickly grilled lamb steak, sprouted mung beans, tomatoes and black olives in a vinaigrette dressing.

PREPARATION and COOKING: about 1¹/₂ hours, plus 3 hours soaking   SERVES 4

1 Put the wholewheat grains in a bowl, cover with cold water and leave to soak for 3 hours. Drain and rinse the wholewheat, then put into a saucepan with 1 garlic clove and enough water to cover. Bring to the boil, then reduce the heat and simmer for about 1 hour or until tender. Drain thoroughly and leave to cool. Discard the garlic.

2 Preheat the grill to moderate. Place the lamb steaks on the grill rack. Crush the remaining garlic clove and mix with the olive oil and a little pepper. Brush the garlic-flavoured oil over the lamb, then grill for 4 minutes on each side or until cooked but still slightly pink in the centre. Remove from the heat and leave to rest on a carving board for 10 minutes.

3 Meanwhile, mix together the sprouted mung beans, tomatoes, celery, rocket and olives in a salad bowl. In a small bowl, make a vinaigrette by whisking together 120 ml extra virgin olive oil, 2 tablespoons red wine vinegar, 1 teaspoon Dijon mustard, a pinch of sugar and seasoning to taste. Add 5 tablespoons of the vinaigrette to the salad with the wholewheat. Toss well together. Carve the lamb into thick slices and arrange on top. Serve at once.

180 g wholewheat grains (wheat berries)
2 garlic cloves, peeled
400 g lean lamb leg steaks, trimmed of visible fat
1 tablespoon olive oil
250 g sprouted mung beans, rinsed and drained
170 g cherry tomatoes, halved
2 celery sticks, thinly sliced
1 cup (45 g) rocket
¹/₂ cup (80 g) black olives, preferably Kalamata, pitted
freshly ground pepper

Each serving provides
2085 kJ, 498 kcal, 26 g protein, 27 g fat (9 g saturated fat), 40 g carbohydrate (2 g sugars), 9 g fibre

COOK'S TIP

● Wholewheat grains (or wheat berries) are available from health food shops. They need pre-soaking and take up to 2 hours to cook, so for a quicker alternative use burghul (bulgur) wheat (which needs to be simmered in twice the volume of boiling water for 15 minutes) or boiled wild brown rice.

ANOTHER IDEA

● For a vegetarian wholewheat salad, replace the lamb in step 2 with 300 g firm tofu, cut into large cubes. Grill until golden and add to the salad with 100 g fetta cubes.

HEALTHY EATING

● Wholewheat grains are the entire grain of the wheat plant, minus the hull. Because the whole of the grain is eaten, they are a good source of dietary fibre and have a low GI.

● Lamb is rich source of protein as well as vitamins B12 and thiamin.

● Sprouted beans are a good source of vitamin C and folate.

SALADS

203

Sweet and spicy lentil salad

PREPARATION and COOKING: about 50 minutes   SERVES 4

1¹/₃ cup (245 g) brown/green lentils, rinsed

1 garlic clove, peeled

good pinch of ground cumin

1 slice of lemon

juice of 1 lemon

3 tablespoons extra virgin olive oil

2 tablespoons finely chopped fresh coriander

freshly ground pepper

1 small red onion, finely chopped

¹/₂ cup (90 g) dried apricots, roughly chopped

1 red, 1 yellow and 1 green capsicum (pepper), seeded and cut into 2 cm squares

100 g broccoli, broken into small florets

50 g firm rindless goat's cheese

2 tablespoons toasted sunflower seeds

Each serving provides
1733 kJ, 414 kcal, 22 g protein, 21 g fat
(4 g saturated fat), 37 g carbohydrate
(14 g sugars), 13 g fibre

1   Put the lentils in a large saucepan, cover with water and bring to the boil, skimming off any scum. Flatten the garlic clove with the side of a knife and add to the lentils with the cumin and lemon slice. Reduce the heat and simmer for about 30 minutes or until the lentils are tender.

2   Meanwhile, to make the dressing, put the lemon juice, olive oil, coriander and seasoning to taste into a large salad bowl, and whisk together.

3   Drain the lentils, discarding the lemon and garlic, and add them to the salad bowl. Toss gently to mix with the dressing.

4   Add the onion, apricots, capsicums and broccoli florets, and mix gently. Roughly dice the goat's cheese and scatter with the sunflower seeds over the salad. Serve immediately.

ANOTHER IDEA

● Use 150 g frozen broad beans instead of broccoli florets. Cook the beans in boiling water for 5 minutes or until tender. Drain, then refresh under cold running water.

HEALTHY EATING

● Like all pulses, lentils are GI 'superfood': they provide hunger-satisfying protein, soluble fibre and low-GI carbohydrate. They also contain B vitamins.

● Dried apricots are an excellent source of beta-carotene and fibre.

● Sunflower seeds are rich in healthy polyunsaturated fats.

Avocado and prawn cups

GI estimate LOW–MED

PREPARATION and COOKING: 25 minutes, plus cooling   SERVES 4

1 Cook the potatoes in a saucepan of boiling water for about 8 minutes or until just tender. Drain and refresh under cold running water. Dry in a clean tea towel.

2 Heat the oil in a frying pan, add the onion and fry for 5 minutes or until softened and lightly browned. Add the garlic, chilli and crushed coriander and cumin seeds, and cook for a further minute, stirring. Stir in the potatoes and fry over a high heat for 3 minutes. Remove from the heat and leave to cool.

3 Peel the avocado, remove the stone and cut the flesh into cubes. Toss with the lime juice then add to the potatoes together with the prawns. Season to taste and toss gently.

4 Mix together the yogurt, fresh coriander and seasoning to taste. Arrange 2 lettuce leaves in each of 4 bowls. Spoon the salad into them and top with the coriander yogurt.

ANOTHER IDEA

● For an avocado, potato and tofu salad, replace the prawns with 250 g plain tofu, drained and cubed. Add the tofu with the garlic and spices in step 2.

600 g new potatoes, scrubbed and diced

2 tablespoons canola (rapeseed) oil

1 small red onion, thinly sliced

1 garlic clove, crushed

1 mild red chilli, seeded and finely chopped

1 teaspoon coriander seeds, roughly crushed

1 teaspoon cumin seeds, roughly crushed

1 large avocado

juice of 2 limes

400 g cooked prawns, peeled (thawed if frozen)

freshly ground pepper

6 tablespoons low-fat natural yogurt

3 tablespoons chopped fresh coriander

8 round or iceberg lettuce leaves

Each serving provides
1844 kJ, 441 kcal, 29 g protein, 25 g fat
(4 g saturated fat), 26 g carbohydrate
(4 g sugars), 4 g fibre

HEALTHY EATING

● Substances in avocados stimulate the production of collagen, which is why they have a reputation for being good for the skin. Avocados are rich in heart-healthy monounsaturated fats as well as vitamin E.

● All types of yogurt provide calcium as well as phosphorus, riboflavin and vitamin B12.

SALADS

HEALTHY EATING

● Fresh sardines are an excellent source of healthy protein as well as heart-healthy omega-3 fats.

● The lemon juice used in the 'souse', or marinade, helps to lower the GI of this dish.

● As soon as vegetables are cut, their vitamin content starts to diminish, so if possible they should be prepared just before serving, as is done for this salad.

Soused fresh sardine salad

Cooking fish and then submerging it in a spicy 'souse' is a tasty way to prepare it, and was once a means of preserving. Here sardines are grilled and marinated, then served on a Moroccan-spiced couscous, chickpea and capsicum salad.

PREPARATION: 25 minutes, plus at least 30 minutes marinating   SERVES 4

1   Preheat the grill to high. To make the marinade, put the lemon zest and juice in a bowl and whisk in the oil. Stir in the chilli, shallot, peppercorns and bay leaf.

2   Line the grill rack with foil and lightly brush with marinade. Tuck 2 lemon slice halves in each sardine cavity, then arrange the sardines on the foil. Brush with more marinade and grill for 2 minutes.

3   Carefully turn the sardines over, lightly brush with marinade again and grill for a further 2–3 minutes or until the skins are slightly crisp and the flesh flakes easily. Immediately transfer the sardines to a baking dish, arranging them in one layer, and pour over the marinade, including any remaining in the grill pan. Roll each sardine over so it is well coated. Leave to cool, then cover and chill for at least 30 minutes.

4   Meanwhile, put the couscous in a bowl and stir in the coriander, turmeric and cayenne pepper. Pour over 600 ml boiling water and stir, then set aside and allow to cool.

5   About 15 minutes before serving, remove the sardines from the refrigerator. Add the chickpeas, spring onions, capsicums and zucchini to the couscous. Stir to mix and fluff up the grains.

6   Divide the spinach leaves among 4 plates and spoon on the couscous. Remove the sardines from the marinade and place 2 fish on each plate. Sprinkle with the parsley and some pepper and serve immediately.

finely grated zest of 1 large lemon

4 tablespoons lemon juice

1 tablespoon garlic-flavoured olive oil

1 red or green chilli, seeded and finely chopped

1 French shallot, finely chopped

6 black peppercorns, lightly cracked

1 bay leaf

8 fresh sardines, cleaned, scaled and heads removed

1 small lemon, cut into 8 thin slices and each slice halved

1$^1/_3$ cups (245 g) instant couscous

1$^1/_2$ teaspoons ground coriander

1 teaspoon turmeric

pinch of cayenne pepper

1 can chickpeas, about 410 g, drained and rinsed

4 spring onions, finely chopped

1 red and 1 yellow capsicum (pepper), seeded and finely diced

1 large zucchini (courgette), grated

140 g baby spinach leaves

fresh flat-leaf parsley to garnish

freshly ground pepper

Each serving provides
1776 kJ, 424 kcal, 33 g protein, 17 g fat (3 g saturated fat), 29 g carbohydrate (5 g sugars), 6 g fibre

Snow pea, grape and fetta salad

GI estimate LOW

Snow peas work well with baby spinach leaves and a little peppery rocket to provide the salad base for tangy fetta and sweet black grapes. Serve this quick lunch dish with thick slices of grainy, low-GI bread or wholemeal pita bread.

PREPARATION and COOKING: about 20 minutes   SERVES 4

grated zest and juice of $1/2$ lemon
$1/2$ teaspoon caster sugar
$1/2$ teaspoon Dijon mustard
freshly ground pepper
1 tablespoon extra virgin olive oil
300 g snow peas (mangetout)
200 g seedless black grapes, halved
200 g fetta, cut into thin strips
45 g rocket, shredded
170 g baby spinach leaves

Each serving provides
1045 kJ, 250 kcal, 13 g protein, 17 g fat
(8 g saturated fat), 13 g carbohydrate
(11 g sugars), 3 g fibre

1   Place the lemon zest and juice in a large salad bowl. Add the sugar and mustard with seasoning to taste. Whisk the ingredients together until the sugar has dissolved in the lemon juice. Whisk in the olive oil.

2   Cut the snow peas across in half. Bring a large pan of water to the boil, add the snow peas and bring back to the boil. Immediately drain the snow peas and refresh under cold running water. Add them to the salad bowl, and turn and fold to coat them with the dressing.

3   Add the grapes, fetta, rocket and spinach to the bowl. Mix the salad gently but well, so that all the ingredients are coated with dressing. Serve at once.

SOME MORE IDEAS

● Instead of rocket, add 6 chopped spring onions.

● For a garlicky dressing, add 1 finely chopped garlic clove with the sugar and mustard.

● Add extra crunch by sprinkling the salad with 2 tablespoons toasted pine nuts just before serving.

● Make a pear, grape and spinach salad with blue cheese dressing. For the dressing, crumble or chop 50 g blue cheese and place it in the salad bowl, then stir in 1 tablespoon cider vinegar and 2 tablespoons extra virgin olive oil. Halve and core 2 ripe but firm pears, then cut them across into slices. Add the pear slices to the blue cheese dressing as they are prepared. Add the halved black grapes and mix well, then add 45 g watercress, 200 g baby spinach leaves and 2 tablespoons chopped walnuts. Toss together gently and serve immediately.

HEALTHY EATING

● Snow peas contain low-GI carbohydrate. As they are eaten pods and all, they provide plenty of dietary fibre. They have a deliciously sweet taste and tender texture, and are a good source of vitamin C.

● Fetta is high in fat and salt, but because its flavour is strong a little can go a long way in a salad. As with other cheeses, it is a good source of protein, calcium and phosphorus, and provides useful amounts of B vitamins and vitamin E.

SALADS

Crab and avocado salad

PREPARATION and COOKING: 40 minutes, plus cooling   SERVES 4

200 g burghul (bulgur) wheat

1 tablespoon extra virgin olive oil

3 tablespoons lemon juice

3 tablespoons chopped fresh flat-leaf
    parsley

1 tablespoon snipped fresh chives

2 medium-sized tomatoes, diced

freshly ground pepper

340 g fresh white crab meat

2 avocados

2 sweet green apples

2 cups (150 g) bean sprouts

3 tablespoons low-fat mayonnaise

3 tablespoons low-fat natural yogurt

1 tablespoon lemon juice

small pinch of cayenne pepper

small leaves taken from the hearts of
    2 lettuces, such as cos or iceberg

1/2 cup (50 g) walnut halves, toasted
    and roughly chopped

Each serving provides
2650 kJ, 633 kcal, 28 g protein, 37 g fat
(6 g saturated fat), 46 g carbohydrate
(16 g sugars), 16 g fibre

HEALTHY EATING

● Like other low-fat dairy products,
yogurt is a GI 'superfood', providing
protein with a low GI score. It also
contains calcium, which is needed
for healthy bones and the healthy
functioning of muscles and nerves.

● Walnuts have a high fat content,
but this is mostly in the form of
'good' polyunsaturated fats.

1 Put the burghul wheat in a large saucepan with 1.3 litres cold water. Bring to the boil over a high heat, then reduce the heat and simmer for 10–15 minutes or until the grains are just tender. Drain in a large sieve, pressing down well to squeeze out all the excess water. Leave to cool.

2 Combine the olive oil, lemon juice, parsley, chives and diced tomatoes in a large mixing bowl. Add the burghul wheat and mix thoroughly, then season to taste. Leave to stand at room temperature.

3 Pick over and flake the crab meat, discarding any fragments of shell. Halve, stone and peel the avocados, then chop the flesh. Add to the crab. Quarter and core the apples, then thinly slice them. Add to the crab with the bean sprouts.

4 Mix the mayonnaise with the yogurt until smooth. Add the lemon juice and cayenne pepper. Spoon onto the crab mixture and toss very gently until just combined.

5 Pile the burghul salad onto a serving platter and arrange the lettuce leaves on top. Spoon the crab salad onto the leaves and scatter over the walnuts. Serve immediately.

Fennel, apple and trout salad

PREPARATION and COOKING: 45 minutes   SERVES 4

1 Rinse the fish. Pour the cider and stock into a large saucepan and add the shallots and bay leaf. Cover and simmer for 10 minutes. Add the fish and continue simmering for 8 minutes or until the flesh looks opaque. Remove the trout and set aside to cool. Strain the cooking liquid and reserve 270 ml.

2 Put the couscous in a bowl and pour over the reserved fish cooking liquid. Cover and leave to soak for about 10 minutes or until the couscous has absorbed all the liquid. Add the mint, parsley and 1 tablespoon of lemon juice, and fluff up the grains with a fork.

3 To make the dressing, in a small bowl stir together the rest of the lemon juice, mustard, mayonnaise and yogurt until smooth, then stir in the dill. Quarter, core and dice the apple. Put the apple, cucumber, fennel, spring onions and hazelnuts into a bowl and stir in half of the dressing. Season to taste.

4 Remove the skin from the fish and carefully take the fillets off the backbone. Use tweezers, if necessary, to remove any remaining bones. Flake the flesh into large pieces and mix gently with the remaining dressing.

5 Pile the couscous onto individual plates and arrange the apple salad and fish on top. Garnish with dill sprigs or fennel fronds and serve.

2 trout, about 500 g in total, cleaned and heads removed
120 ml dry cider
360 ml salt-reduced vegetable stock
2 French shallots, sliced
1 bay leaf
200 g instant couscous
2 tablespoons chopped fresh mint
3 tablespoons chopped parsley
2 tablespoons lemon juice
1 tablespoon Dijon mustard
2 tablespoons low-fat mayonnaise
4 tablespoons Greek-style yogurt
2 tablespoons fresh dill, chopped
1 sweet red apple
$1/2$ cucumber, diced
1 small bulb of fennel, diced
3 spring onions, finely chopped
$1/3$ cup (45 g) hazelnuts, toasted and chopped
freshly ground pepper
sprigs of fresh dill or fennel fronds to garnish

Each serving provides
1607 kJ, 384 kcal, 31 g protein, 16 g fat (3 g saturated fat), 27 g carbohydrate (13 g sugars), 4 g fibre

HEALTHY EATING

● Oily fish is a healthy source of protein as well as providing vitamins A and D. It also contains heart-healthy omega-3 fats.

SALADS

211

HEALTHY EATING

● Burghul wheat is a good source of low-GI carbohydrate. Because it retains the particularly nutritious outer layers of the wheat grain, it contains useful amounts of B vitamins, particularly thiamin.

● Goat's cheese is a tasty source of protein and calcium and lower in fat than cheeses such as cheddar and parmesan.

Tabouleh with goat's cheese

GI estimate LOW

This satisfying salad originated in Lebanon. While the burghul wheat is soaking, you have just enough time to chop the vegetables and herbs, and make the dressing. Serve with wholemeal pita bread.

PREPARATION: about 30 minutes   SERVES 4

1 Put the burghul wheat in a mixing bowl, pour over enough boiling water to cover and stir well. Leave to soak for about 15-20 minutes.

2 Meanwhile, make the salad dressing. Whisk together the cumin, garlic and lemon juice in a small bowl, then whisk in the olive oil.

3 Drain the burghul wheat in a sieve, pressing out excess water, then return it to the bowl. Add the capsicum, tomatoes, onion, cucumber, carrot, parsley, coriander and mint, plus the chilli, if using. Pour the dressing over the top and season to taste. Fold gently to mix well.

4 Arrange the lettuce leaves on 4 plates or a serving platter. Pile the burghul salad on the leaves and sprinkle the goat's cheese over the top. Garnish with the radishes and serve.

SOME MORE IDEAS

● Use fetta cheese instead of goat's cheese.

● For an apricot tabouleh side salad, mix the soaked burghul wheat with the yellow capsicum and red onion, plus 4 chopped celery sticks and 115 g chopped dried apricots (omit the other vegetables and the herbs, as well as the goat's cheese). Add 1/2 teaspoon ground cinnamon to the dressing.

● For a spicy tabouleh with chicken to serve 6, replace the goat's cheese with 2 cooked skinless, boneless chicken breasts (fillets), about 280 g in total, cut into cubes. Mix the soaked burghul wheat with the chicken, capsicum, onion, carrot and parsley (omit the other vegetables and herbs). For the dressing, gently warm 3 tablespoons olive oil in a small frying pan with 1 finely chopped garlic clove. Add 1/2-1 teaspoon each of ground cumin, ground coriander, dry mustard and curry powder, and continue cooking for 1 minute. Stir in 2 tablespoons lemon juice and seasoning to taste. Pour the dressing over the salad and stir gently to combine. Garnish with slices of cucumber.

1²/₃ cups (290 g) burghul (bulgur) wheat

1/4 teaspoon ground cumin

1 small garlic clove, very finely chopped

1 tablespoon lemon juice

3 tablespoons extra virgin olive oil

1 yellow capsicum (pepper), seeded and chopped

20 cherry tomatoes, quartered

1 small red onion, finely chopped

10 cm piece of cucumber, seeded and chopped

1 large carrot, grated

5 tablespoons chopped parsley

2 tablespoons chopped coriander

2 tablespoons chopped mint

1 small red chilli, seeded and finely chopped (optional)

freshly ground pepper

200 g rindless, soft goat's cheese, crumbled

lettuce leaves and 12 radishes, sliced, to serve

Each serving provides
2286 kJ, 546 kcal, 20 g protein, 30 g fat
(12 g saturated fat), 49 g carbohydrate
(6 g sugars), 15 g fibre

Cajun-style ham and beans

GI estimate LOW

PREPARATION: about 25 minutes   SERVES 4

160 ml low-fat yogurt

1 tablespoon tomato sauce

15 g fresh coriander, finely chopped

1^1/$_2$ teaspoon Cajun seasoning

hot chilli sauce

freshly ground pepper

2 cans black-eyed or cannellini beans,
    about 400 g each, drained and
    rinsed

350 g corn (sweetcorn) kernels, from
    about 3 cobs, cooked and drained

3 celery sticks, sliced

1 small red onion, chopped

1 green capsicum (pepper), seeded and
    diced

200 g piece of smoked ham, cut into
    1 cm dice

sprigs of fresh coriander to garnish

Each serving provides
1453 kJ, 347 kcal, 30 g protein, 4 g fat
(1 g saturated fat), 62 g carbohydrate
(10 g sugars), 21 g fibre

1 To make the dressing, put the yogurt, tomato sauce,
coriander, Cajun seasoning, 2 shakes of chilli sauce and
seasoning to taste in a large bowl. Whisk together, then
taste and add more chilli sauce, if liked.

2 Add the beans, corn, celery, onion, capsicum and ham to the
bowl, and stir until everything is well mixed. Garnish with
sprigs of coriander and serve at once.

COOK'S TIP

● To save time, use a can of corn (sweetcorn), about 340 g,
drained and rinsed, instead of cooking corn cobs.

HEALTHY EATING

● Like all pulses, canned beans are a GI 'superfood':
they provide hunger-satisfying protein, soluble fibre
and low-GI carbohydrate. They also provide useful
amounts of thiamin.

● Corn offers vitamins A (from beta-carotene), C and
folate as well as dietary fibre. Fresh or frozen corn
retains more vitamins than canned corn, although
canned corn is more convenient.

Chicken liver and raspberry salad

GI estimate LOW

PREPARATION and COOKING: about 20 minutes   SERVES 4

1 Trim the chicken livers, removing any cores and green bits. Cut any large pieces in half. Pat dry with a paper towel and set aside.

2 Arrange the lettuce and spinach leaves on a platter. Sprinkle with the parsley and chives. Set aside.

3 Heat 2 tablespoons of the olive oil in a large non-stick frying pan. Add the shallots and garlic and fry over a low heat for about 3 minutes or until softened, stirring occasionally. Increase the heat to moderate and add the remaining 1 tablespoon of oil to the pan. Add the chicken livers and fry, stirring occasionally, until they are cooked through.

4 Turn the heat to high, add the raspberry vinegar and stir. Season to taste. Pour the hot liver mixture over the salad, scatter on the raspberries and serve at once.

COOK'S TIP
● Red wine vinegar can be used instead of raspberry vinegar.

ANOTHER IDEA
● Instead of raspberries and raspberry vinegar, use fresh blueberries and blueberry vinegar. The flavours work well with chicken livers. Blueberry vinegar is available from speciality food shops and delicatessens.

400 g chicken livers

150 g mixed lettuce leaves, such as lamb's (mâche), cos and red coral

100 g baby spinach leaves

4 tablespoons chopped fresh flat-leaf parsley

4 tablespoons snipped fresh chives

3 tablespoons olive oil

100 g French shallots, finely chopped

1 large garlic clove, crushed

3 tablespoons raspberry vinegar

freshly ground pepper

1 cup (125 g) raspberries

Each serving provides
1106 kJ, 264 kcal, 20 g protein, 18 g fat (3 g saturated fat), 6 g carbohydrate (4 g sugars), 3 g fibre

SALADS

215

HEALTHY EATING

● Buy the meatiest sausages you can as these will be lower in fat. Try a local butcher, who might sell sausages with interesting flavours. Red meat such as lamb and beef provide excellent amounts of iron and B vitamins.

● Like all pulses, puy lentils are a GI 'superfood': they provide hunger-satisfying protein, soluble fibre and low GI carbohydrate. They also provide useful amounts of many B vitamins, particularly thiamin and B6, and iron.

Lentil and sausage salad

GI estimate LOW

French puy lentils have a slightly nutty texture and flavour, and are perfect in salads as they keep their shape well once cooked. Here they are mixed with grilled sausages and Mediterranean vegetables, plus a handful of fresh rocket leaves.

PREPARATION and COOKING: about 1 hour   SERVES 6

1   Preheat the grill. Rinse the lentils and put them in a large saucepan of water. Bring to the boil, then reduce the heat, cover and simmer gently for about 25 minutes or until just tender. Drain, reserving a little of the cooking liquid.

2   While the lentils are cooking, rub the skins of the capsicums and zucchini with a little of the oil. Arrange the vegetables, skin side up, in the grill pan, in one layer. Add the sausages. Grill for 10–15 minutes, turning the sausages occasionally, until they are cooked and browned and the vegetables are tender. Transfer the capsicums to a plastic bag and leave until cool enough to handle, then peel off the skins.

3   Heat the remaining olive oil in a large frying pan and add the onions, celery, garlic and potatoes. Stir-fry for about 10 minutes or until tender.

4   Roughly chop the sausages and the grilled capsicums and zucchini, then add them to the frying pan. Also add the cooked lentils, thyme, parsley, vinegar and mustard. Stir well, and add a little of the lentil cooking water to moisten the mixture slightly. Season to taste.

5   Transfer to a serving bowl and serve warm or cool. Toss in the rocket leaves just before serving.

ANOTHER IDEA

● For a quick version of this salad, replace the dried lentils with 2 cans lentils, about 300 g each, drained and rinsed. Slice the sausages and chop all the vegetables, including the capsicums and zucchini. Stir-fry them all together for 10 minutes or until the sausages are cooked. Add the lentils in step 4.

$1^1/_2$ cups (300 g) French-style green (puy) lentils

2 red capsicums (peppers), halved and seeded

4 zucchini (courgettes), halved lengthwise

3 tablespoons olive oil

450 g high-meat-content beef or lamb sausages

2 small white or red onions, cut into wedges

2 celery sticks, thinly sliced

2 garlic cloves, thinly sliced

300 g new potatoes, scrubbed and cut into small cubes

2 tablespoons chopped fresh thyme

4 tablespoons chopped fresh flat-leaf parsley

2 tablespoons sherry vinegar

1 tablespoon German or Dijon mustard

freshly ground pepper

45 g rocket

Each serving provides
2026 kJ, 484 kcal, 24 g protein, 29 g fat (11 g saturated fat), 31 g carbohydrate (4 g sugars), 12 g fibre

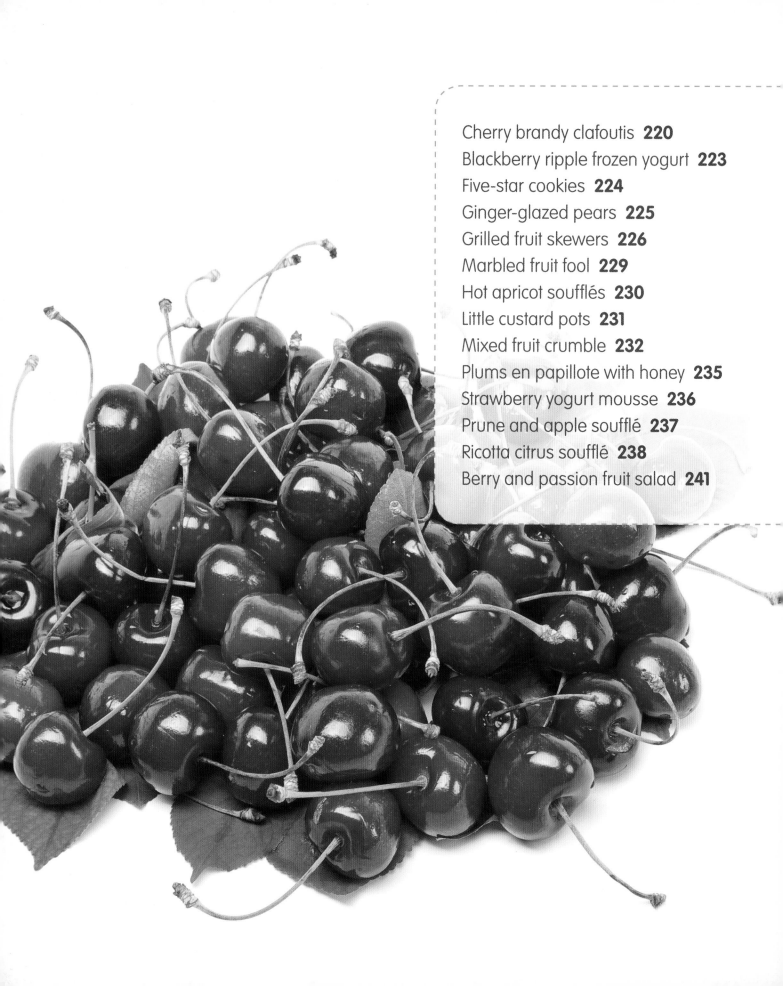

Cherry brandy clafoutis **220**
Blackberry ripple frozen yogurt **223**
Five-star cookies **224**
Ginger-glazed pears **225**
Grilled fruit skewers **226**
Marbled fruit fool **229**
Hot apricot soufflés **230**
Little custard pots **231**
Mixed fruit crumble **232**
Plums en papillote with honey **235**
Strawberry yogurt mousse **236**
Prune and apple soufflé **237**
Ricotta citrus soufflé **238**
Berry and passion fruit salad **241**

Sweet treats

Cherry brandy clafoutis

Clafoutis is a classic French dessert in which fruit is baked in a sweetened batter. Both canned and fresh fruit are suitable, so this is an ideal dessert to make whatever the season. Serve warm from the oven with Greek-style yogurt.

PREPARATION: 10 minutes   COOKING: 20 minutes   SERVES 4

2 cans pitted cherries in fruit juice, about 425 g each
2 tablespoons brandy
1/2 cup (75 g) plain flour
1/4 cup (55 g) light brown sugar
1 cup (250 ml) lite or low-fat milk
3 eggs
1 teaspoon pure vanilla extract
icing sugar to dust (optional)

FOR LOWER GI
Use fresh sweet cherries, pitted, instead of canned cherries.

Each serving provides
1094 kJ, 261 kcal, 11 g protein, 4 g fat
(1 g saturated fat), 41 g carbohydrate
(27 g sugars), 1 g fibre

1 Preheat the oven to 200°C (Gas 6). Drain the cherries, then tip them onto a paper towel and pat dry.

2 Divide the cherries equally among four 300 ml individual flan dishes, or other ovenproof dishes, spreading them in an even layer. Drizzle the brandy over the cherries. Set aside.

3 Sift the flour into a bowl and add the sugar. In a jug, beat the milk and eggs with the vanilla extract, then whisk into the flour mixture to make a smooth batter. Alternatively, combine the ingredients in a food processor and process until smooth.

4 Pour the batter slowly over the fruit. Bake for 20 minutes or until lightly set and pale golden. Dust with icing sugar, if you like, and serve warm.

SOME MORE IDEAS
● Bake in one dish, if you prefer. Use a 25 cm round china flan dish and bake for 20-25 minutes.

● When fresh peaches are in season, replace the canned cherries with 4 ripe but firm peaches, peeled and sliced, and use peach schnapps instead of the brandy. Add 1 teaspoon ground mixed spice to the flour and omit the vanilla extract.

● The tiny black seeds scraped from half a vanilla pod can be used as an alternative to the vanilla extract.

HEALTHY EATING

● Cherries, especially the fresh fruit, have a very low GI. They have a delicious flavour and provide fibre and thiamin.

HEALTHY EATING

● Blackberries are not only an excellent source of vitamin C, they are also one of the richest fruit sources of vitamin E.

● This delicious frozen yogurt is much lower in sugar (and therefore has a lower GI) than most commercial frozen yogurts or ice creams. Using low-fat milk means it is lower in fat and calories, too.

Blackberry ripple frozen yogurt

GI estimate MEDIUM

Most commercial ice creams have a high GI, but here is a recipe that offers a moderate GI and is low in fat and calories too. Creamy Greek-style yogurt, flavoured with a hint of orange and fresh blackberry purée, makes this dish a summertime treat.

PREPARATION and COOKING: about 35 minutes, plus cooling and freezing SERVES 4

1 Warm the milk in a heavy-based saucepan with the orange zest until scalding hot. Meanwhile, put the whole egg, egg yolks, sugar, cornflour and vanilla extract in a mixing bowl, and whisk together until pale and creamy.

2 Stir the milk into the egg mixture, then return to the pan and cook over a low heat, stirring constantly, until thickened. Do not allow the custard to boil. Remove from the heat and set aside to cool.

3 When the custard is cold, beat in the yogurt. Pour the mixture into an ice-cream machine and churn according to the manufacturer's instructions until the mixture is thick and slushy. Alternatively, pour the mixture into a freezerproof container and freeze for 2 hours or until beginning to set around the edges. Tip out into a bowl and whisk well with a balloon whisk or electric mixer to break down the ice crystals, then return the mixture to the container. Freeze for a further 1¹/₂ hours.

4 Meanwhile, make the purée. Put half of the blackberries in a saucepan with 1 tablespoon sugar and 1 tablespoon orange juice. Heat until the berries are soft and juicy, then bring to the boil and boil for 1–2 minutes to reduce slightly. Remove from the heat and cool. Press the blackberries through a nylon sieve to make a smooth purée.

5 If using an ice-cream machine, transfer the frozen yogurt to a rigid plastic container, then lightly stir in the blackberry purée to make a ripple effect. If frozen in a container, tip out into a bowl and whisk well until softened, then swirl in the blackberry purée and return to the container. Freeze for a further 3 hours, or overnight, until firm. (The frozen yogurt can be kept, covered, in the freezer for 3 months.)

6 About 45 minutes before serving, remove the frozen yogurt from the freezer so it can soften a little. Scoop into glasses and decorate with the rest of the berries.

300 ml lite or low-fat milk
finely grated zest of 1 orange
1 large egg
2 large egg yolks
¹/₄ cup (55 g) caster sugar
1 teaspoon cornflour
1 teaspoon pure vanilla extract
1 cup (250 g) Greek-style yogurt
2 cups (260 g) blackberries
1 tablespoon caster sugar
1 tablespoon orange juice

FOR LOWER GI
Use ¹/₄ cup concentrated fruit juice, agave syrup, maple syrup or pure floral honey as a sweetener instead of sugar.

Each serving provides
1139 kJ, 272 kcal, 11 g protein, 10 g fat (5 g saturated fat), 34 g carbohydrate (33 g sugars), 4 g fibre

Five-star cookies

PREPARATION: 20 minutes   COOKING: 10–15 minutes   MAKES 16 cookies

¹/₂ cup (60 g) chopped hazelnuts

¹/₂ cup (60 g) sunflower seeds, chopped

¹/₃ cup (60 g) dried apricots, finely chopped

¹/₃ cup (55 g) finely chopped dates

1 tablespoon light brown sugar

¹/₂ cup (50 g) barley flakes

¹/₂ cup (50 g) self-raising wholemeal flour

¹/₂ teaspoon baking powder

2 tablespoons canola (rapeseed) oil

4 tablespoons apple juice

FOR LOWER GI

Substitute dried sour cherries or cranberries for the dates.

Each serving provides
450 kJ, 107 kcal, 2 g protein, 7 g fat
(<1 g saturated fat), 10 g carbohydrate
(5 g sugars), 2 g fibre

1 Preheat the oven to 190°C (Gas 5). Mix the chopped hazelnuts, sunflower seeds, apricots and dates together in a bowl. Add the sugar, barley flakes, flour and baking powder, and stir until all the ingredients are thoroughly combined.

2 Mix together the oil and apple juice, and pour over the dry mixture. Stir until the dry ingredients are moistened and clump together. Add a little more apple juice if necessary to make the mixture clump.

3 Scoop up a large teaspoonful of the mixture and, with dampened fingers, lightly press it together into a ball about the size of a large walnut. Then press it into a small, thick cookie about 5 cm in diameter. Neaten the edge with your fingers. Place on a large greased baking tray. Repeat with the remaining mixture.

4 Bake the cookies for 10–15 minutes or until slightly risen and browned on top. Transfer to a wire rack and leave to cool. They can be kept in an airtight container for up to 4 days.

HEALTHY EATING

● Barley is believed to be the world's oldest cultivated grain. It is low in fat and rich in low-GI carbohydrate. It contains gluten, but is useful for those following a wheat-free diet.

● Sunflower seeds are a good source of the antioxidant vitamin E, which protects against free-radical damage, and polyunsaturated fats – the 'good' fats.

Ginger-glazed pears

PREPARATION and COOKING: 35–40 minutes, plus 2 hours soaking and cooling   SERVES 4

1 Put the ricotta and chopped stem ginger with the soaked raisins in a small bowl and mix well. Set aside. Preheat the grill to moderate.

2 Quarter the pears lengthwise. Peel them, then scoop out the core with a teaspoon to make a cavity in each quarter. Arrange the pear quarters on their sides on the grill rack.

3 Mix together the honey, lemon juice and ginger syrup, and brush all over the pears. Grill for 4–6 minutes or until just tinged with colour. Turn over and cook the other sides for 2–3 minutes.

4 Turn the pears cavity side up and brush again with the syrup mixture. Divide the ricotta and raisin mixture among the pear cavities, mounding the mixture up slightly. Try to ensure that the raisins aren't exposed, or they may burn during grilling.

5 Return the pears to the grill and cook for 3–4 minutes or until the filling is lightly browned. Leave to cool. To serve, drizzle the remaining syrup over the pears and garnish with sprigs of fresh mint.

COOK'S TIP

● Instead of rum, soak the raisins in orange liqueur or, for an alcohol-free version, orange juice.

HEALTHY EATING

● Pears are a GI 'superfood' because of their high natural sweetness yet low GI. They are also a good source of potassium.

● Raisins contain useful amounts of fibre, iron and potassium as well as natural sugar. They are not a low-GI food, but the small amount used in this recipe will not affect the overall GI of the dish.

$^1/_3$ cup (40 g) raisins, soaked for
    2 hours in 1 tablespoon dark rum

$^2/_3$ cup (160 g) ricotta

2.5 x 5 cm piece stem ginger in syrup,
    drained and finely chopped

3 large, firm but ripe dessert pears

2 teaspoons pure floral honey

1 teaspoon lemon juice

3 tablespoons ginger syrup (from the
    jar of stem ginger)

sprigs of fresh mint to decorate

Each serving provides
1135 kJ, 271 kcal, 5 g protein, 5 g fat
(3 g saturated fat), 51 g carbohydrate
(37 g sugars), 5 g fibre

Grilled fruit skewers

Cooking fruit on skewers, just long enough to heat the fruit through and slightly caramelise its sugars, is an easy and fun way of enjoying fresh fruit. The tiny amount of caster sugar used keeps the GI low.

GI estimate LOW

PREPARATION: 20 minutes   COOKING: 6-7 minutes   SERVES 4

225 g raspberries

grated zest and juice of $^1/_2$ orange

$1^1/_2$ tablespoons caster sugar plus
    4 teaspoons for grilling

$^1/_2$ medium-sized ripe pineapple

2 just ripe, firm bananas

2 ripe but firm pears

4 ripe but firm fresh figs

2 ripe but firm peaches

juice of 1 lemon

cape gooseberries to decorate (optional)

FOR EVEN LOWER GI
Use pure floral honey, agave syrup or maple syrup as a sweetener in step 1.

Each serving provides
939 kJ, 224 kcal, 4 g protein, 1 g fat
(0 g saturated fat), 50 g carbohydrate
(45 g sugars), 10 g fibre

1   Soak 8 bamboo skewers in water for 20 minutes. Meanwhile, make the coulis. Purée the raspberries with the orange zest and juice and $1^1/_2$ tablespoons of sugar in a blender or food processor. If you like, sieve the purée to remove the raspberry pips. Taste the coulis and add a little more sugar, if necessary. Set aside.

2   Preheat the grill. Prepare the pineapple, bananas, pears, figs and peaches, peeling as necessary and cutting into attractive bite-sized pieces. Thread the fruit onto the soaked skewers, alternating them to make a colourful arrangement.

3   Sprinkle the kebabs with half of the lemon juice and 2 teaspoons of sugar. Grill them for 3-4 minutes or until lightly tinged with brown, then turn over, sprinkle with the remaining lemon juice and 2 teaspoons of sugar and grill for a further 3 minutes or until the second side is lightly browned and caramelised a little.

4   While the kebabs are being grilled, pull back the papery skins on the cape gooseberries to form a star-like flower round the fruit.

5   Place 2 fruit kebabs on each plate, drizzle round the coulis, decorate with cape gooseberries and serve hot.

SOME MORE IDEAS
● Use nectarines instead of peaches.
● Use apples when peaches or figs are not in season.
● Serve the fruit kebabs raw, just the fresh fruit skewers resting in a pool of the coulis.

HEALTHY EATING

● This recipe provides useful amounts of vitamin C and beta-carotene. As the fruit is heated for only a very short time, most of the vitamin C is retained.

● This colourful array of fruit has a low GI and is full of dietary fibre, which helps to keep the digestive tract healthy.

HEALTHY EATING

● Dried fruit is a concentrated source of many nutrients, including iron. The vitamin C in the orange juice aids the absorption of iron from the dried fruit.

● Mixing low-fat yogurt with whipped cream produces a rich-tasting dessert that is delightfully low in calories. The yogurt also adds a pleasant hint of sharpness to contrast with the sweet fruit purée.

Marbled fruit fool

Dried prunes and peaches have a concentrated flavour and sweetness; add a dash of peach schnapps or brandy and you have a really special fruit fool. This is an attractive dessert for times when fresh fruit is unavailable.

PREPARATION and COOKING: 30 minutes   SERVES 4

1 Cut a third of the peaches and a third of the prunes into small dice. Put into a bowl, pour over the schnapps or brandy, and set aside to marinate.

2 Place the remaining peaches and prunes in 2 separate saucepans and pour 100 ml orange juice into each. Bring to the boil, then reduce the heat and simmer gently for about 10 minutes or until the fruit is tender.

3 Purée the peaches and prunes separately in a blender or food processor until smooth, adding a little extra orange juice if needed. Leave to cool.

4 Whip the cream in a mixing bowl until thick. Add the yogurt and whip to mix with the cream.

5 Layer alternate spoonfuls of the peach purée, prune purée and cream mixture into 4 stemmed glasses, swirling slightly for a marbled effect. Spoon the marinated fruit on top just before serving.

SOME MORE IDEAS

● For an alcohol-free version, use extra orange juice instead of the peach schnapps or brandy.

● For a rhubarb fool, cook 300 g washed and chopped rhubarb with 2 tablespoons caster sugar and 1 tablespoon orange juice. Cool, then purée. Make the cream and yogurt mixture as in the main recipe, then lightly swirl in the rhubarb purée. Spoon into individual glasses or dishes. Decorate with 1 tablespoon toasted flaked almonds.

● To make a plum fool, halve and stone 300 g red plums and poach gently in a covered pan with 15 g caster sugar and 1 tablespoon orange juice until tender. Cool, then purée until smooth. Make the cream and yogurt mixture as in the main recipe. Reserve 4 tablespoons of the plum purée, then swirl the rest in with the yogurt and cream mixture in stemmed glasses. Top each with a spoonful of the reserved purée.

1 cup (145 g) dried peaches

2/3 cup (140 g) pitted prunes

2 tablespoons peach schnapps or brandy

200 ml orange juice, or as needed

150 ml whipping cream

150 g low-fat natural yogurt

Each serving provides
1404 kJ, 335 kcal, 6 g protein, 16 g fat (10 g saturated fat), 37 g carbohydrate (32 g sugars), 6 g fibre

Hot apricot soufflés

PREPARATION: about 10 minutes   COOKING: 15 minutes   SERVES 4

GI estimate LOW

1 Preheat the oven to 200°C (Gas 6) and place a baking tray inside to heat. Lightly grease four 175 ml ramekins and dust the sides with the almond meal, shaking out the excess.

2 Put the apricot halves, egg yolks, cream, sugar, vanilla extract and lemon juice in a food processor or blender and process until smooth.

3 Place the eggwhites in a clean bowl and whisk until soft peaks form. Sift over the cream of tartar and whisk until stiff peaks form. Spoon the apricot mixture over the eggwhites and use a large spoon to fold together, taking care not to overmix and deflate the eggwhites.

4 Divide the apricot mixture among the prepared ramekins. Use a round-bladed knife to mark a circle in the centre of each soufflé; this helps the tops to rise evenly.

5 Place the ramekins on the heated baking tray and bake in the centre of the oven for 15 minutes or until the soufflés are well risen and golden brown on top. Immediately dust with icing sugar, or a mixture of icing sugar and cocoa powder, sifted through a sieve, and serve at once.

ANOTHER IDEA

● For double-fruit soufflés, drain a second can of apricot halves and finely chop the fruit. Flavour the apricots with a little very finely chopped preserved stem ginger or ground mixed spice. Prepare 6 ramekins, instead of 4. Make the soufflé mixture as above. Divide the chopped fruit among the ramekins, then top with the soufflé mixture and bake.

1¹/₂ teaspoons almond meal (ground almonds)

1 can apricot halves in natural juice, about 400 g, well drained

2 eggs, separated

2 tablespoons whipping cream

1 tablespoon caster sugar

¹/₂ teaspoon pure vanilla extract

¹/₂ teaspoon lemon juice

¹/₂ teaspoon cream of tartar

icing sugar, to serve

cocoa powder (optional)

Each serving provides
531 kJ, 127 kcal, 4 g protein, 7 g fat
(4 g saturated fat), 11 g carbohydrate
(10 g sugars), 1 g fibre

HEALTHY EATING

● Using fruit canned in natural juice, rather than in syrup, cuts the sugar and therefore lowers the GI as well as the calories.

● Eggs are a first-class source of protein - an essential nutrient for good health. They also provide a wide range of vitamins and minerals.

Little custard pots

GI estimate LOW

PREPARATION: 15 minutes   COOKING: 25-30 minutes   SERVES 6

1 Place the milk and vanilla pod in a saucepan and heat until almost boiling. Remove from the heat, cover and set aside to infuse for 15 minutes.

2 Preheat the oven to 160°C (Gas 3). Put the whole eggs, egg yolks, caster sugar and cornflour into a bowl and lightly whisk together. Bring the milk back to boiling point, then remove the vanilla pod and pour the hot milk over the egg mixture, whisking all the time. Strain the mixture into a jug, then divide among 6 lightly greased 120 ml ramekins.

3 Set the ramekins in a roasting pan or baking dish and pour in enough hot water to come halfway up the sides of the ramekins. Bake for 30-35 minutes or until lightly set – the custards should still be slightly wobbly, as they will continue cooking for a few minutes after being removed from the oven. Lift them out of the hot water and allow to cool. Once cold, chill until ready to serve.

4 To make the cherry compote, put the raw sugar and 6 tablespoons water in a saucepan and heat gently until the sugar has dissolved. Bring to the boil, then reduce the heat and add the cherries. Cover and simmer gently for about 4-5 minutes, stirring occasionally, until tender. Lift out the cherries with a draining spoon and place in a serving bowl.

5 Mix the arrowroot with 1 tablespoon cold water. Stir into the cherry juices in the saucepan and simmer for 1 minute, stirring, until thickened and clear. Allow to cool for a few minutes, then pour over the cherries. (The compote can be served warm or at room temperature.) Spoon a little over the top of each custard pot, and serve the rest of the compote in a bowl.

600 ml lite or low-fat milk
1/2 vanilla pod, split
2 eggs
2 egg yolks
40 g caster sugar
1/2 teaspoon cornflour
30 g raw (demerara) sugar
450 g fresh cherries, pitted
2 teaspoons arrowroot

Each serving provides
753 kJ, 180 kcal, 9 g protein, 4 g fat
(1 g saturated fat), 29 g carbohydrate
(26 g sugars), 1 g fibre

HEALTHY EATING

● Cherries have a low GI, are rich in potassium and provide useful amounts of vitamin C.

● Adding extra egg yolks in this recipe boosts the content of vitamins A, D and E as well as B vitamins.

Mixed fruit crumble

A traditional apple crumble is given a flavoursome twist with the addition of exotic fruit. The rolled oats and chopped nuts in the crumble topping help to lower the GI.

GI estimate LOW–MED

PREPARATION: 35 minutes   COOKING: 20-25 minutes   SERVES 6

1 kg sweet red apples

4 tablespoons blueberries

4 tablespoons orange juice

100 g cape gooseberries, papery skins discarded, peeled lychees or grapes

1 tablespoon raw (demerara) sugar

125 g plain flour

100 g non-hydrogenated soft margarine

1/4 cup (55 g) caster sugar

1/2 cup (50 g) rolled oats

1/2 cup (60 g) chopped hazelnuts or walnuts

grated zest of 1 orange

FOR EVEN LOWER GI

Use agave syrup, maple syrup or pure floral honey as a sweetener in steps 2 and 3 (omit the water in step 3).

Each serving provides
1896 kJ, 453 kcal, 6 g protein, 21 g fat (2 g saturated fat), 62 g carbohydrate (37 g sugars), 7 g fibre

1   Preheat the oven to 200°C (Gas 6). Peel the apples, cut them into thick wedges and remove the cores. Place them in a saucepan with the blueberries and orange juice. Cover the pan and cook over a low heat for 10 minutes or until the apples start to soften and release their juices.

2   Add the whole cape gooseberries (or the peeled lychees or grapes), and raw sugar to the apples and stir. Transfer the fruit filling to a 1.5 litre, deep baking dish.

3   In a mixing bowl, rub the flour and margarine together until the mixture resembles fine breadcrumbs. Stir in the caster sugar, oats, hazelnuts or walnuts, and orange zest, then mix in about 1 tablespoon water to give a very rough, crumbly mixture. Spread the crumble topping gently and evenly over the fruit. Do not press down.

4   Bake for 20-25 minutes or until the topping is golden brown and the fruit juice is bubbling up round the edges. Serve hot, with custard.

SOME MORE IDEAS

● Replace the cape gooseberries with 100 g of chopped rhubarb. If liked, add a handful of strawberries, too.

● 2 tablespoons desiccated coconut can be mixed into the crumble topping.

HEALTHY EATING

● Oats are a GI 'superfood'. They are an excellent source of soluble fibre which helps to slow the absorption of glucose into the bloodstream, resulting in a gentler rise and fall in blood sugar levels. They have other health benefits, too, including lowering cholesterol.

HEALTHY EATING

● Plums have natural sweetness and a low GI. They contain a useful amount of vitamin E.

● Pecans, like other nuts, are rich in fat but most of it is the healthy type. They also provide generous amounts of vitamin E.

● Yogurt, along with other dairy products, has a low GI and is a valuable source of calcium.

Plums en papillote with honey

GI estimate LOW

En papillote is a method of cooking food in the oven in parcels of paper, thus sealing in all the delicious juices. When the parcels are opened for serving, a wonderful spicy aroma is released.

PREPARATION: 10 minutes   COOKING: 20 minutes   SERVES 4

1   Preheat the oven to 200°C (Gas 6). Take 4 large squares of baking paper and in the centre of each put a quarter of the plum slices, a knob of butter or margarine, a piece of cinnamon stick and 3 whole cloves. Drizzle 1 tablespoon of honey over each portion of plums.

2   Use a zester to take fine shreds of zest from the orange, or thinly pare off the zest with a vegetable peeler and then cut it into fine shreds. Squeeze the juice from the orange. Add a quarter of the orange zest and juice to each portion of plums, sprinkling the zest and juice over the fruit evenly.

3   For each parcel, bring two opposite sides of the paper together over the fruit filling and fold two or three times. Fold over the other ends twice, then tuck them underneath to make a neatly sealed parcel.

4   Place the parcels on a baking tray and bake for 20 minutes. The paper parcels will puff a little and brown slightly, and the fruit mixture inside will be bubbling hot.

5   Place the parcels on individual serving plates, carefully open up each one and top with a scoop of frozen yogurt. Sprinkle with the pecans and drizzle with extra honey, if you like. Serve immediately.

8 large plums, stoned and quartered

30 g butter or non-hydrogenated soft margarine

2 cinnamon sticks, halved

8 whole cloves

4 tablespoons pure floral honey

1 large orange

4 scoops vanilla frozen yogurt to serve

3 tablespoons coarsely chopped pecans to serve

extra honey for drizzling (optional)

Each serving provides
888 kJ, 212 kcal, 2 g protein, 6 g fat
(4 g saturated fat), 38 g carbohydrate
(36 g sugars), 4 g fibre

COOK'S TIP

● It is important to use baking paper for the parcels as it is more moistureproof than greaseproof paper.

SOME MORE IDEAS

● For pineapple and banana en papillote, replace the plums and spices with 1 small ripe pineapple, peeled, cored and chopped, and 4 bananas, thickly sliced. Add 2 star anise to each parcel, then drizzle with the honey and orange zest and juice.

● You can use foil for the parcels rather than baking paper, but transfer the fruit compote to bowls for serving.

Strawberry yogurt mousse

PREPARATION and COOKING: 20 minutes, plus at least 2 hours chilling   SERVES 4

1 tablespoon powdered gelatine

3 cups (450 g) strawberries

50 g caster sugar

2 cups (500 g) low-fat natural yogurt

³/₄ cup (115 g) redcurrants or blackcurrants, plus a few extra on stalks to decorate

³/₄ cup (90 g) raspberries

1 tablespoon framboise (raspberry liqueur) or kirsch

Each serving provides
810 kJ, 193 kcal, 13 g protein, 1 g fat
(<1 g saturated fat), 29 g carbohydrate
(29 g sugars), 6 g fibre

1. Sprinkle the gelatine over 3 tablespoons cold water in a small mixing bowl and leave to soak for 5 minutes or until spongy. Set the bowl over a pan of hot water and stir until the gelatine has dissolved. Remove the bowl from the heat and leave to cool.

2. Meanwhile, put the strawberries and half of the sugar in a bowl and mash with a fork. Add the dissolved gelatine and then the yogurt, mixing well. Divide among 4 glasses or serving dishes of 200 ml capacity. Cover and chill in the fridge for at least 2 hours or until set.

3. Meanwhile, make the sauce. Put the currants, the rest of the sugar and 2 teaspoons water in a small saucepan and bring to the boil, stirring to dissolve the sugar. Simmer for just 1 minute, then remove from the heat and add the raspberries. Purée in the pan with a hand-held blender, or crush with a fork, then press through a sieve.

4. Pour a little of the sauce over the top of each mousse and decorate with a stalk of redcurrants or a few loose currants. Serve the remaining sauce separately.

COOK'S TIP

● If you can't find fresh blackcurrants or redcurrants, use frozen berries, thawed.

ANOTHER IDEA

● Use blueberries instead of redcurrants or blackcurrants and blackberries instead of raspberries.

HEALTHY EATING

● Berries provide natural sweetness (as long as they are ripe) and have a low GI. They are a good source of vitamin C and other antioxidants.

● All types of yogurt are a GI 'superfood', providing bone-building calcium as well as phosphorus and vitamins B12 and thiamin, plus a low GI score. Low-fat natural yogurt is the best choice.

Prune and apple soufflé

PREPARATION: 20 minutes, plus overnight soaking   COOKING: 20 minutes   SERVES 4

1. Heat the prunes in the apple juice until they start to simmer, then simmer gently for about 5 minutes or until very tender. Purée in the pan with a hand-held blender, or in a blender or food processor.

2. Preheat the oven to 200°C (Gas 6), and put a baking tray in to heat. Lightly grease a 1 litre soufflé dish that is 15 cm in diameter.

3. In a mixing bowl, lightly whisk together the egg yolks and cream, then stir in the prune purée.

4. In another bowl, clean and grease-free, whisk the eggwhites until stiff. Stir 2 tablespoons of the eggwhites into the prune mixture to loosen it, then carefully fold in the rest with a large spoon.

5. Pour the mixture into the soufflé dish. Set on the hot baking tray and bake for 20 minutes or until the soufflé is risen and just slightly wobbly when very gently shaken. Quickly dust the top with the icing sugar, then serve immediately.

125 g pitted dried prunes, soaked overnight in 120 ml apple juice
3 large eggs, separated
2 tablespoons whipping cream
2 teaspoons icing sugar, sifted

Each serving provides
752 kJ, 180 kcal, 7 g protein, 9 g fat (4 g saturated fat), 19 g carbohydrate (15 g sugars), 2 g fibre

HEALTHY EATING

● Prunes are naturally sweet and provide useful amounts of iron, potassium and vitamin B6. The vitamin C in the apple juice will help the body to absorb the iron from the prunes.

● Although fruit juices like apple have little fibre - unlike the original fruit - they still retain the other nutrients such as good amounts of vitamin C and other antioxidants.

● Eggs are a useful and convenient food, suitable for both sweet and savoury dishes. They also boost your intake of many essential nutrients including protein, vitamins B12, A and E, and zinc.

SWEET TREATS

Ricotta citrus soufflé

GI estimate LOW–MED

These deliciously light, individual soufflés will be a tempting and refreshing end to any meal. Ricotta is low in fat and provides valuable nutrients such as calcium without adding too many calories. The strawberry coulis makes the perfect accompaniment.

PREPARATION: 30 minutes   COOKING: 15-20 minutes   SERVES 6

15 g non-hydrogenated soft margarine, melted

1/2 cup (115 g) caster sugar

4 eggs, separated

1/4 cup (30 g) cornflour

1 cup (250 g) ricotta

finely grated zest of 1 lime

finely grated zest of 1 small orange

300 g ripe strawberries, halved

2 teaspoons icing sugar, or to taste, sifted

dash of liqueur, such as kirsch (optional)

FOR LOWER GI

Dust the inside of the soufflé dishes with almond meal (ground almonds) instead of the sugar in step 1.

Each serving provides
988 kJ, 236 kcal, 10 g protein, 10 g fat (4 g saturated fat), 27 g carbohydrate (22 g sugars), 1 g fibre

1 Preheat the oven to 190°C (Gas 5). Brush 6 individual 200 ml soufflé dishes or ramekins with the melted margarine, then coat with caster sugar, using 30 g in total.

2 Put the egg yolks, 30 g of the caster sugar, the cornflour, ricotta and citrus zests in a food processor and blend until smooth and creamy.

3 In a clean mixing bowl, whisk the eggwhites until stiff. Gradually whisk in the remaining caster sugar. Carefully fold the whisked eggwhites into the ricotta mixture.

4 Spoon the mixture into the prepared soufflé dishes and set them on a baking tray. Bake for 15-20 minutes or until well risen and golden brown.

5 Meanwhile, make the strawberry coulis. Purée the strawberries in a blender or food processor until smooth. Sweeten with the icing sugar, then stir in the liqueur, if using.

6 Serve the hot soufflés straight from the oven, dusted with a little icing sugar and with the coulis alongside.

SOME MORE IDEAS

● Instead of flavouring the soufflés with lime and orange zests, try lemon and orange, or pink grapefruit and orange.

● Coat the greased dishes with 15 g finely crushed macaroons or ground hazelnuts instead of caster sugar.

● For a mixed berry soufflé, grease a 1.7 litre soufflé dish with melted non-hydrogenated soft margarine and dust with caster sugar. Make the soufflé mixture as in the main recipe, flavouring with the finely grated zest of 1 lemon and 1 lime. Put 350 g mixed berries, such as raspberries, strawberries and blackberries, into the prepared soufflé dish. Spoon the soufflé mixture over the fruit, covering it completely, and bake for 30 minutes or until well risen and golden brown. Dust with sifted icing sugar and serve.

HEALTHY EATING

● Ricotta is made from whey, the liquid that separates from the curds when cheese is made. It is a mild, soft cheese that is naturally low in fat and a good substitute in recipes that would normally call for fat-laden creamy cheeses.

● Eggs are a good source of protein as well as zinc, a mineral that is vital for growth, reproduction and efficient working of the immune system.

Berry and passionfruit salad

GI estimate LOW

Sweet, juicy berries come in a wide array of types, ranging from bright and delicate raspberries to fleshy strawberries and plump little blueberries. The passionfruit adds a fragrant tart edge to tingle the tastebuds.

PREPARATION: 10–15 minutes   SERVES 6

1 Mix the strawberries, raspberries, blackberries, blueberries, redcurrants and blackcurrants together in a bowl.

2 Cut the passionfruit in half. Holding a sieve over the bowl of berries, spoon the passionfruit flesh and seeds into the sieve. Rub the flesh and seeds briskly to press all the juice through the sieve onto the berries. Reserve a few of the passionfruit seeds left in the sieve and discard the rest.

3 Add the sugar and lemon or lime juice to the berries. Gently toss together. Sprinkle over the reserved passionfruit seeds. Serve straightaway or cover and chill briefly.

SOME MORE IDEAS

● Instead of passionfruit, add 3 tablespoons crème de cassis. Chill until ready to serve.

● Omit the passionfruit and instead serve the berries with a peach and apricot sauce: peel and purée 2 ripe peaches and flavour with 2–3 tablespoons caster sugar, the juice of $1/2$ lemon plus a dash of pure almond extract. Finely dice 8 dried apricots and add to the peach purée. Serve the berries on plates in a pool of the sauce.

● Serve the berry salad spooned over frozen yogurt.

3 cups (450 g) strawberries, cut in half
$1^1/4$ cup (155 g) raspberries
$3/4$ cup (100 g) blackberries
$2/3$ cup (100 g) blueberries
$2/3$ cup (100 g) mixed redcurrants and blackcurrants, stalks removed
2 passionfruit
1 tablespoon caster sugar
juice of $1/2$ lemon or lime

FOR EVEN LOWER GI
Use agave syrup, maple syrup or pure floral honey as a sweetener in step 3.

Each serving provides
255 kJ, 61 kcal, 2 g protein, <1 g fat (0 g saturated fat), 11 g carbohydrate (11 g sugars), 6 g fibre

HEALTHY EATING

● Berries, especially blackcurrants, are bursting with vitamin C. They are also rich in dietary fibre and have a low GI. Berries are also an excellent source of immune-enhancing antioxidants.

● Passionfruit adds beta-carotene to the medley of nutrients in this dish.

Living the low-GI life **244**
Meal plans **246**

Putting it all into practice

LIVING THE LOW-GI LIFE

By now you will understand about the way the low-GI eating plan works and the types of foods that are recommended as well as those best avoided. As already discussed, the low-GI eating plan is not a 'quick fix' diet, but more of a long-term strategy for healthy eating. The easiest way to begin is to make a few simple substitutions (see 'Smart substitutions' on page 17), but after a while you may want to embrace a more whole-hearted approach and that's where the recipes in this book come in. The menu plans on pages 246–9 show you how to incorporate the recipes, but the emphasis is on commonsense and what works best for you.

Smart shopping

Putting the low-GI eating plan into practice begins at the supermarket. You will need to stock up on the right kinds of foods. If you are among the many people who hate the weekly chore of food shopping, there is some good news: there will be whole aisles of the supermarket that you just will not have to walk down. Forget about the shelves of baked goods, confectionery and chips (crisps) – these items won't be on your list. Instead you'll be stopping by the fresh produce, meat and dairy sections.

Even so, the supermarkets can still lead you astray with discount offers and 'specials' that may not be especially good for your diet. But there are a few practical steps you can take to help you to stay on the GI wagon.

● **Plan ahead** Before you head out, make a list – and stick to it. Think of the meals you'll be eating for the week and make a list accordingly. Doing this will save you time and help to avoid buying foods on impulse.

● **Read the labels** Although most of your shopping will comprise fresh produce, there are certain processed foods that come in handy and are useful store cupboard ingredients such as canned tomatoes and beans. But before you buy any kind of processed or packaged food, always take a moment to read the label. You may be surprised to see how the different brands compare. Some

Look for the GI Symbol when shopping

Look for the GI Symbol when shopping. There's a symbol that will help you put the right kind of foods in your supermarket trolley: the GI Symbol. You can't miss it. It's on a wide range of foods from breads and breakfast cereals to yogurts, snack foods, spreads and sweeteners.

What is the GI Symbol? The GI Symbol is your guarantee that the GI value stated near the nutrition information label is accurate. Not only that: foods with the GI Symbol are good for you in other ways, too. To be approved to carry the Symbol, foods must be a good source of carbohydrate and meet a host of other nutrient criteria, including number of kilojoules, total and saturated fat, sodium (salt) and, where appropriate, fibre and calcium.

Who is behind the GI Symbol? The GI Symbol Program is run by the Glycemic Index Foundation, a not-for-profit organisation established by the University of Sydney, Diabetes Australia and the Juvenile Diabetes Research Foundation of Australia. It is one of the world's peak bodies for GI research and education. Manufacturers pay Glycemic Index Ltd a licence fee to use the GI Symbol on their products and the income is then channelled back into education and further research.

come loaded with refined sugars and starches, but you will soon get to know the healthier brands. Keep an eye out for food marked with the GI Symbol (see box on page 244).

When buying margarines, it is important to look for the non-hydrogenated kind, and stick with a trusted brand. Cheap margarines are usually made by a process that forms trans fats, which are worse for your heart than saturated fats – they boost levels of 'bad' LDL cholesterol and decrease 'good' HDL cholesterol. Check the label for a clear statement that the product does not contain trans fats.

The GI store cupboard

You will soon get the hang of what foods and ingredients you need to buy. As a quick reminder, here are some recommendations you can use to form the basis of your regular shopping list:

- Grains: barley, buckwheat and burghul (bulgur)
- Cereals: rolled oats, All-Bran and muesli
- Bread: stoneground wholemeal, soy-linseed and rye
- Pasta and noodles: wholemeal pasta, couscous, glass or cellophane noodles
- Protein foods: canned or dried pulses (lentils, chickpeas, beans), fish, chicken, lean meat, eggs
- Dairy: low-fat yogurt, lite or low-fat milk, low-fat cottage cheese
- Oils and fats: canola (rapeseed) oil, olive oil, non-hydrogenated soft margarine.

Add a little acid

As mentioned on page 14, adding some acidic condiments such as vinegar and lemon juice to your food can lower your blood glucose response to the carbohydrates in a meal. The acid is thought to slow the rate of emptying of food from your stomach to your intestines, so that your blood glucose rises more slowly. Here are a few suggestions for getting these acidic foods into your meals:

- **Always dress for dinner** Add flavour to salads with a vinaigrette dressing. Mix your preferred vinegar (balsamic, rice, sherry, white wine) with an equal amount of olive oil. Add some chopped fresh herbs, mustard or garlic to taste.
- **Spread the mustard** Since it is made with vinegar, mustard is acidic, so use this instead of fat-laden mayonnaise in ham or chicken sandwiches.

Eat a rainbow

Fruit and vegetables make up the bulk of the GI eating plan – remember that half of your plate at every meal should be covered in fruit and veg and you should be aiming for seven servings a day. But which types should you eat? Well the answer is easy: as many as you can and as many different types as you can. Most fruit and vegetables not only have a low GI, they come packed with nutrients, including antioxidants, which boost the immune system and help to fight free radical damage and so slow the ageing process. There are various types of antioxidant, which show up as different colours. So to ensure you are getting the best range, you need to eat a rainbow of colourful fruit and veg.

- **Red** strawberries, radishes, tomatoes, apples
- **Orange** butternut pumpkin, oranges, orange capsicums (peppers), carrots
- **Yellow** lemons, yellow capsicums, yellow zucchini (courgettes), corn (sweetcorn)
- **Green** broccoli, cabbage, green beans, lettuce
- **Blue** blueberries
- **Purple** eggplant (aubergine), blackcurrants, grapes, purple cauliflower

- **Add a pickle or two** The sour taste of pickle comes from vinegar, so put it on your plate. (Watch out for the salt content, though.)
- **Try sauerkraut** This traditional dish from Germany, a form of pickled cabbage, is available from most supermarkets at the deli counter. Serve it with meat dishes.
- **Lemon squeezy** Just sprinkle lemon or lime juice – high in citric acid – on any type of fish or seafood. You can also use it to 'wake up' soups and stews.

Don't forget to drink

The best fluid you can drink is water – and try to drink about eight glasses of it a day. Make it more interesting with a squeeze of lemon or lime. Keeping hydrated will help you to feel less hungry, too.

MEAL PLANS

Healthy eating the low-GI way is easy and delicious. To show you just how easy it is, here are two weeks of meal plans. The daily calorie count comes to roughly 1800–2000 kcal (about 7500–8500 kJ), but remember the emphasis is not on counting calories or kilojoules. Instead, focus on incorporating the principles of low-GI eating as explained in this book. Each meal plan incorporates recipes from the book and has been designed to provide at least seven servings per day of fruit and vegetables, and at least three servings of dairy foods, in line with current nutritional guidelines. The meal plans are meant as a guide, not a strict regimen, so feel free to incorporate your own favourite dishes and swap meals around. After a week or so, you should start to feel the benefits of your new way of eating – you will probably feel more energetic and be well on your way to shedding that unwanted spare tyre.

	DAY 1	DAY 2
BREAKFAST	1 serving **Fruity Bircher muesli** (*page 20*) Tea or coffee	1 serving **Fruit and nut porridge** (*page 23*) Tea or coffee
SNACK	4 wholegrain soy-linseed crackers, sliced tomato, low-fat cream cheese	1 **Five-star cookie** (*page 224*)
LUNCH	1 serving **Japanese miso soup** (*page 54*) 1 serving **Chickpea and vegetable frittata** (*page 161*) 1 apple Water or mineral water	1 serving **Soused fresh sardine salad** (*page 207*) 1 orange or mandarin Water or mineral water
SNACK	1 serving **High-vitality milk shake** (*page 46*)	1 serving **Garlicky fresh cheese** with vegetables (*page 38*)
EVENING MEAL	**Baked whole fish with grapefruit** (*page 130*) 2 small new potatoes, 1 cup of steamed broccoli and snow peas (mangetout) Water or mineral water, or a small glass of wine	1 serving **Fragrant lamb with spinach** (*page 80*) 1/2 cup basmati rice, 1 cup steamed carrots, capsicums (peppers) and green beans Water or mineral water, or a small glass of wine
SNACK/DESSERT	1 serving **Little custard pots** (*page 231*)	1 serving **Ginger-glazed pears** (*page 225*)

	DAY 3	DAY 4	DAY 5	DAY 6
BREAKFAST	1 **Wholesome muffin** (*page 37*) 1 tub low-fat natural yogurt (200 g) Tea or coffee	1 serving **Blueberry and cranberry crunch** (*page 26*) Tea or coffee	1 serving **Strawberry yogurt smoothie** (*page 25*) 1 egg, scrambled, served with $1/2$ cup spinach, mushrooms 1 slice wholegrain toast, with a little non-hydrogenated soft margarine	1 cup fruit salad made with apple, orange, grapes and lychees 1 boiled egg 1 slice rye toast Tea or coffee
SNACK	1 serving (a small handful) **Spiced fruits, nuts and seeds** (*page 47*)	1 cup fruit salad made with apple, orange, grape and kiwifruit	1 **Wholesome muffin** (*page 37*)	1 handful of almonds and dried cranberries
LUNCH	1 serving **Chickpea soup with asparagus** (*page 72*) 1 slice rye toast, with a little non-hydrogenated soft margarine Water or mineral water	1 serving **Tuscan white bean soup** (*page 70*) 1 slice soy-linseed bread Water or mineral water	1 chicken sandwich made with 2 slices rye bread, lettuce, avocado, tomato, lean sliced skinless chicken, and dressing from the recipe on page 211 Water or mineral water	1 serving **Sardine open sandwich** (*page 126*) Water or mineral water
SNACK	1 pear and a handful of walnuts	$1/2$ serving **Sweet potato and celeriac purée** (*page 50*) 2 wholegrain crispbreads, sliced tomato and red onion	1 apple and a handful of almonds	1 cup raw vegetable sticks 1 serving **Turkish eggplant and yogurt dip** (*page 42*)
EVENING MEAL	1 serving **Beef and mushroom pie** (*page 82*) 1 cup steamed snow peas (mangetout) and zucchini (courgettes) Water or mineral water, or a small glass of wine	1 serving **Chinese-style whole fish** (*page 137*) 1 cup steamed broccoli and Asian greens (such as wombok, bok choy, gai lan) Water or mineral water, or a small glass of wine	1 serving **Refried bean burritos** (*page 165*) Water or mineral water, or a small glass of wine	1 serving **One-pot Japanese chicken** (*page 98*) Water or mineral water, or a small glass of wine
SNACK/DESSERT	1 serving **Ricotta citrus soufflé** (*page 238*)	1 serving **Cherry brandy clafoutis** (*page 220*)	1 serving **Grilled fruit skewers** (*page 226*)	1 serving **Marbled fruit fool** (*page 229*)

	DAY 7	DAY 8	DAY 9	DAY 10
BREAKFAST	1 serving **Cottage cheese medley** (*page 28*) $^1/_2$ cup unsweetened orange juice Tea or coffee	1 serving **Apple-berry soufflé omelette** (*page 31*) Tea or coffee	1 serving **Mushroom and herb omelette** (*page 29*)	1 **Orange and oat muesli square** (*page 32*) 1 tub low-fat natural yogurt (200 g) Tea or coffee
SNACK	1 nectarine or kiwifruit	4 wholegrain soy-linseed crackers, sliced tomato, low-fat cream cheese	1 tub low-fat natural yogurt (200 g)	1 apple and a handful of hazelnuts
LUNCH	1 serving **Zesty turkey broth** (*page 64*) 2 slices stoneground wholemeal bread with a little non-hydrogenated soft margarine Water or mineral water	1 lean roast beef sandwich, made on 2 slices oat/barley bread with mustard, finely sliced fennel, lettuce and red onion Water or mineral water	2 slices of rye bread with 1 small can tuna, lemon juice, sliced cucumber 1 pear Water or mineral water	1 serving **Golden lentil soup** (*page 59*) 1 slice soy-linseed bread with a little non-hydrogenated soft margarine Water or mineral water
SNACK	1 tub low-fat natural yogurt (200 g) with a generous handful of stoned cherries	1 serving **Corn fritters** (*page 40*)	1 handful of dried apricots and hazelnuts	1 serving **Gravlax with ginger** (*page 48*) 2 wholegrain crackers
EVENING MEAL	1 serving **Cannellini bean burgers** (*page 164*) 1 bowl mixed green salad Water or mineral water, or a small glass of wine	1 serving **Indian-style grilled chicken breasts** (*page 108*) 1 serving **dal with cauliflower and carrots** (*page 151*) Water or mineral water, or a small glass of wine	1 serving **Spaghetti with a chickpea sauce** (*page 167*) 1 bowl mixed green salad Water or mineral water, or a small glass of wine	1 serving **Lamb, butternut and barley stew** (*page 79*) 1 cup steamed carrots, green beans Water or mineral water, or a small glass of wine
SNACK/DESSERT	$^1/_2$ serving **Spicy vegetable wedges** (*page 44*)	1 serving **Berry and passionfruit salad** (*page 241*)	1 apple and a handful sultanas, stewed with cinnamon and nutmeg in orange juice until soft, served with 1 scoop low-fat ice cream	1 serving **Strawberry yogurt mousse** (*page 236*)

	DAY 11	DAY 12	DAY 13	DAY 14
BREAKFAST	1 serving high-fibre breakfast cereal with 1/2 cup sliced strawberries 1 slice soy-linseed toast with low-fat cream cheese and sliced tomato Tea or coffee	2 slices fruit bread, toasted, spread with low-fat ricotta and jam 1 slice honeydew melon Tea or coffee	1 serving **Boston baked beans** (*page 51*) 1 slice rye toast with a little non-hydrogenated soft margarine Tea or coffee	2 slices stoneground wholemeal toast with peanut butter 1 tub low-fat natural yogurt (200 g) Tea or coffee
SNACK	1 cup fruit salad	1 slice rye toast, with low-fat cream cheese	1 serving **High-vitality milkshake** (*page 46*)	1 peach or 2 apricots
LUNCH	1 chicken sandwich made with two slices sourdough bread, cucumber, avocado and lettuce and lean sliced skinless chicken Water or mineral water	1 serving **Minestrone** (*page 66*) Water or mineral water	1 serving **Tabouleh with goat's cheese** (*page 213*) 1/2 wholemeal pita bread, toasted Water or mineral water	1 serving **Avocado and prawn cup** (*page 205*) 1 slice rye bread Water or mineral water
SNACK	1 tub low-fat natural yogurt (200 g)	1 glass low-fat flavoured milk	1 orange or mandarin	1 handful of walnuts and dried apple
EVENING MEAL	1 serving **Tuscan-style baked polenta** (*page 172*) 1 cup mixed green salad Water or mineral water, or a small glass of wine	1 serving **Fish en papillote** (*page 119*) Water or mineral water, or a small glass of wine	1 serving **Spiced pork with sweet potatoes** (*page 85*) 1 cup steamed Asian vegetables such as wombok or bok choy Water or mineral water, or a small glass of wine	1 serving **Bean and lentil lasagne** (*page 168*) 1 bowl mixed green salad Water or mineral water, or a small glass of wine
SNACK/DESSERT	1 serving **Prune and apple soufflé** (*page 237*)	1 serving **Mixed fruit crumble** (*page 232*)	1 serving **Blackberry ripple frozen yogurt** (*page 223*)	1 serving **Plums en papillote** (*page 235*)

INDEX

A

almonds, 157
Bean hot pot with orange salad, 156
Fruit and nut porridge, 23
Spiced fruits, nuts and seeds, 47
apples, 12, 14, 16, 30, 36, 245
Apple-berry soufflé omelette, 31
Apricot and apple squares, 32
Cottage cheese medley, 28
Crab and avocado salad, 210
Fennel, apple and trout salad, 211
Fruity Bircher muesli, 20
Mixed fruit crumble, 232
Prune and apple soufflé, 237
Smoked mackerel and apple open sandwich, 126
Sweet potato and celeriac purée, 50
Turkey and celery casserole, 112
Wholesome muffins, 37
apricots, 204
Apricot and apple squares, 32
Apricot and coriander tagine, 178
Apricot pecan muffins, 24
Apricot stuffing, 102
Apricot tabouleh side salad, 213
Five-star cookies, 224
Hot apricot soufflés, 230
Millet with spinach and pine nuts, 170
Moroccan-style pumpkin, 146
Peach and apricot sauce, 241
Rich lamb and apricot couscous, 81
Spiced couscous tomatoes, 41
Sweet and spicy lentil salad, 204
asparagus, 10, 73, 150, 181
Chickpea soup with asparagus, 72
Fetta and couscous salad, 193
Penne primavera, 181
Poached eggs with asparagus, 150
Roast vegetable and pasta bake, 162
Salmon baked on asparagus, 130
Spaghetti with brie and tomato, 154
aubergine see eggplant
avocados, 16, 18, 49, 63, 123, 205
Avocado and prawn cups, 205
Avocado and radish salsa, 96
Avocado salsa, 65
Chilled leek and avocado soup, 63
Crab and avocado salad, 210
Swordfish with a Mexican salad, 123
Aztec chicken pie, 101

B

bacon, 15, 70
baked beans, Boston, 51
bamboo shoots, 69, 98, 120

bananas
High vitality milk shake, 46
Honey and banana squares, 32
Mixed fruit shake, 46
Pineapple and banana en papillote, 235
barley, 14, 61, 79, 197, 224, 245
Five-star cookies, 224
Lamb and barley soup, 60
Lamb, butternut and barley stew, 79
Minted barley and beans, 197
Turkey, chestnut and barley broth, 71
barramundi, 135
Chinese-style whole fish, 137
Steamed fish with black beans, 134
Bean and lentil lasagna, 168
bean burgers, Cannellini, 164
bean burritos, Refried, 165
bean chilli, Speedy two-, 171
Bean hot pot with orange salad, 156
bean lasagna, Mixed, 168
bean sprouts, 91, 203
Chinese-style broccoli salad, 201
Chinese-style lemon chicken, 97
Chinese-style whole fish, 137
Crab and avocado salad, 210
Wholewheat and tofu stir-fry, 142
bean terrine, Garlicky, 159
beans see under name eg black beans
beef, 76
Beef and cranberry rolls, 84
Beef and mushroom pie, 82
Beef in red wine, 77
Lentil and sausage salad, 217
Belgian endive/chicory see witlof
berries see under name eg blueberries
Berry and passionfruit salad, 241
Bircher muesli, Fruity, 20
black beans, 135
Butterflied prawns with black beans, 134
Steamed fish with black beans, 134
blackberries, 31, 222
Apple-berry soufflé omelette, 31
Berry and passionfruit salad, 241
Blackberry ripple frozen yogurt, 223
Mixed berry soufflé, 238
blackcurrants, 245
Berry and passionfruit salad, 241
Strawberry yogurt mousse, 236
blue cheese
Roquefort and pear salad, 189
Tagliatelle with broccoli, 176
blueberries, 36, 245
Berry and passionfruit salad, 241
Blueberry and cranberry crunch, 26
Blueberry muffins, 24

Mixed fruit crumble, 232
Wholesome muffins, 37
bok choy
Chinese meatball broth, 69
Chinese-style broccoli salad, 201
Fish en papillote, 119
borlotti beans, 185
Borlotti bean tortilla pie, 101
Couscous pilaf with tahini yogurt, 184
Minestrone, 66
Turkey chilli soup with salsa, 65
Tuscan-style baked polenta, 172
brie and tomato, Spaghetti with, 154
broad beans, 76, 77
broccoli, 16, 64, 91, 176, 185, 245
Chinese-style broccoli salad, 201
Couscous pilaf with tahini yogurt, 184
Ham and baby corn polenta tart, 91
Sweet and spicy lentil salad, 204
Tagliatelle with broccoli, 176
Zesty turkey broth, 64
buckwheat
Buckwheat and seafood salad, 198
Chinese-style broccoli salad, 201
Marinated duck with buckwheat, 200
bulgur see burghul
burghul, 10, 118, 196, 212, 245
Burghul and herb pilaf, 119
Burghul wheat and fetta salad, 196
Burghul wheat and prawn salad, 196
Crab and avocado salad, 210
Tabouleh with goat's cheese, 213
burritos, Refried bean, 165
butter beans
Chunky vegetable crumble, 153
Moroccan-style pumpkin, 146
Salmon and butter bean frittata, 161
butternut pumpkin, 79, 82, 147, 163, 178, 245

C

cabbage, 245
Chicken and cashew pancakes, 107
Couscous pilaf with tahini yogurt, 184
Minted couscous with cabbage, 81
Tuscan white bean soup, 70
cannellini beans
Bean and lentil lasagna, 168
Cajun-style ham and beans, 214
Cannellini bean burgers, 164
Minestrone, 66
Minted barley and beans, 197
Speedy two-bean chilli, 171
Tagliatelle with cannellini beans, 167
Tuscan white bean soup, 70
White bean and yogurt dip, 42

cape gooseberries
  Grilled fruit skewers, 226
  Mixed fruit crumble, 232
capsicum, 113, 139, 245
  Bean and lentil lasagna, 168
  Braised vegetables with falafel, 148
  Cajun-style ham and beans, 214
  Chakchouka, 155
  Chinese-style lemon chicken, 97
  Eggplant casserole with polenta, 147
  Goulash in a hurry, 95
  Ham with pears, 90
  Hungarian-style meatballs, 92
  Lentil and sausage salad, 217
  Mexican pork, 96
  Simple seafood broth, 58
  Soused fresh sardine salad, 207
  Spicy turkey chilli with spaghetti, 110
  Sweet and spicy lentil salad, 204
  Wholewheat and tofu stir-fry, 142
carrots, 12, 16, 61, 64, 126, 151, 245
  Beef in red wine, 77
  Cannellini bean burgers, 164
  Chinese-style lemon chicken, 97
  Chunky vegetable crumble, 153
  Dal with cauliflower and carrots, 151
  Garlicky fresh cheese, 38
  Golden lentil soup, 59
  Minestrone, 66
  Root vegetable purée, 50
  Sardine open sandwich, 126
  Spiced lentil dal, 145
  Vegetable mash, 112
  Zesty turkey broth, 64
cashew pancakes, Chicken and 107
cauliflower, 151, 245
  Dal with cauliflower and carrots, 151
  Spiced lentil dal, 145
  Tagliatelle with broccoli, 176
celeriac
  Minestrone, 66
  Sweet potato and celeriac purée, 50
celery
  Bean hot pot with orange salad, 156
  Cajun-style ham and beans, 214
  Turkey and celery casserole, 112
Chakchouka, 155
cheese, 15, 16, 66, 164, 189, 192, 245
  Cannellini bean burgers, 164
  Garlicky fresh, 38
  homemade, 38, 39
  Oaty red lentil gratin, 175
  Olive and caper, 38
  Refried bean burritos, 165
  Roast vegetable and pasta bake, 162
  see also under name eg ricotta
cherries
  Cherry brandy clafoutis, 220
  Cherry soufflé omelette, 31
  Little custard pots, 231
  Spicy vegetable tagine, 178
cherry tomatoes see tomatoes, cherry

chestnuts
  Stuffed turkey rolls with lentils, 102
  Turkey, chestnut and barley broth, 71
  see also water chestnuts
chicken, 10, 15, 245
  Aztec chicken pie, 101
  Chicken and cashew pancakes, 107
  Chicken satay, 104
  Chinese-style lemon chicken, 97
  Indian-style grilled chicken breasts, 108
  One-pot Japanese chicken, 98
  Spicy tabouleh with chicken, 213
Chicken liver and raspberry salad, 215
Chicken liver mousse, 103
chickpeas, 10, 12, 15, 72, 149, 167, 179, 245
  Braised vegetables with falafel, 148
  Chickpea and vegetable frittata, 161
  Chickpea soup with asparagus, 72
  Pasta with sage and fetta, 177
  Soused fresh sardine salad, 207
  Spaghetti with a chickpea sauce, 167
  Spicy vegetable tagine, 178
chicory see witlof
chilli
  Avocado and prawn cups, 205
  Aztec chicken pie, 101
  Chakchouka, 155
  Chicken and cashew pancakes, 107
  Chilli spiced split pea purée, 50
  Fish with spicy lentils, 129
  Fragrant lamb with spinach, 80
  Fresh fruit soup, 57
  Moroccan-style pumpkin, 146
  Refried bean burritos, 165
  Soused fresh sardine salad, 207
  Spaghetti with clams, 132
  Speedy two-bean chilli, 171
  Spiced lentil dal, 145
  Spicy turkey chilli with spaghetti, 110
  Swordfish with a Mexican salad, 123
  Turkey chilli soup with salsa, 65
Chinese cabbage, 98, 119
Chinese meatball broth, 69
Chinese-style broccoli salad, 201
Chinese-style lemon chicken, 97
Chinese-style whole fish, 137
Cidered pork with herb dumplings, 87
Citrus marinade, 96
citrus soufflé, Ricotta, 238
clafoutis, Cherry brandy, 220
clams, Spaghetti with, 132
cookies, Five-star, 224
corn, 12, 16, 214, 245
  Aztec chicken pie, 101
  Burghul wheat and prawn salad, 196
  Cajun-style ham and beans, 214
  Chinese meatball broth, 69
  Chinese-style broccoli salad, 201
  Corn and wholewheat salad, 195
  Corn fritters, 40
  Eggplant casserole with polenta, 147
  Ham and baby corn polenta tart, 91

  Speedy two-bean chilli, 171
  Turkey chilli soup with salsa, 65
cottage cheese, 28, 171, 245
  Cottage cheese medley, 28
  Garlicky bean terrine, 159
  Garlicky fresh cheese, 38
  Speedy two-bean chilli, 171
  Spinach and smoked trout roulade, 124
couscous, 12, 41, 193
  Couscous pilaf with tahini yogurt, 184
  Fennel, apple and trout salad, 211
  Fetta and couscous salad, 193
  Minted couscous with cabbage, 81
  Rich lamb and apricot couscous, 81
  Soused fresh sardine salad, 207
  Spiced couscous tomatoes, 41
  Spicy vegetable tagine, 178
Crab and avocado salad, 210
cranberries
  Beef and cranberry rolls, 84
  Blueberry and cranberry crunch, 26
  Cranberry stuffing, 84
  Spiced fruits, nuts and seeds, 47
  Spiced pork with sweet potatoes, 85
cream cheese, 25
  Lemon mackerel pâté, 127
  Sardine open sandwich, 126
  Spinach and smoked trout roulade, 124
cucumber
  Braised vegetables with falafel, 148
  Buckwheat and seafood salad, 198
  Burghul wheat and prawn salad, 196
  Corn and wholewheat salad, 195
  Fennel, apple and trout salad, 211
  Fresh fruit soup, 57
  Raita, 108
  Tabouleh with goat's cheese, 213
  Tunisian tuna and egg briks, 138
custard pots, Little, 231

D

dal
  Dal with cauliflower and carrots, 151
  Spiced lentil, 145
  Spicy split pea, 151
dips
  Spicy peanut, 45
  Tangy mustard, 45
  Turkish eggplant and yogurt, 42
  White bean yogurt, 42
duck with buckwheat, Marinated, 200

E

egg noodles, 137
eggplant, 43, 245
  Chickpea and vegetable frittata, 161
  Eggplant casserole with polenta, 147
  Spiced couscous tomatoes, 41
  Turkish eggplant and yogurt dip, 42
  Vegetarian goulash, 95
eggs, 10, 15, 16, 29, 155, 230, 231, 237, 239, 245
  Apple-berry soufflé omelette, 31

251

Apricot pecan muffins, 24
Blackberry ripple frozen yogurt, 223
Blueberry muffins, 24
Chakchouka, 155
Cherry soufflé omelette, 31
Chickpea and vegetable frittata, 161
Corn fritters, 40
Double fruit soufflés, 230
Garlicky bean terrine, 159
Ham and baby corn polenta tart, 91
Hot apricot soufflés, 230
Little custard pots, 231
Mushroom and herb omelette, 29
Pear and ginger soufflé omelette, 31
Poached eggs with asparagus, 150
Prune and apple soufflé, 237
Ricotta citrus soufflé, 238
Scrunch-top filo pie, 158
Spinach and smoked trout roulade, 124
Tunisian tuna and egg briks, 138
Tuscan-style baked polenta, 172
Wholesome muffins, 37
Egyptian lentils with macaroni, 183

F
falafel, Braised vegetables with, 148
fennel
    Baked whole fish with grapefruit, 130
    Buckwheat and seafood salad, 198
    Fennel, apple and trout salad, 211
    Fish en papillote, 119
    Turkey kebabs with relish, 113
fetta cheese, 208
    Burghul wheat and fetta salad, 196
    Fetta and couscous salad, 193
    Olive and caper cheese, 38
    Pasta with sage and fetta, 177
    Snow pea, grape and fetta salad, 208
fish and seafood, 10, 15, 16, 118, 128, 245
    Baked whole fish with grapefruit, 130
    Buckwheat and seafood salad, 198
    Chinese-style whole fish, 137
    Fish en papillote, 119
    Fish with mustard lentils, 129
    Fish with spicy lentils, 129
    Gravlax with ginger, 48
    Malay-style braised fish, 120
    Oat-crusted fish with orange, 116
    Simple seafood broth, 58
    Smoked fish and lentil salad, 190
    Steamed fish with black beans, 134
    see also barramundi; clams; mackerel;
        prawns; sardines; scallops; sea bass;
        skate; swordfish; trout; tuna
flageolet beans, 156, 159
flax seeds see linseeds
frittata
    Chickpea and vegetable, 161
    Salmon and butter bean, 161
Fruit and nut porridge, 23
fruit fool, Marbled, 229
fruit skewers, Grilled, 226

fruit soufflés, 230, 237
fruit soup, Fresh, 57

G
garlic, 43, 95, 245
    Baked whole fish with grapefruit, 130
    Beef in red wine, 77
    Boston baked beans, 51
    Chickpea soup with asparagus, 72
    Chilled leek and avocado soup, 63
    Chinese meatball broth, 69
    Fish en papillote, 119
    Fragrant lamb with spinach, 80
    Garlicky bean terrine, 159
    Garlicky fresh cheese, 38
    Goulash in a hurry, 95
    Indian-style grilled chicken breasts, 108
    Minestrone, 66
    Rich lamb and apricot couscous, 81
    Spaghetti with clams, 132
    Spicy turkey chilli with spaghetti, 110
    Sweet potato and celeriac purée, 50
    Turkey and lentil pâté, 109
    Turkey chilli soup with salsa, 65
    Turkish eggplant and yogurt dip, 42
    Tuscan white bean soup, 70
ginger, 135
    Chicken satay, 104
    Chinese meatball broth, 69
    Chinese-style lemon chicken, 97
    Chinese-style whole fish, 137
    Dal with cauliflower and carrots, 151
    Fragrant lamb with spinach, 80
    Ginger-glazed pears, 225
    Gravlax with ginger, 48
    Japanese miso soup, 54
    Pear and ginger soufflé omelette, 31
    Spiced fruits, nuts and seeds, 47
    Spiced lentil dal, 145
    Spicy vegetable tagine, 178
    Steamed fish with black beans, 134
    Sweet potato and celeriac purée, 50
    Wholewheat and tofu stir-fry, 142
goat's cheese, 212
    Scrunch-top filo pie, 158
    Sweet and spicy lentil salad, 204
    Tabouleh with goat's cheese, 213
Goulash in a hurry, 95
grapefruit, Baked whole fish with, 130
grapes, 17, 245
    Fresh fruit soup, 57
    Snow pea, grape and fetta salad, 208
Gravlax with ginger, 48
Greek-style yogurt
    Blackberry ripple frozen yogurt, 223
    Corn fritters, 40
    Fennel, apple and trout salad, 211
    Fragrant lamb with spinach, 80
    High-vitality milk shake, 46
    Refried bean burritos, 165
    Turkish eggplant and yogurt dip, 42
    White bean and yogurt dip, 42

green beans, 245
    Chinese-style lemon chicken, 97
    Gruyère and ham salad, 192
    Marinated duck with buckwheat, 200
    Minestrone, 66
    Penne primavera, 181
    Trout with green beans and pesto, 121
Gruyère and ham salad, 192

H
ham, 91, 192
    Cajun-style ham and beans, 214
    Gruyère and ham salad, 192
    Ham and baby corn polenta tart, 91
    Ham with pears, 90
haricot beans, 51
hazelnuts, 20, 23
    Fennel, apple and trout salad, 211
    Five star cookies, 224
    Fruit and nut porridge, 23
    Fruity Bircher muesli, 20
    Mixed fruit crumble, 232
Herb dumplings, 87
Herb scones, 60
Honey and banana squares, 32
Hungarian-style meatballs, 92

I, J
Indian-style grilled chicken breasts, 108
Japanese chicken, One-pot, 98
Japanese miso soup, 54

K
kebabs with relish, Turkey, 113
kidney beans, 10, 100, 110
    Aztec chicken pie, 101
    Speedy two-bean chilli, 171
    Spicy turkey chilli with spaghetti, 110
    Swordfish with a Mexican salad, 123
    Turkey chilli soup with salsa, 65
kombu (kelp) seaweed, 54
kumara see sweet potatoes

L
lamb, 80, 203
    Fragrant lamb with spinach, 80
    Lamb and barley soup, 60
    Lamb and wholewheat salad, 203
    Lamb, butternut and barley stew, 79
    Lentil and sausage salad, 217
    Rich lamb and apricot couscous, 81
lasagna, Bean and lentil, 168
leeks, 62, 86
    Chilled leek and avocado soup, 63
    Cidered pork with herb dumplings, 87
    Fish with spicy lentils, 129
    Lamb, butternut and barley stew, 79
    Minted barley and beans, 197
    Moroccan-style pumpkin, 146
    Pork, prune and orange pie, 88
    Roast vegetable and pasta bake, 162
    Turkey, chestnut and barley broth, 71

lemon chicken, Chinese-style, 97
Lemon mackerel pâté, 127
lemons, 127, 206, 245
lentils, 10, 12, 15, 59, 109, 129, 145, 151, 169, 175,
        182, 190, 204, 216, 245
    Bean and lentil lasagna, 168
    Dal with cauliflower and carrots, 151
    Egyptian lentils with macaroni, 183
    Fish with mustard lentils, 129
    Fish with spicy lentils, 129
    Golden lentil soup, 59
    Lentil and sausage salad, 217
    Mixed lentil gratin, 175
    Oaty red lentil gratin, 175
    Smoked fish and lentil salad, 190
    Smoked trout and green lentil salad, 190
    Spiced lentil dal, 145
    Stuffed turkey rolls with lentils, 102
    Sweet and spicy lentil salad, 204
    Turkey and lentil pâté, 109
    Turkey, lentil and sweet potato soup, 71
lettuce, 245
    Bean hot pot with orange salad, 156
    Chicken liver and raspberry salad, 215
    Crab and avocado salad, 210
    Poached eggs with asparagus, 150
    Refried bean burritos, 165
linseeds, 15, 16, 28

M

mackerel, 16
    Lemon mackerel pâté, 127
    Smoked fish and lentil salad, 190
    Smoked mackerel and apple open
        sandwich, 126
Malay-style braised fish, 120
mangetout see snow peas
meal plans, 246–9
meatballs, 69, 92
Mexican pork, 96
Mexican salad, Swordfish with a, 123
milk shakes, 46
Millet with spinach and pine nuts, 170
Minestrone, 66
Minted barley and beans, 197
Minted couscous with cabbage, 81
miso soup, Japanese, 54
Moroccan-style pumpkin, 146
muesli, 12, 15, 17, 20
muesli squares, 32
muffins, 12, 16, 17
    Apricot pecan, 24
    Blueberry, 24
    Wholesome, 37
mushrooms, 175
    Bean hot pot with orange salad, 156
    Beef and mushroom pie, 82
    Beef in red wine, 77
    Corn and wholewheat salad, 195
    Gruyère and ham salad, 192
    Hungarian-style meatballs, 92
    Mushroom and herb omelette, 29

Oaty red lentil gratin, 175
    Penne primavera, 181
    Rich lamb and apricot couscous, 81
    Tuscan-style baked polenta, 172
mushrooms, shiitake, 68
    Chinese meatball broth, 69
    Japanese miso soup, 54
    One-pot Japanese chicken, 98
mussels, 58
Mustard and dill sauce, 48
mustard dip, Tangy, 45

N

new potatoes see potatoes, new

O

Oat-crusted fish with orange, 116
oats, rolled, 12, 14, 15, 20, 23, 32, 116, 175, 232,
        245
    Blueberry and cranberry crunch, 26
    Fruit and nut porridge, 23
    Fruity Bircher muesli, 20
    Mixed fruit crumble, 232
    Mixed fruit shake, 46
    Oaty red lentil gratin, 175
    Orange and oat muesli squares, 32
    Spiced fruits, nuts and seeds, 47
olives, 43
    Garlicky bean terrine, 159
    Grilled polenta and tuna pizza, 139
    Lamb and wholewheat salad, 203
    Marinated duck with buckwheat, 200
    Olive and caper cheese, 38
    Turkish eggplant and yogurt dip, 42
omelettes
    Apple-berry soufflé, 31
    Cherry soufflé, 31
    Mushroom and herb, 29
    Pear and ginger soufflé, 31
orange juice, 30, 56
    Baked whole fish with grapefruit, 130
    Fresh fruit soup, 57
    High-vitality milk shake, 46
    Marbled fruit fool, 229
    Orange and oat muesli squares, 32
oranges, 12, 157, 245
    Bean hot pot with orange salad, 156
    Garlicky bean terrine, 159
    Oat-crusted fish with orange, 116
    Plums en papillote with honey, 235
    Pork, prune and orange pie, 88
    Skate with citrus-honey sauce, 133
    Tomato and orange salsa, 116

P

pancakes, Chicken and cashew, 107
pancetta
    Pasta with sage and fetta, 177
    Penne primavera, 181
Paprika sauce, 92
parsnips, 12, 152
    Chunky vegetable crumble, 153

Golden lentil soup, 59
    Moroccan-style pumpkin, 146
    Root vegetable purée, 50
    Turkey, chestnut and barley broth, 71
    Vegetable mash, 112
passionfruit, 241
    Berry and passionfruit salad, 241
    Fresh fruit soup, 57
pasta, 13, 66, 154, 167, 169, 176, 177, 245
    Bean and lentil lasagna, 168
    Chickpea soup with asparagus, 72
    Egyptian lentils with macaroni, 183
    Minestrone, 66
    Pasta with sage and fetta, 177
    Penne primavera, 181
    Roast vegetable and pasta bake, 162
    Spaghetti with a chickpea sauce, 167
    Spaghetti with brie and tomato, 154
    Spaghetti with clams, 132
    Spicy turkey chilli with spaghetti, 110
    Tagliatelle with broccoli, 176
    Tagliatelle with cannellini beans, 167
pâté
    Lemon mackerel, 127
    Smoked trout, 127
    Turkey and lentil, 109
peaches, 12, 220
    Grilled fruit skewers, 226
    Marbled fruit fool, 229
    Mixed fruit shake, 46
    Peach and apricot sauce, 241
peanuts, 201
    Peanut sauce, 104
    Salad dressing, 201
    Spicy peanut dip, 45
pearl barley see barley
pears, 12, 14, 189, 225
    Cottage cheese medley, 28
    Fresh fruit soup, 57
    Ginger-glazed pears, 225
    Grilled fruit skewers, 226
    Ham with pears, 90
    Pear and ginger soufflé omelette, 31
    Roquefort and pear salad, 189
    Smoked fish and lentil salad, 190
    Snow pea, grape and spinach salad, 208
peas, 181
    Pea fritters, 40
    Penne primavera, 181
pecans, 234
    Apricot pecan muffins, 24
    Plums en papillote with honey, 235
Penne primavera, 181
pies
    Aztec chicken, 101
    Beef and mushroom, 82
    Pork, prune and orange, 88
    Scrunch-top filo, 158
pilaf
    Burghul and herb, 119
    Couscous pilaf with tahini yogurt, 184
    Wild rice and lemongrass, 133

pine nuts, 158, 170
pineapple
  Grilled fruit skewers, 226
  Pineapple and banana en papillote, 235
pineapple juice, 57
pinto beans, 156, 165
pizza, Grilled polenta and tuna, 139
plums, 234
  Plum fool, 229
  Plums en papillote with honey, 235
polenta, 91, 139, 173
  Eggplant casserole with polenta, 147
  Grilled polenta and tuna pizza, 139
  Ham and baby corn polenta tart, 91
  Herbed polenta, 91
  Spinach and smoked trout roulade, 124
  Tuscan-style baked polenta, 172
ponzu sauce, 98
pork, 68, 85, 89
  Chinese meatball broth, 69
  Cidered pork with herb dumplings, 87
  Goulash in a hurry, 95
  Mexican pork, 96
  Pork, prune and orange pie, 88
  Spiced pork with sweet potatoes, 85
porridge, Fruit and nut, 23
potatoes, new, 16, 76, 86, 87, 92, 161
  Avocado and prawn cups, 205
  Chickpea and vegetable frittata, 161
  Chunky vegetable crumble, 153
  Lentil and sausage salad, 217
  Skate with citrus-honey sauce, 133
  Spiced lentil dal, 145
prawns, 196
  Avocado and prawn cups, 205
  Burghul wheat and prawn salad, 196
  Butterflied prawns with black beans, 134
  Malay-style braised fish, 120
  Simple seafood broth, 58
prunes, 89, 237
  Marbled fruit fool, 229
  Pork, prune and orange pie, 88
  Prune and apple soufflé, 237
pumpkin, 16, 146, 163, 245
  Eggplant casserole with polenta, 147
  Lamb, butternut and barley stew, 79
  Minestrone, 66
  Moroccan-style pumpkin, 146
  Roast vegetable and pasta bake, 162
  Spicy vegetable tagine, 178
  Sweet potato and butternut mash, 82
pumpkin seeds, 23
  Fruity Bircher muesli, 20
  Spiced fruits, nuts and seeds, 47
purées
  Chilli spiced split pea, 50
  Root vegetable, 50
  Sweet potato and celeriac, 50

Q
quail's eggs, 150
quinoa, 10

R
radishes, 245
  Avocado and radish salsa, 96
  Buckwheat and seafood salad, 198
  Tabouleh with goat's cheese, 213
raisins, 178, 179, 225
Raita, 108
raspberries
  Berry and passionfruit salad, 241
  Chicken liver and raspberry salad, 215
  Grilled fruit skewers, 226
  Mixed berry soufflé, 238
  Strawberry yogurt mousse, 236
redcurrants
  Berry and passionfruit salad, 241
  Strawberry yogurt mousse, 236
Rhubarb fool, 229
rice, 10, 12, 13, 14, 16, 17
  Chinese meatball broth, 69
  Wild rice and lemongrass pilaf, 133
ricotta, 239
  Bean and lentil lasagna, 168
  Chicken liver mousse, 103
  Ginger-glazed pears, 225
  Grilled polenta and tuna pizza, 139
  Ricotta and witlof salad, 189
  Ricotta citrus soufflé, 238
  Simple seafood broth, 58
rocket
  Braised vegetables with falafel, 148
  Lamb and wholewheat salad, 203
  Lentil and sausage salad, 217
  Pasta with sage and fetta, 177
  Snow pea, grape and fetta salad, 208
rolled oats see oats, rolled
Roquefort and pear salad, 189
roulade, Spinach and smoked trout 124

S
sage and fetta, Pasta with, 177
salads, 123, 124, 156, 189–217
salmon, 16
  Gravlax with ginger, 48
  Salmon and butter bean frittata, 161
  Salmon baked on asparagus, 130
  Salmon en papillote, 119
salsa
  Avocado, 65
  Avocado and radish, 96
  Tomato and orange, 116
sandwiches
  Sardine open sandwich, 126
  Smoked mackerel and apple open
    sandwich, 126
sardines, 16, 126, 206
  Oat-crusted fish with orange, 116
  Sardine open sandwich, 126
  Soused fresh sardine salad, 207
satay, Chicken, 104
sausage salad, Lentil and, 217
scallops
  Scallops with citrus and chive sauce, 133

Simple seafood broth, 58
sea bass, 135
  Chinese-style whole fish, 137
  Steamed fish with black beans, 134
seafood see barramundi; clams; fish and
    seafood; mackerel; prawns; sardines;
    scallops; sea bass; skate; swordfish;
    trout; tuna
seaweed, 54
seeds, Spiced fruits, nuts and, 47
sesame seeds, 23
  Fruity Bircher muesli, 20
  Orange and oat muesli squares, 32
shiitake mushrooms see mushrooms, shiitake
shortcrust pastry, 88
Skate with citrus-honey sauce, 133
smoothies, Strawberry yogurt, 25
snow peas, 199, 208
  Buckwheat and seafood salad, 198
  Chinese meatball broth, 69
  Chinese-style broccoli salad, 201
  One-pot Japanese chicken, 98
  Snow pea, grape and fetta salad, 208
soufflés
  Double-fruit, 230
  Hot apricot, 230
  Mixed berry, 238
  Prune and apple, 237
  Ricotta citrus, 238
spaghetti
  Spaghetti with a chickpea sauce, 167
  Spaghetti with brie and tomato, 154
  Spaghetti with clams, 132
  Spicy turkey chilli with spaghetti, 110
spinach, 80, 125, 158
  Chicken liver and raspberry salad, 215
  Fragrant lamb with spinach, 80
  Millet with spinach and pine nuts, 170
  Minestrone, 66
  Minted barley and beans, 197
  Scrunch-top filo pie, 158
  Snow pea, grape and fetta salad, 208
  Soused fresh sardine salad, 207
  Spaghetti with a chickpea sauce, 167
  Spinach and smoked trout roulade, 124
  Tagliatelle with broccoli, 176
  Tunisian tuna and egg briks, 138
split peas
  Chilli spiced split pea purée, 50
  Spicy split pea dal, 151
spring onions
  Chinese meatball broth, 69
  Garlicky fresh cheese, 38
  Japanese miso soup, 54
stir-fries, 106, 107, 142
strawberries, 24, 245
  Berry and passionfruit salad, 241
  Fruity Bircher muesli, 20
  Mixed berry soufflé, 238
  Ricotta citrus soufflé, 238
  Strawberry yogurt mousse, 236
  Strawberry yogurt smoothies, 25

sunflower seeds, 46, 47, 152, 153, 204, 224
swedes, 86, 87
sweet potatoes, 12, 17, 83, 85
    Couscous pilaf with tahini yogurt, 184
    Ham with pears, 90
    Spiced pork with sweet potatoes, 85
    Spicy vegetable wedges, 45
    Sweet potato and butternut mash, 82
    Sweet potato and celeriac purée, 50
    Sweet potato mash, 82
    Turkey, lentil and sweet potato soup, 71
    Vegetable mash, 112
sweetcorn see corn
swordfish, 123
    Spicy swordfish wraps, 123
    Swordfish with a Mexican salad, 123

T

tabouleh side salad, Apricot, 213
tabouleh with chicken, Spicy, 213
Tabouleh with goat's cheese, 213
Tagliatelle with broccoli, 176
Tagliatelle with cannellini beans, 167
tofu, 10, 143
    Japanese miso soup, 54
    Wholewheat and tofu stir-fry, 142
tomatoes, 41, 155, 245
    Aztec chicken pie, 101
    Bean hot pot with orange salad, 156
    Boston baked beans, 51
    Chakchouka, 155
    Crab and avocado salad, 210
    Egyptian lentils with macaroni, 183
    Goulash in a hurry, 95
    Grilled polenta and tuna pizza, 139
    Minestrone, 66
    Minted barley and beans, 197
    Pasta with sage and fetta, 177
    Refried bean burritos, 165
    Rich lamb and apricot couscous, 81
    Scrunch-top filo pie, 158
    Simple seafood broth, 58
    Spaghetti with a chickpea sauce, 167
    Spaghetti with brie and tomato, 154
    Spaghetti with clams, 132
    Speedy two-bean chilli, 171
    Spiced couscous tomatoes, 41
    Spiced lentil dal, 145
    Spiced pork with sweet potatoes, 85
    Spicy turkey chilli with spaghetti, 110
    Spicy vegetable tagine, 178
    Swordfish with a Mexican salad, 123
    Tomato and orange salsa, 116
    Tomato salad, 124
    Tunisian tuna and egg briks, 138
    Turkey chilli soup with salsa, 65
tomatoes, cherry
    Braised vegetables with falafel, 148
    Cannellini bean burgers, 164
    Chicken satay, 104
    Gruyère and ham salad, 192
    Lamb and wholewheat salad, 203

Spaghetti with brie and tomato, 154
Tabouleh with goat's cheese, 213
Turkey chilli soup with salsa, 65
tortillas, 100, 101, 165
trout, 121, 125
    Fennel, apple and trout salad, 211
    Smoked trout and green lentil salad, 190
    Smoked trout pâté, 127
    Spinach and smoked trout roulade, 124
    Trout with green beans and pesto, 121
tuna, 139
    Grilled polenta and tuna pizza, 139
    Tunisian tuna and egg briks, 138
Tunisian tuna and egg briks, 138
turkey, 64, 110
    Hungarian-style meatballs, 92
    Spicy turkey chilli with spaghetti, 110
    Stuffed turkey rolls with lentils, 102
    Turkey and celery casserole, 112
    Turkey, chestnut and barley broth, 71
    Turkey chilli soup with salsa, 65
    Turkey kebabs with relish, 113
    Turkey, lentil and sweet potato soup, 71
    Zesty turkey broth, 64
turkey livers, 109
Turkish eggplant and yogurt dip, 42
turnips, 152
    Chunky vegetable crumble, 153
    Couscous pilaf with tahini yogurt, 184
    Lamb, butternut and barley stew, 79
Tuscan-style baked polenta, 172
Tuscan white bean soup, 70

V

vegetable crumble, Chunky, 153
Vegetable mash, 112
vegetable tagine, Spicy, 178
vegetable wedges, Spicy, 45
Vegetarian casserole, 98
Vegetarian goulash, 95
Vegetarian wholewheat salad, 203

W

walnuts, 210
water chestnuts, 97
watercress, 149
    Braised vegetables with falafel, 148
    Gruyère and ham salad, 192
    Roquefort and pear salad, 189
    Sardine open sandwich, 126
    Smoked fish and lentil salad, 190
wheat germ, 23, 27
    Blueberry and cranberry crunch, 26
    Fruit and nut porridge, 23
    High-vitality milk shake, 46
White bean and yogurt dip, 42
white bean soup, Tuscan, 70
wholewheat, 143, 194, 203
    Corn and wholewheat salad, 195
    Lamb and wholewheat salad, 203
    Vegetarian wholewheat salad, 203
    Wholewheat and tofu stir-fry, 142

Wild rice and lemongrass pilaf, 133
witlof
    Garlicky bean terrine, 159
    Garlicky fresh cheese, 38
    Poached eggs with asparagus, 150
    Ricotta and witlof salad, 189

Y

yogurt, 12, 14, 15, 245, 205, 210, 228, 234, 236
    Avocado and prawn cups, 205
    Braised vegetables with falafel, 148
    Cajun-style ham and beans, 214
    Corn fritters, 40
    Couscous pilaf with tahini yogurt, 184
    Crab and avocado salad, 210
    Fragrant lamb with spinach, 80
    Garlicky fresh cheese, 38
    High-vitality milk shake, 46
    Spiced lentil dal, 145
    Spicy turkey chilli with spaghetti, 110
    Strawberry yogurt mousse, 236
    Strawberry yogurt smoothie, 25
    Tangy mustard dip, 45T
    Turkish eggplant and yogurt dip, 42
    White bean and yogurt dip, 42
    Yogurt marinade, 108
yogurt, frozen, 46, 222
    Blackberry ripple frozen yogurt, 223
    Marbled fruit fool, 229
    Plums en papillote with honey, 235

Z

zucchini, 245
    Braised vegetables with falafel, 148
    Chicken satay, 104
    Couscous pilaf with tahini yogurt, 184
    Fetta and couscous salad, 193
    Lentil and sausage salad, 217
    Marinated duck with buckwheat, 200
    Moroccan-style pumpkin, 146
    Simple seafood broth, 58
    Soused fresh sardine salad, 207
    Turkey chilli soup with salsa, 65
    Turkish eggplant and yogurt dip, 42
    Vegetarian goulash, 95

A note about the recipes

Australian metric cup and spoon measurements have been used throughout this book: 1 cup = 250 ml; 1 tablespoon = 20 ml and 1 teaspoon = 5 ml. If using the smaller imperial cup and spoon measures (where 1 cup = 235 ml and 1 tablespoon = 15 ml), some adjustments may need to be made. A small variation in the weight or volume of most ingredients is unlikely to adversely affect a recipe. The exceptions are yeast, baking powder and bicarbonate of soda (baking soda). For these ingredients adjust the recipe accordingly. All cup and spoon measures are level, unless stated otherwise. Ingredients are generally listed by their metric weight or volume with cup measurements given for convenience, unless the conversion is imperfect, whereby the ingredients are listed by metric weight or volume only.

Each recipe is accompanied by a nutrient profile showing kilojoules (kJ), calories (kcal), protein, fat (including saturated fat), carbohydrate (including sugars) and fibre. Serving suggestions, garnishes and optional ingredients are not included in the nutritional analysis. For the recipe analysis we used FoodWorks ® based on Australian and New Zealand food composition data.

In line with current nutritional recommendations, we have kept the salt content of the dishes to a minimum and advocate using salt-reduced stock and soy sauce wherever possible.

The recipes in this book recommend non-hydrogenated margarine (which does not contain trans fats). Trans fats are worse for your heart than saturated fats – they boost levels of 'bad' LDL cholesterol and decrease 'good' HDL cholesterol. When buying margarine, check the label for a clear statement that the product does not contain trans fats.

The GI Cookbook contains some material first published in the following Reader's Digest books: *A Passion for Pasta; Beautiful Baking; Cook Smart for a Healthy Heart; Eggs, Milk & Cheese; Fresh Fish & Seafood; Fresh Fruit & Desserts; Light Bites and Lunches; Meat Classics; Perfect Poultry; Pies, Tarts & Puddings; Rice, Beans and Grains; Soups & Casseroles; Super Salads; Vegetables for Vitality.*

Alternative terms and substitutes

capsicum = sweet pepper
corn cob = mealie/miele
eggplant = aubergine, brinjal
fish substitutes
   blue-eyed cod = hake or other
     firm white fish
   ling = hake, cod or other firm white fish
   snapper = firm white fish
wholemeal = wholewheat

Photography credits

Photographs pp 22, 28, 36, 111, 166, 180: **Photographer** Andre Martin (*stylist* Gabrielle Wheatley, *food preparation* Grace Campbell)

All images except the following are the copyright of Reader's Digest.
endpapers *(all)* Shutterstock; **1** Shutterstock; **5** *(left, top to bottom)* Shutterstock, Shutterstock, iStockPhoto, Shutterstock *(right, all)* Shutterstock; **8** *(all)* Shutterstock; **11** Shutterstock; **13** Shutterstock; **14** Shutterstock; **16** *(all)* Shutterstock; **18** Shutterstock; **34** Shutterstock; **52** Shutterstock; **74** Shutterstock; **114** iStockPhoto; **140** Shutterstock; **186** Shutterstock; **218** Shutterstock; **242** Shutterstock

Book code: AU 0564
Product codes: 041-3986 (H/B) 041-3988 (P/B)